Corporate Research Foundation is a
aims to inform a wide audience abou
management and corporate strategie
behind the success of leading compar
consisting of analysts, journalists,
associations and specialists in hui.
reviewed in this book has been interviewed and assessed by members
of CRF's team of writers.

Britain's Top Employers

A Guide to the Best Companies to Work For

The Corporate Research Foundation
Editor Paul Donkersley

HarperCollins*Publishers*

HarperCollins*Publishers*
77–85 Fulham Palace Road,
Hammersmith, London W6 8JB

Published by HarperCollins*Publishers* 1999
1 3 5 7 9 10 8 6 4 2

Corporate Research Foundation
Lauderdale House,
25, Duke Street,
London W1M 5DB
+44 (0) 171 486 2603

The Corporate Research Foundation asserts the moral right to
be identified as the editor of this work

A catalogue record for this book
is available from the British Library

ISBN 0 00 257068 8

Set in Linotype Meridien

Printed and bound in Great Britain by
Clays Ltd, St Ives plc

Contents

Foreword

Who says that the companies featured in this book are Britain's Top Employers? Well, Corporate Research Foundation (CRF) does, this being a team comprising a panel of 'experts' in human resources, recruitment and management consultancy, business analysts Dun & Bradstreet and researchers from CRF. They carried out the initial research and selection processes to whittle down a comprehensive list of hundreds of companies long before the army of business journalists from national newspapers and freelance writers like myself were let loose on the companies.

This is no definitive list, and companies appear in the book in alphabetical order. It's contentious enough for anyone to decide which are the very best companies to work for in Britain, at this moment in time as a famous football manager once said, let alone rank them.

And there's the point. There are excellent companies out there which are not featured in this book, some of which might have strong claims to being among the best. But what the companies selected by CRF in this book do have in common, apart from being excellent businesses, is that they are all doing something fairly special that allows them to count themselves deservedly among 'Britain's Top Employers'.

They might be highly successful businesses, or operating in fast-growing markets. They may offer superlative training or the chance to really enhance your CV and future employability in the time you are with them. They might offer high earning potential, or are such open meritocracies that the only limit to promotion opportunity is your own ability. Or they might be at the leading edge in current trends in employment thinking, such as striking an effective balance between work and life issues.

They are all companies though – whether British, multinational or foreign-owned; whether publicly quoted, subsidiaries, or private. They are companies because that's what we wanted to write about. At the highly successful launch party of the first edition of this book at

London's Atlantic Bar in 1997, someone asked me, 'Why didn't you do a book on the public sector instead?' To me, that's like being asked by your grandmother to try on one of the two ties she has just bought you for Christmas, only to reappear and be hit by the question 'What's wrong with the other one?' CRF is interested in *companies*.

And, just as unashamedly, we have targeted this book at primarily a professional and executive readership. Graduates, young executives, 'first bouncers', professional job-seekers, company analysts and watchers, managers, human resources and personnel specialists. In short, anyone interested in working as a professional – and discerning about whom to work for.

In writing many of the profiles in this book I've met an awful lot of companies – but no awful companies – and I've heard my share of buzz words, clichés and jargon. You will therefore read a lot along the lines of 'people are our greatest asset', 'we aim to be the employer of choice', 'world class', and my own personal favourite: 'lots of companies say they are a people business, but we really mean it'. And of course solutions are always 'tailor-made', businesses are suddenly 'customer-facing', salaries are invariably 'competitive' and pitched, unerringly, at 'the upper quartile' to the extent that if anyone else crowds on to this narrow ledge of remuneration, they'll all fall off.

Is it fair of me to mock, from my lofty perch as a professional copywriter whose mother tongue is the richest in the world, when companies earnestly volunteer these well-meant phrases? No, of course not. Because even when someone uses a word like 'proactive' – and I don't like 'proactive' – we all know what is meant. Call it common usage, call it communication, call it dumbing-down – it doesn't matter. We are quite clear about what that person or company is actually saying. Or are we?

Because if I have just one piece of advice to offer a job-seeker faced with the bewildering task of processing such claims, it is to retort with the question 'How do you achieve that?' Now this is where the companies in this publication really begin to differentiate themselves. They may *say* similar things, but they 'walk the talk' and actually *do* something to justify their claims and achieve their aspirations. They don't just have vision – they have what it takes to make that vision a reality. They are also confident enough to have their approach committed to print. 'How?' has always been the most difficult of the questions to answer, because it cannot rely on facts – it needs ideas, commitment and courage. These are the real hallmarks of the top employers.

When Carole Pemberton, writing in the first edition of this book, said, 'All of the profiles describe excellence. In reading this book, I would encourage you to see yourself as a partner in the process and identify those things which are important to you,' she was absolutely right.

I would like to take that argument further. Because it would be wrong to look at any list of companies as if you are selecting from a menu. It is not a matter of choosing a company that is 'right' for you. Nothing is that static, and companies are not just waiting there to be chosen. I think that it is far more important that you listen to what they are saying – because they are also listening to you.

The employment contract has probably never been so open or dynamic. Enlightened employers know that the rules are changing all the time – competitive forces (which are global), the expectations of employees in balancing home life and work, the unrelenting impact that technology has on everyday life, but particularly the workplace. And employers – or anyway the best employers – admit that they don't have all of the answers: which is why they want to hear the views of current and future employees. In that way, they strive to forge a relationship based on understanding, delivering achievable results and making life richer.

It all makes eminent sense really. In our personal lives we enjoy the freedom and creativity to pursue and achieve whatever we want. So why change that happy formula at work? Yet companies have often done precisely this, setting frameworks, policies, hours, guidelines, organisational charts, regulations, parameters and paradigms. Why on earth not instead unleash the potential and the creativity of individuals by letting them drive at least part of the agenda?

Fortunately, there are many companies now grasping the nettle. Not out of some charitable gesture but out of simple business sense. Happy employees are productive ones, and why in any case restrict your access to the 'best' people that every company says it sets out to recruit, by not being flexible in the area of age, ethnic or cultural diversity, working parents, or the myriad other people whose busy lives involve many things as well as their jobs?

I am encouraged to witness the reality of flexible hours, home, part-time and tele-working, open and honest psychological contracts, 'fun' being encouraged in the workplace, sabbaticals, 'school term' years, self-managed careers. This is not the future – it's the present.

Information technology has had a phenomenal impact. It continues to revolutionise businesses and the winners are those who apply it effectively. And young people, to whom the latest technology such as the Internet is second nature, have a lot to teach companies.

It adds up to a staggering rate of progress – if companies had only been like this when I started! There is again one company in this edition of the book that I have worked for. Had I my time again, I might have been drawn to any of today's top employers.

My final thanks go to the many, many contacts at the companies and the team of willing writers, without whom I would not have this long grey beard. If people enjoy reading even part of this book, it has all been worthwhile.

Paul Donkersley
Editor

Research Team

Editor:

Paul Donkersley

Writers:

Lisa Buckingham
Alex Brummer
Roger Cowe
Paul Donkersley
Jim Dow
Sue Hayward
David Kirk
Kevin Pratt
Roger Trapp
Barry Turnbull
David Vickery

Sources and Advisers:

The Reward Group
People in Business
Association of Career Advisory Services (AGCAS)
Sanders & Sidney
Association of Graduate Recruiters
Business in the Community

Britain's Top Employers

3i

3i is Europe's leading venture capital company with 28 offices across Europe. With its headquarters in London and 18 offices throughout England, Scotland and Wales, 3i's financial expertise is found in all Britain's major business centres. 3i has 10 offices in France, Germany, Italy and Spain, and a presence in Asia with an office in Singapore as well as a joint venture in Japan. In the year ending 31 March 1998, 3i invested around £1 billion in 647 businesses. In total, 3i has 790 employees.

Scorecard:

Remuneration and benefits	★★★★★
Progressive attitude	★★★
Opportunity for promotion	★★★★★
Training, development and education	★★★★
Working atmosphere and environment	★★★

Biggest plus:
Fascinating, challenging work, sets your career up for life

Biggest minus:
A lot of pressure to get investment deals done

3i plc
91 Waterloo Road
London SE1 8XP
Tel: 0171 928 3131
Fax: 0171 928 9318
website: www.3igroup.com

3i

The Business

'Our purpose is to help businesses succeed,' says 3i, something it has been doing successfully for over 50 years. 3i is often described as the 'university of venture capital', the training ground for an alumni pursuing successful careers in venture capital, finance and industry. 3i is certainly a 'CV enhancer'.

3i's own business aim is to achieve capital and dividend growth for shareholders, deriving its own success from the success of its portfolio companies. As a measure of success, 3i floated on the London Stock Exchange in July 1994 and joined the prestigious FTSE-100 Index in September of the same year.

3i helps businesses which do not have access to capital markets by providing equity capital and long-term loans at any stage of their development. In fact, 3i is committed to being Europe's leading venture capital company and has always leaned towards higher risk situations, investing at an early stage including start-ups, management buy-ins and buy-outs.

3i will invest in any business sector – it is easier to identify which sectors it doesn't invest in. That said, investment in high technology industries, with IT and biotechnology companies to the fore, is an important area of specialisation and one of significant growth internationally. 3i's portfolio also has a higher weighting towards manufacturing companies than 'UK plc', but the proportion of service industries is increasing.

Company Culture and Style

3i is a well-known business with a powerful brand image and reputation second to none for training its investment professionals. The air at 3i is highly professional, confident and successful. People attracted to 3i aspire to high professional standards, exclusivity even, and this is recognised within the company. This is a very intellectual, challenging and performance-driven environment.

Individuals joining 3i are amazed at how much autonomy and responsibility they have, particularly at the lower levels. And especially in an industry which remains highly regulated. Having the leeway to work on their own initiative, within agreed boundaries, is highly valued by 3i staff.

Teamwork still has an important role at 3i, which does not have a culture of the individual. There is a tremendous desire to put together the best investment team for the job, drawn from experts with a breadth of skills, experience and backgrounds.

Certain core values are fundamental to the way 3i does business – fairness, honesty, professionalism, respect for others and a continual search for improvement and innovation head the list. They are included in the 3i booklet 'Our Company' given to all employees and sent out with each job offer, and on 3i's innovative and interactive web site, which also includes an entertaining 'entrepreneurial test'!

So the type of person 3i looks for is bright, with strong analytical and decision-making skills. They must also be capable of building excellent business relationships with a wide range of people to 'get the deal done' and cope with the inevitable pressure. Confidence, flexibility, energy and empathy are valuable personal characteristics.

'This all makes for a stimulating company,' suggests Adam Quarry, marketing director. 'It's the people you meet and the relationships you develop that really make the job rewarding.'

3i necessarily has a serious nature, but it is very personal as well. There are social events and parties, and 3i supports the involvement of its employees in the community, matching the charity funds they raise.

Human Resources

3i's human resources activity is centred on attracting, motivating and retaining the best and brightest people. The HR team supports the growth of the business through resourcing, training and development, and compensation and benefits.

Over half of 3i's employees are directly involved in investment, the other half in other professional services including accountancy, legal, corporate finance and marketing. People often join 3i from the practices, but also direct from industry. The company occasionally takes graduates straight from university, but people with 3–5 years' relevant work experience are more typical.

3i receives a vast number of speculative approaches regarding career opportunities, from the Far East, the US and many other far-away places as well as the UK. The company replies to everyone and even meets some people despite there being no suitable vacancy at the time. It is all part of being a market leader and setting high standards. 3i is to be commended for this, but it all helps to extend the network.

Indeed, there is a scheme where employees can introduce someone to the business and even receive a fee if their candidate is subsequently hired and the referral proved to be of good quality. In a more planned campaign, 3i has links to the international business schools, uses specialist recruitment consultancies to accelerate searches, and sometimes advertises.

Career Opportunity and Development

All new investment executive recruits go through 3i's one-year investment skills training programme – the 'technical training'. Each investment team is headed by a local director, who is responsible for the development of all staff in his or her team and will assign a 'mentor' – a senior executive who will advise and guide an individual's performance, training and development.

A major strength of 3i is that many of its managers have been developed within the business. They are skilled on the 'people side' of management, and take a very professional approach to people skills, really wanting to motivate and develop their staff.

3i supports the concept of people moving around the business, and tries to take account of individuals' career aspirations. You can discuss your career development at any time – with your line manager, mentor, director or with HR, or at the annual appraisal. It's an open policy, and if someone wants a move, the company (or more directly, the head of department), doesn't stand in their way.

There are secondments within the business, and people are also seconded from outside the business. Again, the 3i network benefits. This gives people the chance to gain new experiences and perspectives, and they can return to their own department or seek a more permanent career change.

Internationally, 3i knows that businesses prefer to deal with locals. Initially, however, experienced and 'approved' 3i people might go anywhere in the world, to establish a new office, and to recruit and develop a highly effective local team. 3i's Singapore office is a case in point.

If people do leave, it usually takes a major offer or step up to tempt individuals who can normally achieve all that they want at 3i. Over time, professional, talented people with drive can accumulate considerable wealth.

Remuneration

Pay is market- and performance-driven. All employees are eligible for annual profit-sharing and individual performance-related bonuses which could be up to as much as 100% of salary in some areas.

Benefits include an excellent non-contributory pension scheme for every UK employee, which provides two-thirds of salary after 25 years' service. Free private medical insurance is available for employees and spouses, and 3i also offers subsidised mortgages. Many employees are also eligible for the company car scheme (or cash alternative), share options, and long-term share-based incentive schemes.

The Future

3i has strong ambitions to be a world-class business and is already the European leader. It still has a large proportion of its businesses in the UK, but is actively spreading its business interests outside.

It will be careful not to be too 'British' in the way it goes about this, conscious of the fact that most of its experts have lived, worked and run businesses in Britain. That is why a greater exposure to local culture and business methods is sought by recruiting local staff. The European venture capital industry is far less mature than the UK's, and its products and markets are less well known. The competition is relatively fragmented, but there are local players.

The HR team is also looking at in-house provision of a 'total concept of learning', incorporating the whole process of appraisal, career development plan, education and learning so that individuals can integrate and monitor their own development.

'We are always looking to improve the internal services and communications we provide for our staff,' says John Cushing, human resources operations manager. That includes an Intranet designed to expand information available to employees and to make it more interesting and 'friendly', and a recently implemented Employee Assistance Programme – a helpline without any back-referral – where employees can seek advice on life issues.

3i offers a stimulating environment, promotes self-development and actively encourages its people to build on their skills. Everyone at 3i has the opportunity to be innovative – it's a personal challenge as much as a corporate one.

3M UK plc

3M is one of the world's leading technology companies. 3M manufactures more than 50,000 innovative products, including adhesive tapes, pharmaceuticals, abrasives, reflective materials, fibre optic connectors, respirators and fabric protectors. 3M uses over 100 different technologies in 40 business units in the manufacture of products for a wide variety of industrial, commercial, healthcare and consumer markets. US-owned 3M had worldwide sales of $15 billion in 1998 and over 70,000 employees. 3M UK and Ireland is one of the largest subsidiaries outside the USA, and is involved in the vast majority of 3M's incredibly wide product range. 3M has 4,200 people in 15 locations in the UK.

Scorecard:

Remuneration and benefits	★★★★
Progressive attitude	★★★★★
Opportunity for promotion	★★★★
Training, development and education	★★★★★
Working atmosphere and environment	★★★

Biggest plus:
A standard bearer for best practice and innovation

Biggest minus:
Almost too caring for its employees and communities

3M UK PLC
3M House
PO Box 1, Market Place
Bracknell
Berkshire RG12 1JU
Tel: 01344 858000
Fax: 01344 862367
e-mail: innovation@uk.mmm.com
website: www.3M.com

3M

3M UK plc

The Business

In 1953, a 3M laboratory assistant working on the development of a fluorochemical liquid coolant spilled a few drops on her tennis shoe. When she tried to scrub the spots with soap and water, alcohol and other solvents, nothing worked. Then came a flash of insight, if the sample couldn't be removed with water, it might make a good rain repellent. If it was impervious to solvents, it could protect fabrics from stains.

This insight was the innovation that led to the family of Scotchgard™ Protectors used widely today on clothing, carpets, furniture, wood and leather.

Not all new products come about through lucky accident, though. 3M takes innovation seriously. As a result, 3M today is a much-admired global company which creates, manufactures and sells an array of 50,000 technology-based products in some 200 countries. Familiar products include Post-it®Notes, Wetordry™ Sandpaper and the signature Scotch™ adhesive tape brand, but it has many more where it applies the very latest technologies such as micro-replication and fibre optics.

The company looks to produce around 1,000 new products every two years and typically, 30% of total sales each year are from products no more than four years old.

Company Culture and Style

Innovation is virtually compulsory at 3M. But innovation is more than products – it's the way everyone in the company does business. 3M prides itself on forming innovative relationships within the organisation: with suppliers and customers; between domestic and international business units – relationships that respect individual and cultural differences and result in products which make life better for everyone. It's a culture which appeals to imaginative, flexible and inquisitive people with an emphasis on teamwork.

Strong and interactive customer relationships are absolutely funda-mental. 3M's Customer Technical Centre in Bracknell welcomes some 3,000 visitors each year looking for technology-based solutions to their business or manufacturing problems. 'But the company also races ahead, innovating in new technologies and products to identify needs that customers haven't yet realised or expressed,' says Dr John How-ells, 3M UK's technical director.

Internally, 3M exhibits strong values of loyalty. 'The company has been around for an amazing 100 years, and there is a strong sense of joining a company in which you can invest your life,' says Paul Davies, human resources development manager, Europe. 'Many do, because they love the work and respect the company's values.'

It's the relentless innovation, a dedication to 'better living through technology', new product flow and diversity that sustains this culture. And 3M valued differences long before diversity entered legislation and corporate language. 'It's great to watch the sparks between tech-nologists working in a haphazard scientific environment alongside the offices of those who have to deal with this wild skill and bring the products to market,' says Wayne Brown, managing director of 3M in the UK.

'Bootlegging' is a highly productive culture somewhat peculiar to 3M. The company's scientists are allowed to spend up to 15% of their time on projects of their own choosing. Some have been known to spend more than 50%! The important message is that people have licence to be creative. In encouraging risk-taking, 3M believes that it is better to ask forgiveness rather than permission. 'Put fences around people and you get sheep,' said William McKnight, one of the earliest and most visionary chief executives, over 50 years ago.

Human Resources

3M encourages the pursuit of long-term careers and is rightly proud of its emphasis on promotion from within. Chief executive Livio DeSi-mone champions long-term employment, believing that secure and happy employees are more likely to be productive at work.

3M's HR function is therefore particularly interested in recruiting and developing individuals and helping them maximise their contri-bution and potential. Development is a partnership, involving the indi-vidual, the company and the supervisor. Personal development is built into the performance management process which includes 360-degree feedback. The whole process impacts directly on salary reviews and personal action plans.

Closely involved in leadership succession, HR is working hard to maintain the same strength in leadership roles. 'We know that as the organisation becomes leaner, it creates more demanding jobs and bigger steps between levels,' says Paul Davies. 'The job learning curve is steepening all the time.'

Recruitment remains of great importance and while the company often takes 'risks' in putting people in different jobs, it is aware that today, jobs are ever more complex and demanding and more care is needed. HR also supports people in coping with inevitable change and behaving differently when they go into something new.

3M's Management Team Review process is an annual event where managers meet to consider the challenges within the company and the abilities and aspirations of their own people. Managers must only discuss individuals from first-hand experience. HR supports the management team to do this well, and the process instils a sense of commitment across the team to 'make things happen'.

The 3M Staff Opinion Survey has a high response rate (60–70%) and among other things, provides a test of how its leadership initiatives are working. The survey is also used to establish HR priorities in the wider sense, and there is a determined effort to 'do something about it'. Responses, after all, will be measured in the next survey.

At its European Employee Forum in Brussels, the most positive feedback came from the translators employed, who were amazed at the great lengths the company went to with its employees!

Career Opportunity and Development

3M has a huge diversity of businesses. With six major market groups, and research, manufacturing and sales operations in over 60 countries, it can offer a diverse range of career opportunities in all major disciplines. It gives 3M great scope to offer people 'career shots in the arm', and means that it should be able to interest and retain the people it wants to.

International work experience is highly valued, and is an essential part of the development process for the future senior management of the company. 70% of 3M's top executives have worked abroad for at least three years. Most have grown their successful careers within 3M.

3M has a fairly unusual structure in that individuals can follow the conventional leadership or management line, or alternatively climb the 'dual ladder'. This parallel track allows scientific and technical professionals to remain firmly within their specialisation yet still attain the higher levels of the organisation and reach director level as corporate scientists.

There is a fundamental and substantial commitment to training at 3M. In addition to the range of work-related and competency/skills courses, further education is available for formal qualifications and 3M makes a generous contribution towards fees, allowances and study leave.

Remuneration

3M's salary policy is to ensure that each employee is paid according to their level of responsibility and individual contribution to the company's success. After setting salary ranges, 3M aims to pay competitively, benchmarking against its peer group. It tends not to have a high variable pay element, but exceptional things in work, however small, are recognised and rewarded.

Higher up the line, remuneration can be linked more directly to the fortunes of the company. Share options are provided for middle management, while senior managers also have a complex 'Pay at Risk' profit-sharing arrangement.

There are no financial bonuses for innovation, which is considered 'part and parcel of the job', but achievement is recognised and rewarded. For top scientists it could be election to the elite Carlton Society, and the dual ladder facilitates higher promotion for scientists.

The Future

3M is embracing many challenges in the global marketplace. Shorter product cycles, customers wanting fewer, more sophisticated suppliers, and the world of electronic commerce are all putting pressure on the logistics of research/manufacture/distribution. 3M has introduced its 'Pacing Plus' initiative to prioritise and accelerate the development of new products it has identified as winners, and is pursuing supply-chain excellence. It is working ever closer with customers, and also, in an attempt to secure stronger customer loyalty, will be taking a more rational approach to the use of the powerful 3M brand.

3M really does go the extra mile with its employees, and the culture is still one of long-term employment. But in an increasingly competitive world, some of its generous values and ethical attitude may come under scrutiny and certainly under economic pressure. Employability rather than employment may creep into the culture, and the company also expects to become 'less hysterical' about staff turnover.

But the company's trump card will always be its pioneering, innovative spirit. There is a genuine joy in innovation and invention at 3M. It has always been willing to invest in research for its own sake, 'for happy outcomes which emerge from unpromising starts'. That the company has increased revenues and profits almost every single year since 1985 suggests that this innovative company knows precisely what it is doing.

Abbott Laboratories

Abbott Laboratories has been manufacturing and selling quality healthcare products for over 100 years. Its mission is to improve lives by providing cost-effective healthcare products and services. Headquartered in Chicago, Abbott has had a UK presence for 45 years. Today, it is a $12 billion business employing over 54,000 people, 2,200 of whom work in the UK. The company markets its diverse portfolio of products in over 130 countries worldwide.

Scorecard:

Remuneration and benefits	★★★★★
Progressive attitude	★★★★★
Opportunity for promotion	★★★★
Training, development and education	★★★★★
Working atmosphere and environment	★★★★

Biggest plus:
A dynamic company where everybody does essential work

Biggest minus:
Definitely not for the nine-to-fivers of this world!

Abbott Laboratories Limited
Abbott House
Norden Road
Maidenhead
Berkshire SL6 4XE
Tel: 01628 773355
Fax: 01628 644115

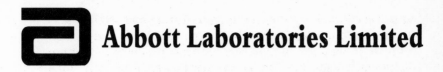 **Abbott Laboratories Limited**

Abbott Laboratories

The Business

Unlike many companies in its sector which have a narrow, pharmaceuticals-intensive product line, Abbott is a broad-based healthcare business. The structure of the UK company mirrors that of the group as a whole: the company is divided into three main divisions comprising pharmaceutical products, hospital products and nutritional products. There is also Abbott Diagnostics, which has made two acquisitions in the last three years: MediSense, Inc. and Murex.

The pharmaceutical division is a big player in this marketplace, making and selling antibiotics as well as a range of other products. The antibiotics are used in treating respiratory problems, ulcers, prostate conditions and others. The division has a turnover of around £41 million.

Abbott's nutritional division (Ross) is the market leader and has actually caused this market to grow in recent years. From a turnover of around £7 million eight years ago, the division is now worth £48 million. This impressive growth has been driven by its ethical nutritional products, including enteral feeding and sip feed lines.

The hospital division is also enjoying a period of rapid growth, forecast to continue into the next millennium. Its products are mainly in the area of anaesthetics used in operating theatres and intensive care. Its turnover is £22 million.

The diagnostics arm produces high-technology equipment for blood-testing, allowing hospitals and blood-banks to test for various diseases. It offers a full service of manufacturing, selling, maintenance and engineering, and has a turnover of £28 million. MediSense is one of the leaders in the diabetic market through its successful blood-testing strips for glucose monitoring. Murex also produces blood-testing equipment.

Company Culture and Style

In some ways, the culture at Abbott is typical of many US companies: fast-paced and demanding. Yet it also has its own style. There's a real sense of positive energy among its people. Despite the highly regulated nature of its markets, the company has avoided excessive bureaucracy. It's also very financially based and results-driven, so numerical ability is important for would-be managers.

There is a growing acknowledgement at Abbott that its people are its greatest asset, and great efforts are being made to retain and reward its stars. The nature of the work and the company suits people who like being busy, enjoy constant challenges, and are confident in their own skills. There are no cosy backwaters here; virtually everyone is doing vital work. It's a company at the cutting-edge of an exciting, rapidly developing marketplace, and for those who relish that sort of opportunity, Abbott is an ideal place to be.

The vast majority of staff are educated to first degree level or beyond. In its 25–30 graduate hires each year, the company looks for life science graduates, as well as pharmacists, engineers and chemists. Overall, Abbott is a company full of very bright people, committed, conscientious, goal-oriented and results-focused. Anyone interested in going on to management also needs good interpersonal skills. People who join at higher levels rather than as graduate recruits need to have all those abilities plus proven experience and performance. Abbott also stringently checks that managers have the right attitude towards developing their staff before appointing them from outside.

Human Resources

The HR department works in partnership with line management and is very much part of the decision-making process. The HR people are genuinely valued for their input. They are all generalists and the team is multi-skilled. The company is not unionised, but HR handles issues such as legal requirements and employee relations.

The company measures employee satisfaction, with the goal of having at least 70% of its employees rating it as an excellent employer by the year 2003. In working to achieve that goal, the company is focusing on ensuring that communication channels are good and that individual jobs fit smoothly with overall corporate goals.

Recently, the goal-setting approach has changed to one of shared rather than inward-looking personal goals. This is facilitated by bringing senior people throughout the company together for a one-day discussion in a hotel, a new trend but one which will continue.

Career Opportunity and Development

Abbott Laboratories has a 'Targeting Success' scheme, whereby about 12 of the brightest graduates (and others) are brought together to work on real, work-based projects once a year. This can lead to formal management assessment. However, others are equally well served, with business skills workshops, mentoring and much more to aid their development.

Abbott Laboratories tries to fill vacancies internally, fuelled by succession planning meetings twice yearly for all staff. With four divisions there is plenty of opportunity for career development, since each division maintains its own sales, marketing, product development and other teams.

There are opportunities for working overseas. Not surprisingly, given the US parentage, the main movements are between the UK and the USA. Currently this tends to operate at a relatively senior level, but the company is actively seeking to drive this process downwards through more junior levels. One plan currently under discussion is to offer sales representatives in the UK the chance to swap jobs for a year with a colleague from (for example) Australia. When overseas development opportunities occur, language skills, especially Spanish, can be an advantage.

Career development is organised with the aid of annual appraisals (which look backwards) and personal development plans (which look forwards). These sessions allow the company to consider what is needed to get the individual where he or she wants to be.

Training is important at Abbott. An international training manager looks after Europe and masterminds the management development programmes. Many training courses are internal, but the company also maintains links with some well-known training organisations. It will consider sponsoring people for self-study where that study is relevant for either the current or future role. This support can include full or partial funding and study leave.

Remuneration

Abbott continuously compares itself with the top 25 pharmaceutical companies and aims to be a median payer – although upper quartile performers will receive upper quartile pay. This marketplace is traditionally a good payer in any case. Remuneration is performance-based, linked to appraisals and taking into account personal performance as well as the market value for that job.

Benefits include all one would expect of a top company: a good final salary contributory pension scheme (4% from employees, 14% from the company) with the right to make AVC contributions; a year-end gratuity which can be spent in part or whole on company shares at preferential rates; free private healthcare; good life cover and accident insurance; 25 days' holiday; a company car scheme with five levels of car; and annual parties depending on the location.

The Future

The prospects for Abbott Laboratories look rosy. In the last ten years, Abbott has grown at an average rate of 24% a year. This can be contrasted to the US stock market, which has grown at only 15–16% a year over the same period. Indeed, over the last quarter of 1998 the US stock market fell by 10% while Abbott grew by 6%.

This consistent growth is backed by the company's broad-based approach. Growth has been consistent across the four divisions, so that if one is performing less impressively for a time, another may be doing particularly well. The biggest challenge for the pharmaceutical arm is to find new products, especially important when development from idea to marketable drug can take 12 years. A number of new products are planned for launch over the next few years.

The industry is a highly competitive one, so Abbott needs to attract and retain the best people to keep its edge. However, it seems to be doing exactly this. One aspect which could help to retain staff is that Abbott's chairman has gone on record to state that the company is not interested in taking part in a big merger. It is large enough to resist hostile attention from others, and will make only small, strategic acquisitions itself. This can be an important factor in the pharmaceutical world where 'mega-mergers' often mean staff reductions.

Overall, Abbott Laboratories looks well placed for the future: its international resource, its broad base, its oncoming products and above all its bright, committed and motivated staff look to stand it in good stead.

Abbott Mead Vickers·BBDO Limited

Abbott Mead Vickers·BBDO is the leading advertising agency in the UK by billings (turnover), which reached £356 million in 1997, and the winner of numerous creative awards. Abbott Mead Vickers was created in 1977 by the three people in the company's name. In 1991 Abbott Mead Vickers bought BBDO London; at the same time, BBDO's parent Omnicom acquired a 25% share in Abbott Mead Vickers plc, and in 1999 it acquired the rest of the equity. Today the AMV group is one of the largest marketing services companies in the UK, the result of a number of acquisitions, and BBDO Worldwide the world's fourth largest agency network. Some 335 people work for Abbott Mead Vickers·BBDO.

Scorecard:

Remuneration and benefits	★★★★
Progressive attitude	★★★★★
Opportunity for promotion	★★★★
Training, development and education	★★★★
Working atmosphere and environment	★★★★★

Biggest plus:
Creative, caring, fun, focused

Biggest minus:
Most advertising agencies, happily, lack too much structure

Abbott Mead Vickers·BBDO Limited
151 Marylebone Road
London NW1 5QE
Tel: 0171 616 3500
Fax: 0171 616 3600
website: amvbbdo@amvbbdo.co.uk

Abbott Mead Vickers·BBDO Limited

The Business

Abbott Mead Vickers·BBDO (AMV·BBDO) is all about *advertising*, and highly creative advertising at that (though it does take very seriously the need to make a profit). In the advertising business, an agency's reputation and track record of creative and effective advertising is everything. And AMV's is second to none.

Take their clients' word for it. *Marketing Week*'s annual reputations survey of the people who matter had AMV·BBDO as first for creativity, the highest valued criterion.

AMV·BBDO's impressive client list includes BT, *The Economist*, Guinness, Gillette, Dulux, Pepsi-Cola, Pizza Hut, Sainsbury's, Volvo and the RSPCA. An agency with ethics and discerning taste – it will not work for tobacco companies but enjoys the challenge of charity and social conscience advertising – it considers its compatibility with potential clients as much as they judge AMV·BBDO.

The relationship with BBDO has proved to be a fruitful one, and international advertising now accounts for around one third of the agency's income; these opportunities are increasing all the time. AMV·BBDO is the centrepiece of the AMV group, a web of related marketing services companies linked by the craft of persuasive communications.

Company Culture and Style

AMV·BBDO claims a unique culture, a 'family' environment with an informal style, free of back-stabbing and full of nice, talented people living and breathing their work. It's cohesive, perhaps surprisingly so for its size (the smallest big agency in the UK perhaps?), and is well led. David Abbott, Peter Mead and Adrian Vickers, who knew each other as friends for twenty years before they started AMV, are still involved with the agency.

'No room for disruptive geniuses,' says deputy chairman Adrian Vickers. 'We have no faith in creation through conflict.' AMV·BBDO far from discourages opinions, but it does look for a team effort to secure the end result. It wants bright, talented people to come to work, enjoy it, and celebrate success together.

And there's ample opportunity for that. AMV·BBDO scooped no fewer than 21 creative awards in 1998, and won 12 new business assignments over the year. And that's not including birthdays, weddings and other parties!

A recent move to a new building (still on Marylebone Road) gave the agency the chance to refresh and improve the working environment, and offer facilities such as free breakfast (Adam Smith was sort-of wrong), and a subsidised bar in the evenings. Jazz nights, a softball team, showers and tumble dryers (swimming is a popular lunchtime pastime) show a subtlety of touch in social activities.

In the words of David Abbott: 'You will almost certainly enjoy working at AMV·BBDO. You will sometimes put in unbelievably long hours, you will be frustrated by colleagues and clients alike; you will feel burdened by deadlines; but the exhilaration will always outweigh the exhaustion.'

Human Resources

AMV·BBDO takes a professional approach to managing its human resources – somewhat uncommon in the advertising industry – which shows that the agency 'walks the talk' in describing people as 'our principal asset'.

Regular management meetings help shape policy and provide feedback on staff issues, while the HR team analyses and provides training requirements, remuneration packages and ensures that staff are always treated fairly.

The agency also 'does what it takes' to support any individual and personal crises. It has allowed long lay-offs, provided company loans to ease people through financial difficulty, runs stress management seminars, helps with tax returns, and maternity, paternity and compassionate leave is generous. In the creative business perspiration can be as important as inspiration, and to foster an atmosphere where people are willing to work hard for the cause, a sympathetic touch is needed.

AMV·BBDO recruits graduates and direct-entry professionals. The agency also has a relatively novel and high-powered despatch department. A few graduates who missed the first cut at account management or planning are given a second 'bottom-up' chance; a number of people have made it through this way.

Working hard to maintain its culture despite being a 'big' agency, AMV·BBDO puts time and effort towards internal communication and helping people familiarise with each other – and with the ever increasing number of other companies in the group. It's vital that individuals frequently come into contact with their colleagues – the advertising industry would find it difficult to operate from remote locations.

Diversity happens quite naturally at AMV·BBDO and it needs no policy – it employs anyone who brings real talent to its business and over 50% are women.

Career Opportunity and Development

AMV takes a long-term view of its business, and treats each person who joins the agency as *potentially* being there for a long-term career.

There are at least six types of career specialisation available at AMV·BBDO: creative, account management, planning, media, finance and production.

As brand leader, AMV·BBDO receives a lot of job applications and requests for work placements. Applications are invited from anywhere, and the company visits 4–5 universities and a number of regional centres. In competing for the best talent, the agency believes that it is fighting perceptions. 'People think that they can retire at 30 if they enter investment banking or management consultancy,' suggests Cilla Snowball, head of account management, 'so we need to portray the long-term attractiveness of the advertising business.'

Once it has found its people, AMV·BBDO aims to keep them – by constant training, development, evaluation and improvement.

Graduates start with six weeks of intensive training run by agency personnel, to provide the basics needed to do the job. After this grounding, people are given specific accounts and, as part of an account team, continue to learn and develop new skills. Progress is also monitored by a mentor assigned to each individual and there are regular assessments.

It might appear surprising that graduates are let loose on clients so quickly. But the advertising industry is one where you can do something 'useful' very early on. If there is one inherent characteristic of successful graduates who fight their way through the odds to join AMV·BBDO, it is confidence (without arrogance).

'The Knowledge' is AMV·BBDO's specially designed course to assist account managers and planners as their career progresses in a wide variety of topics from understanding the production process, to managing bosses, to new media, to how to brief creative teams. The sessions are run by both internal and external speakers, spanning national and international perspectives alike. 'The Knowledge' is also an excellent forum for meeting, mixing, sharing experiences and polishing core skills.

AMV·BBDO has long since recognised the importance of training – it motivates people, hones skills and instils confidence. But the economics of the advertising agency are such that you cannot have too many people 'not in at the deep end'. 'And anyway,' says Adrian Vickers, 'this obliges us to provide the best kind of development, combining theory with on-the-job training.'

The link with BBDO has brought overseas opportunities and people frequently find themselves waving their passport at the airport. Secondments to client companies also feature.

Remuneration

AMV·BBDO hires the best talent and is prepared to offer competitive pay and benefit packages to find it. Its high retention rates (staff as well as clients) support this. There is no pay grading system, but managers have pay brackets in their heads. And it always remains a meritocracy.

Bonus schemes are various, with some spontaneous and informal varieties alongside the annual ones. Incentive schemes are there for senior management, linked to the company's profitability and share price performance.

Benefits include life assurance, health insurance and company cars. AMV·BBDO takes its company pension scheme *very* seriously, not only offering an attractive scheme but actively encouraging its younger staff to understand pensions.

The Future

The AMV group is already benefiting from the trend (driven by clients) towards integrated marketing communications. That should provide tremendous opportunities for a new breed of multi-skilled person to emerge – someone with expertise in the other marketing communications disciplines just as much as advertising.

AMV·BBDO is regarded as a great place to work, and many talented people already do. But the best people are always in demand by others and, to retain them, AMV·BBDO must continue to motivate, train and stretch them.

Creative work is the lifeblood of the agency. Primacy of ideas and creativity will remain absolutely fundamental to AMV·BBDO, with everyone motivated, driven and fascinated by the creative product.

At the time of the advertising agency's twentieth birthday in 1997, *Campaign* magazine wrote: 'Throughout its history, Abbott Mead Vickers·BBDO has never pursued size for its own sake, but focused only on achieving excellence. Yet, by concentrating on the latter, it has achieved the former. By hiring the best people and treating them with respect and decency, AMV has created a cycle in which virtue brings success. It is hard to see how that virtuous circle could be broken.'

Ove Arup & Partners

Ove Arup & Partners is an international firm of consulting engineers, providing engineering design, planning and project management services for civil, industrial, building and transport developments. It employs 5,500 people worldwide, 2,500 in the UK.

Scorecard:

Remuneration and benefits	★★★★
Progressive attitude	★★★★★
Opportunity for promotion	★★★★
Training, development and education	★★★★
Working atmosphere and environment	★★★★

Biggest plus:
Extensive opportunities for secondment overseas

Biggest minus:
If you want cosy traditionalism, don't consider working here!

Ove Arup & Partners
13 Fitzroy Street
London W1P 6BQ
Tel: 0171 636 1531
Fax: 0171 580 3924
website: www.arup.com

Ove Arup & Partners

The Business

Ove Arup & Partners was founded in 1946 by Ove Arup, a British engineer of Danish descent. The firm started life by handling structural engineering for buildings: from there, it expanded into mechanical and electrical engineering, and thereafter into more specialised work such as civil engineering, industrial engineering, car design, acoustics, fire safety design, risk analysis and much more. Throughout its operations, the firm is known as a highly innovative business which invests considerable sums in research.

Among its many projects, Ove Arup & Partners is a member of the London & Continental Railways consortium for the Channel Tunnel Rail Link; responsible for engineering design and commissioning, the firm sponsored the route which was adopted by the government. It also handled project planning, structural, mechanical and electrical engineering and fire safety design for Heathrow's Terminal 5; did structural, mechanical and electrical engineering, communications and IT for the John F Kennedy International Airport, New York; and structural engineering for the 800-bedroom Shanghai Hilton.

In 1977, the founding partners vested their interest in a trust for the benefit of all employees. Part of the earnings are now shared among members of staff. In 1998, for instance, £6.9 million was set aside for profit sharing.

Today, 50% of the firm's work is UK-based, with the remaining 50% from its worldwide operations: Ove Arup & Partners has offices in 73 countries. The London offices are the largest group, followed by Hong Kong.

Company Culture and Style

In 1970, Ove Arup delivered an address to partners known an 'The Key Speech'. This included a statement of corporate aims which continue to drive the company forward. Those principles include a humanitarian attitude, creating a philanthropic and friendly organisation; no discrimination on grounds of sex, race or religion; and a belief that work should be excellent, interesting and rewarding while benefiting society.

Arup focuses on quality engineering. Stella Littlewood, personnel director: 'We are an organisation which balances profitability with very strong feelings about people and how to treat them properly.' Even so, Arup is no place for the passive. A challenging environment encourages employees to take active responsibility, and people who need to be told what to do at every step are likely to fall by the wayside.

Everyone works as a member of a project team, which can range in size up to 600 people. Project engineers and group leaders play a pastoral as well as a technical role, acting as mentors, reviewing performance and helping to develop competencies. Enjoyment at work is regarded as essential.

In Stella Littlewood's words, the firm is 'Anything but bureaucratic!' Instead, the culture is one where people take responsibility early on and very much shape their own careers.

Human Resources

Arup recognises that people are its greatest asset. As a result, HR is a high priority for the firm, and is represented on the main board. The personnel strategy clusters around five key issues: resourcing (creating a global skills database and an Intranet vacancy system); development and training (succession and leadership development, a competency framework, a graduate programme, career development and global appraisal); reward (links with performance and competence, open structure, global profit-sharing and benchmarking); international (mobility strategies, modern tax and pay policies, global career development, consistency for local staff employment terms, and international titles); and personnel support (local access personnel information system, modern care policies and consistent employment terms).

The HR strategy overall is to encourage its people to be highly adaptive, given the changing and unpredictable nature of its markets. The firm aims to be a global player: as a result, it seeks to give its business leaders the skills to identify patterns of change and predict market forces shaping the future. Skills and resourcing will continue to be at the forefront for the firm in its area.

Career Opportunity and Development

As part of its support for engineering staff attempting to gain professional qualifications, Arup provides not only on-site experience but also off-the-job training. All candidates receive personal guidance with access to a supervising engineer. The firm even offers courses in essay writing and presentation skills for those sitting exams.

Arup aims to provide several days' off-site training for all employees each year. A wide range of modules includes interviewing skills, motivating project teams, highways and bridge design, emergency first aid and client care. Arup's annual training budget is £2.5 million, and a two-year programme is currently investing substantially in new ways to benefit people strategically. This includes working with Reading University to develop an MSc in project management, linked to national vocational qualifications – the first of its kind in the UK. The firm is also starting to give people wider cultural skills for operating internationally.

The firm has no formal fast track of management development. The appraisal system identifies those individuals with the ability to move forward, and the Bright Lights programme also develops people through communication groups which operate as shadow boards.

Abundant opportunities exist for secondment overseas, so many, in fact, that the firm cannot always find enough employees to fill them. At any given time, approximately 20% of the UK office will be working overseas, amounting to 500 members of staff.

Numerous examples may be found of employees rising through the ranks. Arup's chairman Duncan Michael and joint deputy chairmen Bob Emerson and Mike Shears all joined as graduate engineers. Most promotion is internal. Arup is committed to developing its own management team, although external recruitment has been stepped up in recent years. The company maintains an active graduate recruitment programme, taking on 160 applicants in 1998. A number of these applied via the Internet.

Remuneration

Staff receive significant profit-share payments every year. Additionally, there is an annual pay round for all staff, with interim increases which also recognise exceptional performance. The firm is looking at developing a new remuneration and benefits package that fits a global business and improves its ability to move people around the world.

Senior staff receive company cars. After two years' service 24 days' holiday is standard, and all employees over the age of 21 can now choose between a final salary or money purchase pension scheme. The firm also provides life insurance (four times salary), accident cover (five times salary), generous maternity and paternity leave, 'well woman' screenings, and other benefits. Arup sponsors a wide range of sports activities including golf, sailing and cricket clubs.

The Future

Duncan Michael, Arup's chairman, identifies a range of critical issues for the future. First, he wants Arup to become a truly transnational organisation, not merely international. At the same time, it must remain close to the prime centres of capital spending. Third, the business should endeavour to balance size, success and financial security with retaining a rapid response. In so doing, the firm needs to take Arup's beliefs and attitudes across cultural barriers, and to spread appreciation internally and externally of the value of its endeavours. Finally, Duncan Michael insists that the firm must stay young in its attitude, remain outward looking and avoid introspection. 'None of these challenges has an easy solution,' he comments. 'All require continuous effort and can only be met by working hard.'

Arup is expanding internally far more than ever before. As a result, where it traditionally recruited engineers, it now looks for a whole range of business people, including economists and planners. But despite this strategic shift in the way it operates, Arup intends to remain a creative force in providing engineering solutions.

Stella Littlewood: 'Our firm is exceptional; we attract and retain the best. Nevertheless, there is a real need for us to respond to the global call and to take a step change in the whole area of people management and development.'

Above and beyond all these challenges, Arup remains guided by one key principle: to maintain the highest standards of professional integrity in an increasingly competitive and money-minded world.

AXA Sun Life Assurance Society plc

AXA Sun Life is the fourth largest company in the life and pensions industry in the UK, employing over 4,500 people. It currently trades under two brands: 'Sun Life', selling through Independent Financial Advisers (IFAs) and 'AXA Insurance' in the direct market. AXA Sun Life is a member of the global AXA group, one of the largest insurance and asset management groups in the world. It operates in over 50 countries and has almost 85,000 employees.

Scorecard:

Remuneration and benefits	★★★★
Progressive attitude	★★★★
Opportunity for promotion	★★★★
Training, development and education	★★★★
Working atmosphere and environment	★★★★

Biggest plus:
Being part of a large company which sees people management as vital

Biggest minus:
If you're inflexible and afraid of change, look elsewhere!

AXA Sun Life Assurance Society plc
Sun Life Centre
Brierly Furlong
Stoke Gifford
Bristol BS12 6SW
Tel: 0117 989 9000
Fax: 0117 989 1810

AXA Sun Life Assurance Society plc

The Business

AXA Sun Life was formed in 1997 with the merger of the Sun Life Group and AXA Equity and Law. The new company has a combined total of almost 350 years' expertise in financial services. Between them, the two companies have won the prestigious Financial Adviser '5 Star Service Award' 11 times.

Following the merger, AXA Sun Life launched its 'Mission Challenge' (developed in consultation with staff), designed to bring everyone together behind a common vision: to be 'Recognised as Leaders – Recommended as the Best'.

The Mission Challenge also established shared goals and a clear strategy, a key element of the latter being a commitment to investing in staff. The company recognises that it will only continue to be a successful business if all employees are encouraged to learn, supported to deliver, and valued and rewarded.

As a further indication of the company's ambition, the profile of AXA in the UK has recently been raised with the sponsorship of the FA Cup, costing £25 million over four years.

Company Culture and Style

The merger created the challenge of unifying two cultures. This task was made easier by the companies having many cultural similarities, but inevitably with two such large organisations, this was not achieved overnight. Throughout 1998 and into 1999, a considerable amount of work has been and will be done to ensure the cultures mesh together seamlessly.

At the heart of the new culture are seven values: ambition, commitment, imagination, loyalty, pragmatism, pride and team spirit. For its employees, AXA Sun Life is committed to encouraging learning, supporting them to deliver, and valuing and rewarding good performance. The aim is to reward success at every level, an initiative enhanced by performance management systems.

Michael Baker, general manager (human resources and office services), describes the culture at AXA Sun Life as 'Open, honest and performance-driven. It's a culture which seeks to give people more opportunity to develop and grow.' The approach is to train people in terms of knowledge, skills and competencies and test them against those criteria – and then empower them. The philosophy is to bring decision-making as close to the customer as possible.

The stars of the AXA Sun Life's future are likely to be innovative, customer-serving, and above all, flexible. Self-motivated people do well, aided by the company's Personal Development Portfolio. The company sees attitudes and behaviours as more important than academic qualification. It can provide all the training anyone needs – but that's useless without the right approach!

AXA Sun Life is well served when it comes to internal communications. It has its own Communications Manager whose team produces the award-winning company newsletter and other items. One is *Kick Off!* a monthly magazine arising out of AXA's sponsorship of the FA Cup (which also gives staff access to cup game tickets).

Each year, the company holds a Challenge Day under the aegis of its community partnership coordinator. Over 600 people regularly take part, helping with community projects in and around its Bristol and Coventry office sites: painting the homes of the old and infirm, making toys, clearing rubbish from sites and transforming them into play areas, and so on.

Human Resources

The company's human resources policy is embodied in its mission challenge, which is all about setting new standards in everything it does. The key areas are: motivated and highly skilled people; totally professional distribution channels; innovative products and services; superior investment performance; fast, friendly and fault-free service; and competitive costs.

Considerable resources are devoted to human resources: a group HR department of around 60 people, as well as 50 dedicated training staff within the business areas. HR issues are regularly on the agenda at general management level, and the Corporate Plan has a section on HR. Each department then has its own plan to be implemented, arising out of the overall plan. Targets are set through the corporate planning process, published, and reviewed regularly. Staff are surveyed and the results published and followed up.

Career Opportunity and Development

AXA Sun Life has a graduate recruitment programme. Some opportunities exist particularly in certain specialist areas: actuarial departments, for instance, want maths and science graduates, while IT graduates are sought for special projects. The company also recruits a number of MBAs each year.

Career development is fostered by moving within the company (including a growing number of overseas opportunities through the AXA group). The chief executive, Les Owen, has stated that he wants senior management to have had exposure to different parts of the business. Another part of career development is to work exclusively on a special project, for three to six months. Such people are usually middle managers chosen for their ability and potential. Managers have their own development programme, run by a management development manager.

The company operates a 360-degree appraisal system right up to chief executive level. This means that your boss, your colleagues, your reports and your customers, as well as you, have an input into your appraisal which takes into account everything from competencies and behaviour to attitudes. This is obviously more time-consuming than some systems, but also seems to produce more constructive and balanced results.

The company recognises that the old 'jobs for life' adage has gone forever. Nevertheless, for those who want a long-term career (and the current average length of service is nine years), AXA Sun Life offers plenty of career development and continual challenge. It's also quite possible to move through the ranks: chief executive Les Owen joined as an actuarial student at the age of 22. Michael Baker joined at the age of 16 and has worked in many areas – he is doing his second stint in HR!

Training is taken seriously at AXA Sun Life, evidenced by high levels of training expenditure. Each of the 25 customer services departments has its own full-time trainer, as does every sales channel. There is a blend of internal and external training. Management training includes at least a week at the AXA University in Bordeaux, offering excellent facilities in superb surroundings. People are also encouraged to enhance their professionalism by taking relevant insurance, actuarial or management exams. This takes the form of offering day release, and paying examination fees and sometimes bonuses for passing.

Remuneration

The company sees itself as a median payer – although in the upper quartile when it comes to total earnings. Individual salaries are in fairly wide bands: for instance, the average middle manager's salary is

£30,000 while the highest is £50,000. These wide bands are in place throughout the organisation, and movement between bands is entirely performance-driven. Managers can award individual merit increases up to 10% of salary, arising out of performance against targets. There are also team-related bonuses where the team makes savings against its budget while meeting its customer-service standards.

There is a wide spread of benefits. These include: an employee assistance programme whereby employees can get independent, expert and confidential advice on anything from finance and law to personal health; a group-wide profit-sharing scheme; an SAYE scheme; a non-contributory pension plan; free life assurance cover; free private medical insurance; sports club membership; a season ticket loan; and a career break scheme.

Another benefit is the brand new head office, completed at the end of 1996. This landscaped facility brings together over 2,000 employees in one area, and offers excellent sports, eating and entertainment facilities as well as a crèche.

The Future

The main challenge for AXA Sun Life is to ensure continual growth. A key way of doing so is to attract and retain the best staff, so as to have the right skills in place to manage the business through continual transition while delivering its business targets. The merger allows the company to draw on the synergies created by bringing together two leading UK players and also gives access to a more global corporate organisation, creating better opportunities for international growth.

Another challenge is to operate more flexibly. As Michael Baker puts it, 'We will be offering different types of employment packages in the future. I'm sure we'll be staying open for longer hours. Some people may work shifts, others will perhaps work from home. The changing needs of the business will continue to affect us here, as elsewhere. Our challenge is to stay on top of those changes.'

Bacon & Woodrow

Bacon & Woodrow is the largest independent partnership of actuaries and consultants in Europe. As a member of Woodrow Milliman, an international network of actuarial and consulting firms, Bacon & Woodrow operates in over 30 countries worldwide. It is also joint venture partner in Callan Bacon & Woodrow, a global investment consultancy. Bacon & Woodrow employs nearly 1,000 staff and partners.

Scorecard:

Remuneration and benefits	★★★★★
Progressive attitude	★★★★★
Opportunity for promotion	★★★★★
Training, development and education	★★★★
Working atmosphere and environment	★★★★

Biggest plus:
Innovative, blue-chip reputation – and treats people
as individuals

Biggest minus:
Fast-paced and intellectually challenging, so not a company
for everyone!

Bacon & Woodrow
Parkside House
Ashley Road
Epsom
Surrey KT18 5BS
Tel: 01372 733000
Fax: 01372 733218
website: www.bacon&woodrow.co.uk

BACON & WOODROW

Bacon & Woodrow

The Business

Bacon & Woodrow was founded in 1924 as an actuarial consulting practice. This remains part of the firm's remit, as does its independence: it is a UK-based, equity-owned business, the shares being held by 45 partners of the firm. In other ways, however, Bacon & Woodrow is a far cry from the traditional view of actuaries. Today, it prides itself on solving complex problems in practical, commercial and cost-effective ways, pushing back the boundaries of traditional financial consultancy with a range of sophisticated analytical tools.

The focus nowadays is very much on providing strategic, financially focused consultancy advice. Working in multi-disciplinary teams, the firm uses its experience and skills to help clients resolve strategic issues and solve complex financial problems. Its expertise embraces employee benefits, insurance and investment, as well as specialist areas such as healthcare, IT and communications. Bacon & Woodrow is deservedly known as an innovative and creative company. It was the first in its sector to provide on-line advice, offers leading-edge dynamic modelling packages, and spends over 10% of its annual revenue on investment in technological and product development.

Bacon & Woodrow has offices in seven locations in the UK, one in France and one in Germany, and will shortly open a Netherlands office. It has subsidiaries in Ireland, Mauritius, Trinidad and Guernsey.

Company Culture and Style

The firm comprises a mix of people. Although the core remains those with actuarial training, the business increasingly employs accountants, lawyers, insurance specialists, economists and even those with medical expertise. What they all have in common, though, is intellect. Bacon & Woodrow demands a lot from its people and looks for those who thrive on mentally challenging work. The work is intellectually fast-paced and employees need to be able to cope with that. Of course, for those who can, this is an ideal environment.

Paula Cook, personnel director: 'We employ very intelligent people who are, or want to become, specialists. We place a premium on those who combine teamworking with an ability to champion their own cause. This means that they're individuals, and we want them to stay that way. We welcome their diversity, even their foibles. It's very much a case of the firm providing the frame and the canvas and letting our people pick the colours they want to paint with.'

Much of the work involves getting across highly complex information in simple, business-oriented language. Furthermore, Bacon & Woodrow people work closely with their clients. For these reasons, the culture favours self-starting entrepreneurs with good communication and interpersonal skills. The firm also looks for those with leadership potential, insight, the desire for continual self-development and the ability to create research-based hypotheses.

As an independent partnership, the firm can still allow itself to be paternalistic in the good sense of that word. For instance, loan schemes are provided, and wedding gratuities are still paid to staff about to marry. There is a real buzz in the company's offices and a willingness to use high technology to assist its problem-solving techniques: but at the same time, a strong sense of nurturing its people and treating them as individuals is maintained.

Human Resources

Until 1996, HR at Bacon & Woodrow was seen more in the traditional light of simply administering staff. No longer. Today, HR has a high priority. Paula Cook, who was the firm's first board appointment for HR, explains: 'We now have a four-quadrant system, focusing on clients, people, growth and finance. This is replicated throughout the firm. Our HR team works within the firm, getting to know our staff as people and helping them focus on those quadrants.' The result of this sharper HR emphasis is a significant improvement in employee retention.

The firm has an annual staff attitude survey, commissioned externally. Of the questions asked, 75% relate to standard corporate policies, allowing the firm to compare itself to its market peers, while the remaining 25% focus on Bacon & Woodrow specifics. The latest survey showed a strong level of satisfaction with the way the firm operates.

Career Opportunity and Development

In 1998, Bacon & Woodrow hired 44 graduates, and in 1999 will take on 56: 40 actuarial, 10 investment-focused and six management consultancy trainees. Graduate recruits in its UK offices start at over £19,000 and can expect to earn over £35,000 plus benefits upon completion of professional exams, which the firm believes should be achieved in under four years. The firm also hires a number of specialists each year – usually graduates with relevant work experience.

Career development is all about competencies. The firm's framework mirrors its corporate scorecard of four quadrants, with an added evaluation of personal effectiveness. To be promoted, a candidate needs to demonstrate competency in these areas, as measured by the appraisal system. Other factors may also be considered, from broader work experience to joint initiatives. Candidates for promotion to all senior positions are seen by the management group, which will always feed back its analysis of the person's effectiveness.

Bacon & Woodrow people can move around within the UK if they wish: the firm has offices in Cardiff, Birmingham, Bristol, Epsom, Leeds, London and St Albans. Vacancies are openly advertised, and anyone who successfully applies will receive relocation support. Experience is also gained by working within teams and benefiting from shared expertise. Overseas, secondments are available in the USA, Trinidad, France, Germany and elsewhere, either on a short-term (two to three year) basis or longer. There are also international projects which pull in expertise from many countries. With clients all over the world, this could appeal to someone who relishes the prospect of global travel.

Training is taken seriously. Internal personal and business skills training is linked to the competency framework, while the firm also works with specialist training partnerships. Everyone, including each of the partners, receives a minimum of six days' training a year. This will rise to ten days minimum by the year 2000. Professional qualification is also encouraged by fee paying, study leave and other means, particularly for graduate recruits who in some cases have one day in every week off for professional study.

Remuneration

Paula Cook: 'We want people to work here for more than just the money! Having said that, we see ourselves as above-median for payment. We will pay to recruit and retain the right people. We have broad payment bands, but can and do go beyond those to attract and keep exceptional performers.'

Basic pay is assessed against achievements by section and by individual, but bonuses are also an important part of remuneration at Bacon & Woodrow. These depend on the firm's profits and are allocated by team, in the form of equity.

Benefits include a good pension scheme, private health cover, BUPA, a car scheme with a cash alternative, discount schemes with local shops, season ticket loans, car parking payment, and various sports and social activities which vary by office location. Supporting charities by organising events is also popular, often backed by the firm financially.

The Future

One challenge for Bacon & Woodrow is to grow globally without compromising its independence. Paula Cook: 'We want to expand our operations, but at the same level of quality we have here in the UK. We want to be the best of breed wherever we are, and this is a challenge, especially in the current "big is beautiful" environment.'

Another challenge is to retain the firm's innovative edge, which naturally depends on retaining the highest calibre of people.

Last but not least, the firm intends to retain its quality client base. 'We want to build on our high quality client base to increase the proportion of our clients which are FTSE-250 firms,' says Paula Cook. 'We are at our best when working for clients who are leaders in their fields.'

These challenges will require continued effort on the part of the firm; but the sheer dedication and work appetite of its highly motivated people make them look distinctly achievable.

The W & G Baird Group, Antrim

The W & G Baird Group is the dominant force in printing, book manufacturing and document management in Northern Ireland, with major publishing subsidiaries in England. Several of its present seven member companies were pioneers in the printing and publishing industry well back in the nineteenth century but its focus is firmly on the future. Through a total commitment to technological excellence and personal development, it is on course to achieve its target of a £45 million turnover by the end of the year 2000 and the development of a wider base in the communications industry.

Scorecard:

Salary and benefits	★★★★
Profit-sharing and other extras	★★★★★
Internal promotional mobility	★★★
Education, training and development	★★★★★
Working atmosphere and environment	★★★★

Biggest plus:
An exciting company committed to keeping ahead
in the future

Biggest minus:
Need for a more co-ordinated group culture and strategy

W & G Baird (Holdings) Ltd.
Caulside Drive,
Antrim BT41 2RS
Tel: 01849 463911
Fax: 01849 466266

W & G Baird Group, Antrim

The Business

The W & G Baird Group has grown from a small print shop started in Belfast in 1862 to become one of Northern Ireland's leading companies and one of the most progressive and technically advanced printing and book manufacturing groups in Britain. Its product range stretches from food packaging to digital document management technology.

The 'core' company, W & G Baird Limited, was brought back into Northern Ireland ownership in 1977 through a management buy-out from the British Printing Corporation led by the group's present chairman Roy Bailie. It has never looked back. Continual investment in leading-edge printing and digital technology, in people, in developing new markets and in strategic acquisitions have increased sales from £400,000 in 1977 to £34 million last year and have it on target to achieve £45 million by year end 2000.

Company Culture and Style

When Roy Bailie took control of the company in 1977 he set his team one target, from which everything else has flowed – simply 'to be the best at what we do'.

That is his style and it has set the pattern for the company's culture ever since – very few formal structures, just do whatever has to be done to achieve the best possible results.

Harnessing technology and managing change, in an industry where change is bewilderingly rapid, are skills at which the company excels, and investment in state-of-the-art equipment and the training to match it have positioned it centre-stage in the British printing industry.

Roy Bailie says that group's ethical stance is based on the belief that the greatest asset an organisation can have is a reputation for integrity. For a company to thrive in the long term and provide opportunities for succeeding generations of people it must have ethical leadership, a sound covenant and a rich culture. 'Management at W & G Baird believe that corporate culture is the day-to-day experience that arises from our fundamental covenants – with our customers, with our staff and with the wider community.'

Directors, managers and staff are encouraged to participate in community and public enterprises and endeavour to make a contribution to their local communities.

W & G Baird Limited is an Investors in People company and all operational companies are ISO 9002 accredited. It is also group policy for all member companies to work towards ISO 14000 environmental accreditation.

The group consists of six companies, diverse in the nature of their business activities and diverse geographically and culturally:

W & G Baird Limited of Antrim has an enviable reputation as one of the UK's most sophisticated and technically advanced printing facilities. Textflow Services in Belfast is a pioneer in using digital technology to convert information in any format to digitally printed 600 dpi form for a wide range of 'on demand' printing. MSO Limited of Belfast designs and manufactures printed packages, boxes and presentation packs and is a leading manufacturer of packaging for the food industry and a growing force in multi-media packaging.

Biddles Limited of Guildford and King's Lynn is a major British book manufacturer and an acknowledged leader in the production of illustrated non-fiction books for publishers across Europe. Blackstaff Press is one of Ireland's most highly regarded, most exciting book publishers, focusing on history, politics, fiction, humour and poetry. Thanet Press – formerly Eyre & Spotiswood of Margate – is a leader in the field of academic, legal, scientific and security printing.

With this diversity, chief executive Ken Lindsay admits it will be some time before a 'group culture' will be achieved, although with a very individualistic leadership blind uniformity would hardly be encouraged. One problem, for example, is the different degree of 'unionisation' among the various workforces, with some plants in England having a traditionally strong union influence which is virtually unknown in the 'home' companies.

Human Resources

The maintenance of the W & G Baird reputation for excellence depends on its ability to recruit, develop and retain people of the highest calibre at each level of the organisation. It does this by a rigorous recruitment procedure, close monitoring during the 'induction' period, and sustained and targeted investment in training.

This training commitment has two aims – to encourage and enable individual people to achieve their full potential and thereby to improve the potential of the business.

W & G Baird strives to be an excellent employer because its management believes that people who are excited, challenged and trained produce the best products, the best service – and the best results. High standards of customer care will follow high standards of employee care, it contends.

There is an awareness that as the business grows, diversifies and faces the challenges of being a major international player in its industry, there will be a need for a stronger top management team, especially at board level, to co-ordinate the activities of the member companies.

Bryan McCabe, managing director of W & G Baird Limited says: 'The company is committed to providing comprehensive training and career opportunities available in the industry. This ensures that every individual in any of our companies achieves the maximum rate and level of career fulfilment possible.'

Roy Bailie: 'People skills, and the technologies to allow them to be deployed, give our companies the edge in very competitive markets.'

Career Opportunity & Development

All staff in W & G Baird Group get the chance to participate in twice-yearly personal development interviews with mutually agreed programmes for the development of skills and aptitudes.

The company believes that this process, the internal route, is the most successful method of progressing into senior positions and considerable efforts are made to identify and develop the talents of staff at all levels. This involves in-house training, specific short external courses and support through degree or specialist courses.

For example, when Baird recently invested more than £1 million in Swiss technology that enabled it to treble the speed of binding and finishing publications, making it a world leader in this area, it flew its key team to Zurich for extensive, exclusive, hands-on training from the Swiss manufacturers.

Baird operations director Henderson Allen says: 'This has been an innovative step. We are committed to developing our people and by taking the team away from production pressures and deadlines they were able to fine-tune their own personal skills on the machines. And while they were on the course they had the chance to network with people from printing companies in Russia and the United States, which was useful to them – and to us.'

Although the company does not go through an annual graduate placement procedure, recruiting only to fill vacancies or new openings that arise through expansion, new employees at W & G Baird can be sure of a working environment that is both stimulating, rewarding and full of opportunity. They have every opportunity and are encouraged to 'make a difference'.

Remuneration

While there is still a lot of work to be done on equalising salary and terms of employment across the companies of the widely scattered group, with their different systems and traditions, generally salaries and benefits are within the upper quartile of remuneration packages.

For upper and middle management, bonus and attractive pension schemes are inducements to performance.

The Future

For the past 20 years, W & G Baird has been building for its future by investing in the training and development of its people and pursuing leading-edge technology. The result is that its opportunities for growth and expansion are virtually infinite.

As its promotional brochure says: 'For over 130 years we have built our reputation on a tradition of quality, innovation and guaranteed personal service to our customers. We look forward to serving you to an even higher standard in the years to come.'

Roy Bailie sums it up: 'The growth of the W & G Baird Group is based on the development of people and an organisational structure which concentrates on raising skills and increasing commitment at all levels. Our future commitment is to the development of a wider base in the communications industry through acquisitions or alliances.'

Birse

Birse Group was formed in 1970 by Peter Birse, who remains as chairman. The principal operating subsidiary is Birse Construction, which is involved in building and civil engineering projects nationwide. In addition to its administrative office at Barton-on-Humber in north Lincolnshire, there are five regional offices and four area offices. Total workforce is just over 1,000, with subcontractors retained on specific projects as required. In the year to April 1998, the group recorded operating profits of £6 million on turnover of £450 million.

Scorecard:

Remuneration and benefits	★★★
Progressive attitude	★★★★★
Opportunity for promotion	★★★★
Training, development and education	★★★★★
Working atmosphere and environment	★★★★

Biggest plus:
Birse is pioneering a new management approach in its sector

Biggest minus:
Jealous rivals may try to catch up by poaching staff

Birse Group plc
Humber Road
Barton-on-Humber
North Lincolnshire DN18 5BW
Tel: 01652 633222
Fax: 01652 633360

Birse

Birse

The Business

It is fair to say that Birse has experienced fluctuating fortunes since the business was established in 1970 by the current chairman, Peter Birse. A period of sustained strong growth led to a stock market flotation in 1990 but the company suffered in the years of recession that followed. Committed and innovative management effort, however, has seen the business rebound so that turnover is now approaching £500 million and profitability is rising.

Birse's main interest is in construction and civil engineering. Notable high-profile contracts of recent years include the East India Dock commercial development, the Reebok Stadium at Bolton, and the Madejski Stadium at Reading. Bread-and-butter work includes retail developments, road building and pipelines.

Company Culture and Style

During the dark days of the early 1990s, Birse decided that a radical approach was required if the business was to survive and prosper. In 1996, it conceived the 'Birse Way', which articulates the company philosophy and identifies a series of 'Stands' to which all employees, at all levels, are encouraged to adhere. Central to the effectiveness of this approach are open and efficient channels of communication – something which is of particular importance in a business where much of its activity occurs on remote, temporary sites.

Birse believes in its people and endeavours to exploit their flair and initiative. For this reason, each site operates as if it were an individual contracting company, with senior management linking them to the regional network. What is more, each individual is expected to take responsibility for their own position so that they know precisely what is expected of them. Then, they are encouraged to suggest ways in which their role and the function of the company as a whole can be improved.

The Birse 'Stands' are what the company stands for. They are: Integrity; Brave and Learning; Open and Honest Communication; Profitability on all jobs; Always working safely; Being paid for what we do when we do it; Dealing with issues at the speed of light; Having a Great Life. The corollary is that the company will not stand for anything which deviates from these objectives. As the company states: 'All of our people are recognised for their extraordinary contribution to the good of the company. Those who would rather serve themselves are invited to leave.'

According to Steve French, the director responsible for safety, culture and people, the new culture is making an impact on the company's bottom line: 'We are set to make profit after years of decline. Everyone is learning how to be more responsible and thinking of new ideas on how to be more effective, save money and serve customers, whether within the company or externally. There is a buzz of excitement constantly kept alive as individuals discover the best way to deliver their true potential.'

As a construction company, Birse is obsessive about safety at work. But in terms of culture, Steve French says there is scope for risk-taking: 'People are taking risks, thinking for themselves, rather than merely following outdated formulas, learning how to really communicate with each other to achieve spectacular results.'

Human Resources

Human resources, as a separate management function, is relatively new to Birse, having been introduced in 1996. Significantly, and in line with the corporate culture, it is called the People Department. It has been charged with implementing a new grading system, which covers all staff and locates them precisely within the organisation, and with ensuring that each employee has a programme of development which will raise their performance and technical skills. Disseminating information and reporting feedback is another key area.

Recruitment of the right staff is also an important role of the HR facility. As well as technical ability, candidates must demonstrate the right attitude and be willing to adopt the Birse Way and adhere to the Birse Stands. The department also acts as a sounding board so that the cultural development of the company can be monitored. Exit interviews with departing staff and consultations with clients provide information on the 'current reality' so that trends can be analysed and problems solved.

The department also shoulders the responsibility for ensuring that the company complies with the welter of legislation and regulation which affects industry in general and its sector in particular. It is the first point of contact for those dealing with legal issues regarding staff and is there to provide expert advice so that litigation can be avoided wherever possible.

Career Opportunity and Development

Birse describes itself as being totally committed to being a learning organisation, which means learning how to serve the customer better, faster and cheaper. Within this overall concept, staff are encouraged to generate their own ideas and to contribute towards the success of their own area and the company as a whole. The open and honest lines of communication espoused in the Birse Stands help to monitor individual development, identify the best prospects and fast-track them through the ranks of the organisation.

Birse also boasts the 'Learning Liberator' programme, which is intended 'to mobilise the combined intelligence of all our people to live the Stands and to add knowledge for profit'. Its core elements are to demonstrate the importance of team learning; to unleash enthusiasm and ability to learn and grow in order to increase self-worth through achievement; to equip staff with the tools and opportunities to improve; to combine learning with business functions to benefit the bottom line; to enable lessons to be learned from good and bad situations; to strengthen relationships within teams; to create and share learning opportunities.

While it does not have a formal process for moving staff between disciplines, Birse encourages secondments from one site to another so that staff can gain experience of different tasks and locations. Certainly, staff might be expected to want to move as appropriate in order to enhance their personal development. Wherever possible, the company looks to fill senior positions by recruiting from within its own ranks.

Another significant factor, given the industry in which the company operates, is its 'Women on Board' initiative, which is designed to advance the careers of female staff. Louise Williamson has been appointed a director with responsibility for site productivity and technical excellence. Women will generally be given as much encouragement as possible at Birse.

Remuneration

Birse aims to 'retain, reward and develop' its staff through the payment of competitive salaries and an attractive pension scheme. The company's grading system provides each employee with a clear idea of their position relative to everyone else and allows them to 'know where they stand and what is expected of them'. The emphasis is on rewarding performance and initiative, with regular assessment interviews to ensure that remuneration matches achievement. Company cars are seen as essential, given that much of the company's operations take place on-site.

Almost as important as the actual remuneration is the Birse Stand which states that employees will 'Have a Great Life'. Unlike many companies, Birse actually believes that employees should enjoy what they do and that they will perform better if they are happy. One of the problems the company has identified is that its staff tend to work very long hours. It is keen to address this so that its people can make more of their leisure time so it is examining ways in which more can be achieved in fewer hours.

The Future

Birse's revolutionary approach to the management of its employees was hailed as a massive gamble when it was introduced in 1996, but the company's healthy turnover and profitability suggest that the gamble has paid off handsomely. Those who suggested that the modern approach to human resources issues would not work in a gritty industry such as construction and civil engineering have clearly been proved wrong.

The commitment to individual growth within the company necessitates significant senior management input; in other words, the managers who triggered the transformation of the company must continue to supervise its development. It is not a case of setting the business on a certain path and assuming it will reach its destination; constant involvement from the highest levels will be required to maintain the current pace of progress.

Equally, the practical development of the Birse Way has prompted the creation of a fully-fledged human resources facility: the People Department. This has a crucial role in determining the culture of the company but, as its members are the first to acknowledge, it cannot be allowed to dominate the organisation. It must provide the necessary framework within which the culture can flourish, but it must not interfere with the profitable development of the company as a whole.

Peter Birse certainly seems to think that the formula will continue to prove successful: 'Our ongoing cultural change continues to develop and strengthen our senior management teams and I am particularly confident that the people leading the business will continue to underwrite its successful development for some time to come.'

The BOC Group

The BOC Group is a British-based company that is truly global in terms of markets, management, technology and production. Best known for its gases business, the new BOC is being built around four lines of business – Industrial and Special Products, Process Systems, BOC Edwards and Applied Gas Solutions. BOC manufactures in more than 50 countries. In 1997, worldwide turnover was £3,550 million, on which it made a pre-tax profit of £247.2 million. Around 11,000 of the group's 37,000 employees are based in the UK.

Scorecard:

Remuneration and benefits	★★★
Progressive attitude	★★★★
Opportunity for promotion	★★★★
Training, development and education	★★★★★
Working atmosphere and environment	★★★

Biggest plus:
A professional and increasingly energetic style in a truly global company

Biggest minus:
The beginning of restructuring and building the New BOC

The BOC Group plc
Chertsey Road
Windlesham
Surrey GU20 6HU
Tel: 01276 477222
Fax: 01276 471333
website: www.boc.com.

 **THE BOC GROUP**

The BOC Group

The Business

BOC produces 20,000 different gas mixtures for use in the manufacture of just about everything produced by man and machine. Gases represent 'the invisible fabric of life' while vacuum technology is described as 'making nothing out of something'. The scope for new applications appears to be almost limitless.

Today, BOC is changing faster than at any other time in its history. The BOC of old is being regenerated into a modern company, a new BOC designed for success in the new millennium. The job of almost every single person in the group is being affected one way or another.

It had reached a watershed, and was in danger of falling over the wrong side. A harsh conflux of adverse factors put real pressure on the business. The Asian economy – to which BOC had a big exposure – was in crisis. Once a trump card, and surely long term a position of strength, this had a powerful impact. Throw in a strong sterling exchange rate, a slow down in the semiconductor market and the emergence of truly global competitors, and BOC had to change.

Spelling out the challenge, chief executive Danny Rosenkranz said: 'We have got to learn to grow profitable sales more quickly – and the emphasis is on the word "profitable". And we've got to develop a culture where productivity, quality and looking after the customer are absolutely endemic.'

The first step in this direction was for BOC to concentrate its energies, expertise and investment purely on its core industrial gases. Businesses have been sold, trimmed and restructured. The four lines of business, each serving a clearly defined type of customer, have taken on P+L responsibility. Jobs have been taken out of the businesses and IT is helping automate, standardise and avoid replication around the world.

In equipping itself to compete effectively on the global stage, BOC can draw upon many fundamental strengths. Its gases business is the market leader in most of the countries in which it operates. Its vacuum technology business is the preferred supplier to seven of the world's top ten semiconductor manufacturers. Its British origins gave the company a strong presence in the parts of the world 'once coloured pink', from which it has developed tremendous geographic spread.

Company Culture and Style

BOC is a technology-based company which thrives on innovation, patenting new inventions at the rate of one every four days. It takes special kinds of people to support and maintain such business momentum. People with initiative, ability and ambition. People with agile minds who can think laterally to devise radical solutions to complex problems. Above all, BOC needs people who can meet the exacting demands of customers.

Change, though, has been an ongoing process, and BOC has not had to adapt many aspects of its culture. It has always enjoyed excellent relations with its employees, even in difficult times. A willingness to discuss things openly, good people policies and local practices are a way of life at BOC.

Watchwords in the organisation are transparency, accountability, collaboration and 'stretch'. BOC is moving towards a less hierarchical structure, recognising that groups of people working together, supporting each other and challenging each other will grow the business. The organisation will not only be more cost-effective, but also one which stimulates growth. Organisational and business unit heads collaborate and support each other in meeting tough targets, and transparency is seen as the ideal way to leverage best practices across BOC.

'The professionalism and "classiness" of the managers, and the quality in depth of all staff, is impressive,' says Don Beattie, head of human resources. 'A relaxed style – but not a laid back one. People are very results-oriented, with a positive outlook on the opportunities for the group.' Yet BOC is a very open, informal business, and the working atmosphere reflects a non-hierarchical, sensitive and caring company.

This is a tremendously practical and energetic organisation, full of smart people willing to embrace change. 'I can understand why BOC might appear a little staid from the outside', says Alf Turner, HR Manager, 'but it's nothing like that. Any description of it being unexciting with nothing going on just couldn't be further from the truth.'

Human Resources

HR is reorganising away from its traditional model into a more effective way of providing human resources support to line managers and staff. HR plays a strategic role – working as a partner in each new business unit to ensure that HR strategy supports overall business strategy.

In this way, strategic HR is separated from service, although both are important. The development of HR service centres encourages self-help through the use of Intranet technology and helpline support both in back-office locations and in the field.

A 'win–win' scenario beckons, where a professional, supportive human resources function in the areas of recruitment, training and development, remuneration and change management can be provided at lower cost *and* provide a more efficient service.

While BOC's HR professionals face a major change management task, and technology will play a major role, it will make for more fulfilling jobs.

Career Opportunity and Development

BOC offers exciting careers across a range of disciplines, including engineering, finance, information management, commercial, distribution and technical development, as well as in other specialist functions.

Under 'Project Renew', BOC has challenged itself to get the right people resources and the right talent to deliver results in its new business units. Underpinning the business is the annual Organisational and Manpower Review process, which is reviewed within the year and covers succession management planning, development, and performance appraisals.

BOC enjoys a high standing in the graduate recruitment marketplace, and achieves an unusually high acceptance rate. Around 100 graduates in a range of disciplines are recruited each year, 40 from the UK. One attraction is BOC's excellent graduate trainee scheme. BOC also has good relationships with the leading business schools, in the UK and overseas.

The company also recruits direct entry professionals in, say, their mid-20s. The appeal to BOC is to bring in sharp, bright people with some industrial experience who have already been in tight situations. They can go a long way in the company.

Aware that it has previously been a little paternalistic, BOC now encourages individuals to take responsibility for their own careers, 'although the company is always there to help you drive these plans through', adds Alf Turner. Among the support mechanisms are career-planning workshops, comprehensive internal communications, and various programmes to give people the opportunity to 'stop and take a look at yourself in the mirror'. Participation in these workshops is often very enlightening. BOC still sponsors an awful lot of training, development and external courses, including MBAs and Open University degrees.

People do move internationally, through progressive steps of responsibility, and international assignments still play a major part in career development (BOC at any time has around 250 expatriates abroad). Benefits flow both ways – individuals gain valuable personal development and exposure to different international business styles, while BOC gains from the transfer of expertise, with specialists expected to leave behind three or four more 'new' experts after the assignment.

Remuneration

BOC is competitive on pay without entering into pay 'shoot-outs', preferring instead to emphasise other factors like job challenge, personal development, the people you work with, and the ability to increase your employability. In the business BOC wants to become, it will be seeking to reward success more directly.

There are various employee share schemes, with everyone in the UK eligible for the SAYE scheme. Around 350–400 managers are in the company share-option scheme. BOC offers the usual market competitive package of benefits, but is particularly proud of its company pension scheme.

The Future

BOC remains a highly international organisation going through necessary change. Some jobs are being lost (though not a significant number in percentage terms) and individual roles are changing. While not always ideal for employees in the short term, this process of change will make BOC a stronger organisation which they will benefit from.

The need to accelerate the development of managers through the organisation is as important a priority as ever. BOC expects to be 'management hungry' in the next decade and the changing structure of the business units has increased this requirement.

In an age where there is much talk about the concept of employability, BOC is stretching its people and at the same time needs to equip and provide them with the skills, the 'tool set' and attitude of mind to be employable in a fast-changing, modern world.

There has been a lot of soul-searching at BOC. But the reality is that it is now probably ahead of the game. The company reacted quickly in an innovative way to the problems faced in its geographical and business markets, and as a consequence its antennae are sharper. In an industry where there are four or five big players, and further consolidation likely, BOC intends to be in the lead. It's getting its message across.

The Boots Company

The Boots Company is best known for its UK chain of retail chemists, but is in fact a major group of companies operating principally in retailing, the manufacture and marketing of health and personal care products worldwide, and the development and management of retail property. Retail brands include Boots the Chemists, Halfords and Boots Opticians, making it one of the UK's leading retailers. Other businesses are Boots Contract Manufacturing, Boots Healthcare International and Boots Properties, contributing to a combined group turnover of over £5 billion and an operating profit of £538 million in the year to 31 March 1998. Around 79,000 people are employed in the group, of which some 76,000 are in the UK.

Scorecard:
Remuneration and benefits ★★★
Progressive attitude ★★★★
Opportunity for promotion ★★★★
Training, development and education ★★★★★
Working atmosphere and environment ★★★★

Biggest plus:
Huge range of opportunities with a progressive company

Biggest minus:
Working style and culture undergoing organisational change

The Boots Company PLC
Group Headquarters
Nottingham NG2 3 AA
Tel. 0115 950 6111
Fax 0115 968 7151
websites: www.boots-plc.com
www.bootscareers.com

THE BOOTS COMPANY

The Boots Company

The Business

Since it was founded by Jesse Boot in 1877, Boots has maintained a tradition of being a caring company, setting high standards both for its products and its workforce. While pursuing commercial interests, Boots at all times seeks to enhance its reputation as a well-managed, ethical and socially responsible company.

Boots the Chemists is the largest business, accounting for 70% of total group turnover with some 1,350 stores and over 58,000 employees. Its differentiating offer to consumers focuses on beauty and healthcare, positioning Boots as the store that helps customers to 'look good, feel good'. Boots own brand products are very successful and, of course, pharmacy is an integral part of each store. International Retail Development has moved from the pilot phase to 'learning by doing'. By the end of 1999 Boots should have seven stores in the Netherlands, four in Japan and 45 in Thailand.

Halfords is the UK's largest retailer of car parts, accessories, cycles and cycle accessories, with 412 stores and 9,581 staff. Boots Opticians has 285 stores and 4,349 staff.

Boots Healthcare International (1,952 staff) develops and markets consumer healthcare products in the UK, Europe, Africa, the Indian subcontinent, SE Asia and Australasia, including leading brands such as Nurofen and Strepsils. Boots Contract Manufacturing (4,027 staff) is Europe's leading manufacturer of own-label toiletries, cosmetics and consumer healthcare products. The small but profitable Boots Properties business manages the group's property portfolio.

Company Culture and Style

The Victorian paternalism of the founder still influences a strong culture of a caring, open, ethical organisation, and this is balanced with an increasing recognition of the importance of flair and entrepreneurial spirit. Andy Smith, director of personnel (group), says that he sees 'No incompatibility between a culture which demands high performance and a caring company – we try to support people to perform better.'

The company's ability to continue growing profitably depends heavily on the creativity, motivation and passion of its staff at all levels. Boots is devoting considerable resources to developing increasingly capable people and giving them greater freedom to take decisions and create more value.

Boots is an open, listening organisation which values the exchange of views and opinions among its staff. Great importance is attached to the creation of a good working environment for staff, which the company believes will translate into high standards of customer service.

Each business has its own management team and strong identity and culture, but they share the same common values and commitment to the success of the company overall. A recent group-wide project identified the behaviours and capabilities needed to maximise value. Each business unit is now evolving a more participative management style, introducing organisational and cultural changes best suited to its needs.

Boots the Chemists, for example, has embarked upon a fundamental change to improve its way of working, which may serve as a blueprint for other parts of the group. Task responsibility and profit accountability have been driven further down the organisation, while stores and marketing activities have been reorganised to produce a more customer-focused structure. It's all designed to inspire and harness people's energy and imagination and to minimise bureaucratic distractions. Boots Contract Manufacturing (BCM) has introduced self-managed teams to make people feel more involved.

Human Resources

Boots has a well-established reputation for enlightened employment policies including equal opportunity, individual staff development and family-friendly schemes such as job-sharing and career breaks. Some 80% of Boots the Chemists staff are female and over two-thirds return to Boots after maternity leave. There is even a summer play scheme in Nottingham, where Boots is the city's largest employer. Boots was a founder member of Opportunity 2000, and one of the first UK companies invited to use the 'Positive about disabled people' symbol.

Boots has devolved its human resources function further down the individual businesses to make them more effective, efficient, and responsive to customers' needs – and to their own – at the same time retaining an important strategic role for personnel at group level.

Boots invests substantially in training and development at all levels. Competency-related training is a high priority, with BTC's training budget running at £25m annually. Boots has also been involved with NVQs from the beginning and is the largest NVQ user in the country.

Sir Michael Angus, Boots deputy chairman, said: 'It is no coincidence that the company now has three Investor in People Awards, held by Boots the Chemists, Boots Contract Manufacturing and Boots Properties.' Boots the Chemists has also got through the tough reassessment procedure.

Effective communication is an important strand of personnel practice. The group staff magazine *Blueprint* is published monthly, a staff TV programme is produced quarterly and each employee receives an annual review of the plc's performance. Staff participate in weekly team meetings where company information cascades down, while the staff councils give ample opportunity for new ideas and opinions to cascade up.

Career Opportunity and Development

With six individual companies covering different sectors and professions, the Boots Company offers a wide range of career opportunities in retail management, pharmacy, optometry, science & technology, manufacturing, marketing, property management, logistics and telecommunications as well as professional support disciplines of finance, legal, IT and personnel.

Boots graduate recruitment scheme takes 60–70 people each year. The two-year graduate development programme, which is group-wide to offer diverse experience, has been accelerated to give early exposure to business strategies, broad experience across business units, and stretching personal targets. Specialist programmes also exist – for instance, some 350 graduate pharmacists join Boots the Chemists each year.

As Boots continues to develop globally, International Retail Development, Boots Healthcare International and Boots Contract Manufacturing are recruiting and retaining staff with an international capability.

Each employee has an annual performance review, which determines their pay. A separate development review takes place 2–3 months later, which leads to a personal development plan for each member of staff. Assessment centres and psychometric tests play a part in evaluating potential for career advancement.

Boots is keen to develop its own senior manager cadre, and of the top 200 managers working within the group, around half have worked their way up within the company. Direct entry and external hiring feature because Boots also needs to acquire new skills or bring in specific experience, and international expansion virtually demands it. Once on a management fast-track, the opportunities across the group are numerous.

Boots is a learning organisation and training and personal development are taken very seriously. It wants to produce world-class managers. At the top level, there is the opportunity to take part in the company's own executive development programme and an MBA programme at Nottingham University. Ongoing management and personal development is a flexible, self-help programme of on-the-job experience integrated with management and technical skills training.

Remuneration

Boots offers competitive salaries to attract and retain talented people, which can include a profit-related bonus if company targets are met. Good pension schemes are recognised as being increasingly important to staff and, while Boots' own pension scheme is highly rated, it regularly reviews its pension provision arrangements to ensure that its scheme continues to meet future and present needs.

The company encourages staff share ownership through its SAYE scheme, which gives an option to purchase shares at 80% of the market price. Generous staff discounts – between 12.5 and 22.5% – are available to staff on merchandise sold in all of the Boots retail chains.

The Future

Boots, along with the rest of the UK retailing industry, will have to 'tough it out' in the high street. The threat of a consumer downturn is never far away, and there is the additional factor of the trend towards out-of-town shopping. Boots is already expanding into new areas such as retail parks, airports and motorway service stations.

From its strong UK base, there appears to be interesting long-term opportunity for Boots to develop internationally – both in terms of store concepts and own label product. Boots is now rolling out a chain in Thailand, testing the water in the Netherlands, and preparations continue for entry to Japan in 1999.

Boots has backed its judgement that more autonomy and accountability must be entrusted to the individual business units. For a company which has traditionally been paternalistic and centralised functions to a degree, it will have to 'let go', while not missing opportunities to ensure that individual businesses continue to enjoy the advantage of being part of the group.

Lord Blyth of Rowington, chairman, says: 'We are actively seeking new opportunities and setting "stretch" targets for our businesses, challenging them to innovate and test their capabilities to the utmost. As a business, Boots is still far from mature: indeed, we are constantly delighted to find how much more we can do.'

Bristol & West plc

Bristol & West is the leading financial institution in the West Country and also has a national presence through its branch network, its intermediaries and its other distribution channels. The group's profit before tax was £91.2 million and gross residential and commercial mortgage lending reached £1,802 million for the financial year ending 31 March 1998. Bristol & West employs 2,500 people in the UK.

Scorecard:

Remuneration and benefits	★★★★
Progressive attitude	★★★★★
Opportunity for promotion	★★★★
Training, development and education	★★★★
Working atmosphere and environment	★★★★★

Biggest plus:
Has a distinctive strategy which gives it a strong sense of direction

Biggest minus:
Operates in an ever more competitive marketplace

Bristol & West plc
PO Box 27
Broad Quay
Bristol BS99 7AX
Tel: 0117 979 2222
Fax: 0117 929 3787
website: www.bristol-west.co.uk

Bristol & West plc

The Business

Bristol & West was founded in the mid nineteenth century as a building society. It converted to a bank when in 1997 it became part of Bank of Ireland group, creating a major new force in the British personal finance market.

The merger brought a range of benefits to Bristol & West. The relationship is such that Bristol & West enjoys considerable autonomy in its operations while gaining from its parent's strengths. John Burke, chief executive: 'We have better treasury back-up as a result of being part of Bank of Ireland group and also now have a first-class commercial lending department. This allows us to relationship-manage situations we would probably have had to turn away before.'

Bristol & West's strategy remains unchanged by the merger. That strategy, one of the clearest in its industry, is to focus on just three product types: mortgages, savings and investments. In so doing, it positions itself as a specialist rather than a generalist financial services company. Underlying this strategy is the company's belief that consumers would rather buy the best financial planning products than opt for one-stop shopping. The company's successful growth, to the point where it is now holding more than twice its natural market share, certainly appears to bear this strategy out.

Company Culture and Style

Kevin Flanagan, group services director: 'We're heavily focused on people and also on results. Therefore our culture is one where business performance and individual performance are both key. We have a demanding culture – but also a supportive and a rewarding one.'

Compared to many of its competitors, Bristol & West is refreshingly free from office politics, backbiting and the like. Instead, the culture is one of consensus, team-building, close working relationships and empowerment.

People certainly don't get bored at Bristol & West. Ian Kennedy, group operations director: 'There's lots to do here, and our style is very much about getting on with things. The organisation, like any other, may throw up barriers: our approach is not to stop at those barriers but to find a way round, over or through them.'

Fundamental to Bristol & West's culture is a set of principles. These set out such ideas as that people are inherently creative and capable of self-development; that teamwork and partnership are valued; that people are entitled to full and fulfilling private lives; and that support and encouragement bring out the best in people. Far from being empty words, these principles can be seen in action at all levels of the company.

Human Resources

Human resources appears on the highest possible agenda for this Investors In People accredited company: its strategy and business plan. Bristol & West has four principal business goals: to increase its return on equity, to grow its market share, to enhance its competitive advantage and to be a leading employer. Kevin Flanagan: 'We see the leading employer goal as inextricably connected to the others. And, although we have a busy and active HR department, our view is that HR is too important to be left solely in the hands of one department. At Bristol & West, the individual is responsible for his or her own development, and then the line manager has his or her role to play. We view HR as an enabling function, assisting those managers to better aid their people's development.'

Employee satisfaction is measured by questionnaire surveys known as the Partners' Audit. These show strong levels of support for the way the company is developing. A remarkable 90% of staff, for instance, know the corporate strategy, understand it fully, and approve of it. How many companies could say the same of their employees?

Communication includes regular face-to-face meetings, a company newsletter, and an impressive e-mail system. The latter includes a section called 'Reference' which allows any employee to look at the structure of a department, see the salary ranges, and in general get a good feel of any area he or she may be interested in moving to.

Career Opportunity and Development

Jeff Warren, deputy chief executive: 'Bristol & West has better systems for everything to do with staff and employment than any company I've known or worked for. Its attention to training, appraisals, career development and communications are all excellent.' Ian Kennedy concurs: 'What we do very well is give people responsibility and accountability early on. We simply don't have all that many layers of management: there are only three or four levels between me and the most junior recruit, for instance. Admittedly we do have grades within each level, but even these are being reduced. So there's plenty of opportunity to develop quickly.'

The company looks for people who are not afraid of change but instead are able to embrace it, since it operates in such a rapidly developing market. People need to be able to handle pressure and stress. Bristol & West takes on a significant number of graduates each year, but a degree in itself is not a passport to the fast track; ability, commitment and proven performance definitely are.

With a workforce of around 2,500, Bristol & West is large enough to move people around its organisation to boost their development. It has 152 branches in a network dominated by the South-west and South of England, but it attains national coverage through its other distribution channels such as intermediaries and telephone/post response. There are also some opportunities for working elsewhere in the Bank of Ireland group, something which is expected to increase over time.

Training, as mentioned above, has a high priority at Bristol & West. In a KPMG cost-benchmarking survey, the average amount of training for the financial sector was 8.5 days per employee; Bristol & West currently provides 16 days per employee. Kevin Flanagan explains why: 'It's a challenging environment, so our aim is to assist our people to become more expert. We focus on appropriate skill development. This includes a link with the University of the West of England, which runs courses including ones which use the participant's day job as a major source of learning.'

Development is not just classroom-based. The company has a strong community involvement which includes such ventures as team challenges to redecorate old people's homes, schools, etc. This is a practical and rewarding way to enhance team building, while providing the community with better resources.

The company is also striving to give women managers more opportunities. This includes greater flexibility for mothers in terms of continuing with their career: job-sharing, career breaks and part-time managerial roles.

Remuneration

The company sees itself as a median payer, but, as Ian Kennedy says, 'The total cash will be upper quartile if the company's performance is also upper quartile.' The bulk of salary is fixed, but there is a profit-related element of pay which can be around 10% for junior staff. For managers, the variable element increases as reward is more closely linked to individual performance.

As part of the Bank of Ireland group, all employees receive a free share issue, equivalent to 3% of salary in 1998. The shares are tax-free if held for three years. There are also share options for directors and their senior managers.

Pension arrangements are currently under review, but there is both a final salary and a defined contribution scheme. Other benefits include four times' salary life cover free; private medical insurance for all, with benefits varying with employment level; a good car scheme; and a generous holiday allowance.

The Future

Jeff Warren sees the future as 'Exciting and tough. There have been tremendous changes in our industry over the last few years, and I expect no less over the coming years.' Ian Kennedy agrees: 'There will be many changes, but because of our size and flexibility, we're able to move much faster than our bigger competitors. Our strategy is also in tune with the consumer marketplace: they want specialists for different needs, and that's exactly what we are.'

John Burke envisages the company spending more time on scenario-planning (the 'what ifs' of the marketplace) and on risk management. In addition, he predicts that: 'Going forward, we will need to address our cost base: through cost management rather than cost-cutting. As productivity increases, systems tend to take over manual jobs. We will need to reskill and redeploy our staff. There is also the challenge of having the right people in the first place, but here I am confident that we will continue to attract good men and women; because this a company which offers them the chance to make an impact from day one.'

British Aerospace

British Aerospace is a world leader in aerospace and defence with annual sales exceeding £8.5 billion and an order book of nearly £24 billion. It is Europe's major proven systems integrator and one of the most successful prime contractors in the world. British Aerospace employs around 46,000 people (41,000 based in the UK) in the design, development, manufacture and testing of civil and military aircraft, guided weapon systems, artillery and ammunition together with other high technology systems and equipment. Around 89% of British Aerospace sales are exported to over 72 countries.

Scorecard:

Remuneration and benefits	★★★★
Progressive attitude	★★★★★
Opportunity for promotion	★★★★
Training, development and education	★★★★
Working atmosphere and environment	★★★★

Biggest plus:
A challenging future in tomorrow's world

Biggest minus:
A tough, demanding business environment

British Aerospace plc
Warwick House
Farnborough Aerospace Centre
Farnborough
Hampshire GU14 6YU
Tel: 01252 373232
Fax: 01252 383000
website: www.bae.co.uk

British Aerospace

The Business

British Aerospace is a proud company whose history dates back to the earliest days of aviation and defence engineering. The company has been established as a pioneering defence and aerospace innovator for more than 90 years.

British Aerospace is Europe's major proven systems integrator and one of the most successful prime contractors in the world, providing total land, air and sea solutions to the most demanding customers worldwide. British Aerospace is the UK's largest exporter of manufactured goods and the fourth largest aerospace and defence company in the world.

While much of the manufacturing base of British Aerospace (BAe) lies within the UK, its markets are global, with customers in 72 countries. BAe supports some 3,000 military aircraft in service with 23 airforces. Similarly in commercial aerospace, BAe supports airliners in service with airline customers worldwide. Its broad customer base includes some 1,900 Airbus aircraft now in service with 160 operators. British Aerospace is a 20% partner in Airbus Industrie.

Some of the best known projects in which British Aerospace is involved include the Airbus family of commercial airliners; the Euro-fighter, Tornado and Nimrod MRA4 aircraft; and Rapier, ASRAAM and Seawolf missiles.

Company Culture and Style

Many companies and organisations today talk about 'partnerships' but in few industries is it as evident, and as important, as in aviation and defence engineering. 'We at British Aerospace view our customers and suppliers as partners, and we see partnership as the key to providing effective solutions,' says Sir Richard Evans, chief executive. 'By working together we can more readily identify the real issues, agree on the optimum way forward and progress as a team towards achieving our mutual objectives.' British Aerospace has no fewer than 29 major international collaborative partnerships.

British Aerospace refers to its 'Value Plan', an initiative coursing through the business aimed at continuing BAe's success story in the face of an aggressive competitive environment. BAe identifies five values on which it focuses its efforts and gives it priorities for action: making customers the highest priority; recognising that its people are its greatest strength; accepting that its future lies in successful partnerships and making them really work; understanding that innovation and technology will give it competitive edge; and a commitment to continuous performance improvement as the key to winning.

Human Resources

'For British Aerospace to become a Benchmark company – and that is our goal – each of us will have to make an even greater contribution every time we come to work. And we all need to really feel we *want* to do that,' is the message in the Value Plan.

Human resources at BAe has concentrated on providing excellent leadership, designing flatter organisations that free up people's talents and break down functional barriers, and on getting the right people for the right jobs. It also looks to create opportunities and encourage everyone to continue learning and developing their capabilities.

Communicating effectively and involving everyone in thinking constructively about operational and business issues has a big role to play, matched by having open and fair systems of recognition and reward.

Technology is a vital differentiator in the aerospace and defence industry. The complexity of high-performance aircraft such as Eurofighter demands the application of advanced technology in the design, engineering and manufacture of such systems. BAe recognises that today systems must work with exacting efficiency, reliability and, above all, at a cost that is affordable to the customer and lower than the competition.

British Aerospace's research and development activities, spread across the businesses but centred on Sowerby, represent a massive investment in the technologies of tomorrow. They cover a wide spectrum, from software development through composite materials to synthetic environments and some 170 highly qualified scientists and engineers are helping to turn science fiction into reality.

Integrated teamworking is central to the way BAe works, whether within the company, or with suppliers. For example, the £2 billion Nimrod MRA4 programme is creating the next generation maritime patrol aircraft for the RAF, by stripping 21 existing fuselages and fitting new wings, engines, avionics and mission systems. An Integrated Project Team is helping to deliver the project, making sure that everyone moves forward together. At a time when most BAe projects involve partners over borders, teams are increasingly made up of people with international backgrounds.

British Aerospace commissioned independent researchers Gallup to find out what its young people thought about working for British Aerospace. On 'I recognise that within this company, development is my responsibility,' 74% agreed; 'Secondments and placements are a valuable method of learning and development' (77% agreed); 'I have the right skills for my current job' (73% agreed).

Career Opportunity and Development

'If you're up for it, British Aerospace offers the world,' the company says. British Aerospace operates in aggressively competitive markets. It's a tough, demanding environment and requires people with drive and ambition. This is one of the UK's most complex and innovative companies where constant challenge is a way of life.

British Aerospace operates a range of business units in the UK and from 65 bases around the world. That adds up to a breadth of opportunity. Some 17,000 people work in manufacturing, where all engineering degrees, production management and business studies are required. British Aerospace represents Engineering Excellence, created by more than 10,000 engineers who apply their expertise to the whole product life cycle, where all engineering disciplines, physics, mathematics, computer sciences and materials science feature.

Then there is the range of professional areas, including finance, human resources, commercial (managing relationships with customers, partners and suppliers) and project management. British Aerospace spends over £3.8 billion each year with suppliers and so the purchasing function plays an increasingly important role. And of course, BAe's competitive advantage relies on realising the potential of information technology.

British Aerospace gives its graduates the opportunity to meet the challenge of developing managerial and technological solutions in its fast-changing, competitive global market. That means meaningful work backed up by a structured training programme, developing function-specific skills alongside management experience. The graduate development programme is great for meeting people from other functions and business units. Even in a company of BAe's size it's still a small world, and this provides a ready-made network.

In addition to an individual's manager, the mentoring system often works on two levels: an on-site mentor for the 'day-to-day stuff', and an external mentor to use as a sounding board.

What do British Aerospace's young people say about the company?

'I love being at the cutting edge, feeling that my advice, makes a difference' (Scott Lachlan). 'Working on the Airbus A3XX is an aerodynamicist's dream' (Afandi Darlington). 'Pilots love Eurofighter Typhoon because it's being designed very much with their needs in mind' (Emma Maxwell). 'The sort of engineering we do here matters' (Claire Bridgwood), who adds: 'On my aeronautical engineering course at university there were only eight women out of 80. In this office there are about 15 women engineers, and lots across the company, so the odds are improving. It's no different for women here – there's nothing to prove.' And 'if you work for British Aerospace, you've made it – you're where it's at' (Philippa Dawson).

At British Aerospace you drive your own development. The company's part of the bargain is to give people the resources and support they need. And it does this comprehensively. Personal development planning is made and tracked with the line manager. In addition to various specific training courses, BAe provides The British Aerospace Virtual University, in conjunction with leading academic institutions across the UK and overseas; a network of Learning Resource centres at its main sites; and the Programme of Assisted Self Study (PASS).

Remuneration

Salaries are competitive and benefits packages comprehensive. Participation in the company's profit-sharing scheme is geared to BAe beating its profit targets. There are also Save As You Earn share-option schemes (executive share-option schemes for senior management) and a company pension scheme.

The Future

In a long-term business like aerospace and defence engineering, some things are known about the future and some things aren't. BAe has a substantial order book of nearly £24 billion, but it needs replenishing continuously. Airbus is a very profitable activity for BAe and so progress on Airbus will be a central focus, especially as it will continue to be under severe pressure from the competition. And the evergreen Al Yamamah contract to provide military hardware and support services to Saudi Arabia will also remain important.

BAe will be looking to increase its overall presence on the Eurofighter programme, and its defence systems business has now got sufficient critical mass to increase contract wins. Consolidation of the defence industries in Europe is probably the most critical factor in British Aerospace's future and bigger, stronger commercial partnerships will hold the key. Fortunately, this is a trend gathering momentum. With firmly held positions in its markets and a long order book, British Aerospace looks set to be one of the major players in this long-term industry providing excellent opportunities for its staff.

British Sky Broadcasting Group

BSkyB is Britain's leading Pay TV provider, which produces and packages eleven channels and has approximately 3.5 million satellite subscribers, with a total reach of 6.9 million subscribers. BSkyB is organised into Sky Entertainment (direct home-to-satellite business), Sky Networks (content) and Sky Sports (sports channels and interests). BSkyB also has a number of joint ventures managed under Sky Ventures. BSkyB's production and management offices are at Isleworth in Middlesex, and its call centre operation at Livingston, Scotland. BSkyB has 4,897 full-time employees in the UK.

Scorecard:

Remuneration and benefits	★★★★★
Progressive attitude	★★★★★
Opportunity for promotion	★★★★★
Training, development and education	★★★
Working atmosphere and environment	★★★

Biggest plus:
Pioneering, different, bold, distinctive, bit of a maverick

Biggest minus:
Bit of a maverick

British Sky Broadcasting Group plc
Grant Way
Isleworth
Middlesex
TW7 5QD
Tel: 0171 705 3000
Fax: 0171 705 3030
website: www.sky.co.uk

British Sky Broadcasting Group

The Business

BSkyB celebrated its tenth birthday in February 1999 after flirting, in its earliest days, with not making it to its first. Loss-making BSkyB came within a whisker of bringing down the entire News Corporation back in the late 1980s, but it's all very different now. Turned around to profitability, BSkyB has gone from strength to strength, and is poised to dominate the digital TV revolution in the UK.

Sky started with four channels when there were two competing satellite TV providers. The two merged to form BSkyB. Now with Sky, third party and joint venture products, BSkyB provides some 40 analogue channels direct-to-home and now, through SkyDigital, up to an amazing 140 channels.

The company has effectively re-invented itself for digital, and already has a major part of the market. SkyDigital was launched successfully on 1 October 1998 and market forecasts are that digital will grow the market considerably. Sky is now in 7 million homes, approximately 30% of households in the UK.

In total, BSkyB has 6.88 million paying subscribers in the UK and Ireland. Direct-to-home, or satellite, has 3.5 million (2.5 million subscribe to Sky Movies, 2.7 million to Sky Sports). The remainder subscribes through cable.

BSkyB performs a dual role of platform distributor and programme maker/content owner, and is organised into three divisions:

Sky Entertainment, the direct-to-home business, is responsible for driving subscriber numbers, distribution, striking deals with channel providers, new business and managing customer relationships through the Subscriber Management Centre.

Sky Networks is responsible for content, namely the entertainment channels, including movies and documentaries, Sky One and Sky News and joint venture channels. It also manages the distribution of these channels through the cable networks, and Sky Box Office.

Sky Sports consolidates all of BSkyB's sports channels and interests and represents the leader in sports television in the UK. It also distributes its award-winning sports channels on cable – a task less onerous because the regulators demand it.

Company Culture and Style

From the beginning, BSkyB has always done things differently – in its posture, in its positioning and in its business. One lynchpin, which has been crucial to the BSkyB's success, is that it did what no-one else had ever done – charge separately for sports rights. Sky Sports is an extremely successful business, and in many ways has been the driver of BSkyB's success. It has invested £1 billion in the FA Premier League since 1992 in what former chief executive Sam Chisholm once described as 'one of the greatest sports romances of the century'.

To the outsider, BSkyB has something of an anti-establishment feel to it. Its 'maverick' card was effectively dealt face-up the moment that it set up something new, something that (in the UK at least) was radically different – it actually had the temerity to *charge* for its TV channels, and they were beamed in from outer space via something called a satellite.

Today, it is still difficult to judge whether BSkyB people still revel in their rebel clothes, or are working extremely hard to stress that they really are nice, normal people, and above all, mainstream, professional broadcasters.

The latter should not be a difficult conclusion to reach. Without question, BSkyB's approach to the quality of programming is top class. It doesn't just give its customers what they want (customers would never have invented the television) – it gives its audiences what they never even imagined. Sky Sports, for example, has revolutionised the treatment, recording and presentation of sports programming, which reveals the company's dynamic culture.

Nevertheless, the company cannot avoid being high profile. Its bid for Manchester United generated a huge amount of publicity and emotional outpouring. Unfairly, this overstates BSkyB's desire to court controversy and overstates its importance to the company, even though it would represent a sizeable investment. As BSkyB says, 'We're not in the football business, we're in the satellite TV business.'

Another ingredient on the culture menu is that BSkyB is part of an international organisation. Especially at the beginning, many people came to BSkyB from 'the colonies', although Americans and Australians might contest the term and the timelines if not the common language (and, quite often and despite verbal jousting, the culture). News International still owns nearly 40% of BSkyB.

Under chief executive Mark Booth, BSkyB has evolved a different management style. While Sam Chisholm was credited with BSkyB's original turnaround, albeit in an aggressive style which earned BSkyB the reputation of being a bit of a maverick, American Mark Booth has the same determination but follows a more consensual approach. There is now a greater appreciation of the sensibilities of 'Middle England' and a strong desire to see Sky as an integral part of the broadcasting establishment.

With the exception of the subscriber call centre, everything at BSkyB happens on one site. Management, programmers, engineers, presenters, production, professional and support staff are all thrown together, happily, in the same place making for an 'interesting' mix. TV production people are typically young, hip and trendy, energised to put together creative shows. Corporate 'suits' are more hard-nosed and running a business. Throw in a few famous personalities in the Sports business and it makes for a unique and colourful combination on site.

That this site is on a Middlesex industrial estate, just off the A4, does not excite everyone – particularly media types perhaps more familiar with London's West End. But try cramming a seven-acre integrated facility into Soho.

After once looking like going under, BSkyB has grown fairly quickly, eventually 'exploding' as subscriber numbers increased beyond all expectations. This helps explain the 'can do' attitude of people who were once staring into the abyss, and the easy, successful, entrepreneurial feel of a confident company.

Human Resources

It's not a cliché that BSkyB uses, but when companies repeatedly say 'people are our greatest asset', it's worth considering some figures. In the year to 30 June 1998, BSkyB had turnover in excess of £1.4 billion, and operating profit of £340 million. It had less than 500 employees.

In thanking employees for 'a truly exceptional performance', chief executive Mark Booth added: 'Their dedication and commitment to the company never cease to amaze me.'

This is not a party. BSkyB is a hard-working, pioneering, customer-focused organisation, and the people who do well in the company have these as natural, rather than acquired, attributes.

Career Opportunity and Development

Tremendous career opportunities are there, but loosely defined. The company is growing too fast. Scope for advancement arises all the time and people do 'come up from nothing'. 'When BSkyB launched, the average age of employees was 25 years. This is a very young company, and people who have stayed all the way have generally been very successful.

The diversity of types of careers in a TV company is enormous. There are completely different career structures in the call centre and customer services operations in Scotland compared to the corporate office in London, and the same can certainly be said of content and programming.

BSkyB's three divisions are given autonomy and run as separate entities, and this fragments into smaller pieces. With a proliferation of joint ventures and individual channels, many people are effectively running their own operation.

And that sets the trend. Within defined parameters, individuals at BSkyB are just that – free to innovate and drive fresh ideas forward. This is a meritocracy where self-starters and motivated people excel.

Remuneration

BSkyB admits to 'probably paying more than other TV companies'. Certainly rewards are seen as being very good and BSkyB has offered high-earning potential. During the set-up period recruitment was necessarily from existing broadcasters and BSkyB tended to pay a premium.

Many people have shared in BSkyB's financial success and senior management incentive schemes are linked closely to performance. That many have seen their total earnings escalate reflects the success of the company and the value of individuals' contribution to this success.

Now in more settled times, it is better to view remuneration at BSkyB as being highly competitive. And among various benefits, each permanent member of staff gets a free SkyDigital subscription (the top-tier level) including installation and the necessary set-top 'box'.

The Future

BSkyB believes, quite firmly, that the future is digitally-led, and the options opened up by digital television may support this. Multi-channel choice, improved quality pictures, and the consumer services opened up through interactive technology are powerful dynamics.

The possibilities for transaction revenues are enormous and BSkyB could become a leader in transaction television, if home-delivery shopping, travel reservations, online banking, computer games and e-mail become commonplace.

BSkyB is still driven by subscriber numbers, however, and future success will be measured by new subscribers and the successful conversion to digital of Sky's analogue customer base.

But BSkyB will be digitally-led. While this technology requires fewer people and more automation, it is where the action is in television, and the whole company will be focused on digital. Given its entrepreneurial success to date, expect it to continue.

H P Bulmer

H P Bulmer is an international long alcoholic drinks business and the world's largest cider maker, probably best known for its Strongbow brand. H P Bulmer Holdings plc has its headquarters in Hereford and employs 1,370 people worldwide, with over 900 in the UK. It has growing sales in over 50 countries and turnover in the year to April 1998 reached £298 million. The Bulmer family retains an approximate 50% shareholding but the company is run, and has to perform, like any independent plc. H P Bulmer is a distinctive business with clearly stated objectives and excellent employee relations.

Scorecard:

Remuneration and benefits	★★★★
Progressive attitude	★★★★
Opportunity for promotion	★★★★
Training, development and education	★★★★★
Working atmosphere and environment	★★★★★

Biggest plus:
Excellent commitment to, and partnership with, its employees

Biggest minus:
Having to work hard to implement necessary change in the traditional drinks industry

H P Bulmer Holdings plc
The Cider Mills
Plough Lane
Hereford HR4 0LE
Tel: 01432 352000
Fax: 01432 352084
website: www.bulmer.com

H P Bulmer

The Business

H P Bulmer (Bulmers) is the clear leader of the UK cider market, with a share approaching 60% of the total sector. Its leading brand, Strongbow, is rising up the league table of UK long alcoholic drinks brands and currently stands at eleventh. Bulmers other main brands are Woodpecker (medium sweet cider), Scrumpy Jack (traditional style, premium cider), and White Lightning (white cider).

Bulmers also applies its brand-building skills to a thriving premium packaged beer distribution business. It holds exclusive UK distribution rights for leading international lagers including Amstel, Red Stripe, San Miguel, DAB and Steinlager.

Bulmers' growing international business now accounts for over 20% of group operating profit and comprises export trading, wholly owned subsidiaries in Australia, Belgium, New Zealand, the USA, and a joint venture in South Africa. 'Cider is emerging as an exciting segment of the international drinks market and Bulmers is developing a leading position in all key markets through partnerships with leading local distribution companies,' says Mike Hughes, chief executive.

The Bulmer family connection and a proud 112-year history help give the company its ethos and a sense of continuity in fast-moving times. The company is also nimble enough to stress that this cannot mean paternalism or jobs for life, and that Bulmers' success will only continue if everyone is keen, customer-focused, quality-mad and highly competitive. As Bulmers encourages its employees to become more employable, the sum of individual change equals corporate change.

Company Culture and Style

Bulmers certainly enjoys an open and strong relationship with its employees. Obviously one of Hereford's major employers, many loyal staff have significant length of service. If that is not the easiest start point for 'Breakthrough' – a culture change programme currently sweeping the business – you might not know it from the positive response.

According to Rob Garner, personnel director, 'Breakthrough is a common sense approach to changing the way we work. It is about everyone "owning" one vision – to make Bulmers a world-class, innovative business that is responsive to the needs of its customers, consumers, shareholders, employees and suppliers.'

Breakthrough is also about harnessing the potential of everyone in the company, encouraging people to work together as a team, and creating a working environment that will make Bulmers 'the place to be'.

Communication has been cast in the leading role. Forums, training sessions and taking groups of employees to hotels to share and shape the vision of the business have all featured. Breakthrough stumbled across the common language of football to provide working analogies. 'Buying the top players to have the best team' and 'second half coaching' have already crept into the Bulmer vocabulary.

Rob Garner believes that communication is 'at least a two-way process' and is 'as much about listening as about talking.' Although some people inevitably viewed change with some anxiety, they have quickly grasped that no change is not an option. In that sense, many Bulmers people are already there. Rob Garner: 'We're encouraging people to get involved in the process of change because we certainly don't want it to be centrally-driven. When you tap into the latent energy of 1,000 people, the rest is not that difficult.' Bulmers has not been deterred by initial scepticism – indeed, it actively encourages people to take as much space as they need to explore the change process.

There must be some design behind any culture change programme, and Bulmers gives its employees every opportunity to learn and gain access to different perceptions. To assist this, a group of over 30 facilitators has been set up to coach and nurture new ways of thinking.

Breakthrough seems to be transforming an energetic company in a sometimes traditional industry. The programme touches everybody and has been successful in moving to a 'just do it' attitude.

'While it won't always be an easy ride,' says Mike Hughes, chief executive, 'I am convinced that by embracing change in this way, we can and will realise the full potential of the company.'

Human Resources

Bulmers' personnel policies focus on reskilling, developing positive attitudes to change, a more international approach, and building a culture appropriate for a creative, entrepreneurial and customer-focused business.

In an industry sometimes perceived as traditional, Bulmers' management style is anything but traditional. Managers pursue innovative methods to engage people to the notion that there are different ways of doing things. In the area of coaching and empowering, the 'Bulmers Disunited' video drew on the football analogy and had senior managers acting out the classic 'game of two halves' to demonstrate two very different styles of management!

The atmosphere of employee relations has been boosted by a highly progressive working partnership with the recognised union, T&GWU. The convenor Bob Hardwick stresses that this is a long-standing aspect of the company's way of being. 'Recent initiatives like Breakthrough are welcome and will only work because they are consistent with a long-term commitment to involvement and partnership.'

Equal opportunity is pursued in the widest sense. Through the Employee Council and the Trade Union, a rigorous equal opportunities policy has been launched. Bulmers also aims to reflect the range of views and aspirations of all its people – the local community in Herefordshire and the professional/managerial population drawn nationally – and has the culture to happily accommodate both.

The company has recently added an excellent health and fitness centre – another initiative driven by the extremely active and now deep-rooted Employee Council. The centre caters for all employees and encourages them to make exercise a regular part of their lives.

Bulmers appears to have as many centres as a box of chocolates. The Innovation Centre, known as the Futures Factory, encourages people to innovate more and change the way the company operates. Director of Innovation Les Murphy said: 'The ethos of the Innovation Unit is to reappraise everything that we do within Bulmers, including developing new products, grasping new opportunities and trying to stimulate "an ideas culture" throughout the business.' Bulmers believes that 95% of great ideas come from people at the sharp-end of business.

Career Opportunity and Development

Bulmers stresses employee development as opposed to management development, underlining its belief that every employee has development potential and challenges every employee to update and improve their skills. Emphasising the link between employability and adaptability, the aim is for everyone to enjoy 'self-driven learning.' The company operates a competency-based performance management system for all employees.

The physical manifestation of Bulmers' learning philosophy is its impressive, on-site Learning Centre, designed, resourced and effectively owned by the employees. Mike Court, deputy chair of the

Employee Council, explains that 'the Learning Centre facilities give employees – and now their families – the opportunity to release their untapped potential by learning in their preferred way and at their own pace.' Learning Centre staff are on hand to help and the centre is open 24 hours a day, so night-shift staff can also use the facilities. Bulmers describes the use of the Learning Centre as 'spectacular'. Staff can just come in and ask 'I'm interested in learning about . . .' Languages, computing and multi-skills all feature, and many people have pursued NVQs.

Although Bulmers does not systematically recruit graduates straight from university, the company does operate fast-track development schemes supported by Development Centres.

The internationalisation of Bulmers business is increasing the opportunities for short or longer-term assignments overseas.

Remuneration

Pay levels are good, both in terms of local rates for factory operatives and nationally comparable packages for senior professionals. Bulmers is in the upper quartile of FMCG companies for managers' and directors' pay. Eligible employees enjoy a flexi-benefits scheme, and everyone can join a medical care scheme with the company paying 50% of the costs. Employees are encouraged to participate in 'Gainsharing' and everyone participates in the deferred profit share scheme. In a good year, this scheme could add more than 5% to basic pay.

The Future

Bulmers recognises that it potentially faces a strong challenge from Canandauga, the North American company which recently took over Matthew Clark – Bulmers' closest competitor. The increasing consolidation of purchasing power in the UK among fewer supermarkets and big brewers is affecting all manufacturers, while cider-makers also face the omni-present challenge of fiscal interference.

As Bulmers develops its international business, it is facing the questions of how best to build truly international brands and how to grow a truly multi-national and multi-cultural business from its Herefordshire base.

Its biggest challenge therefore will be to maintain the heady pace of change it has set itself. Bulmers draws the analogy with the human immune system, where the centre of an organisation doesn't need to know everything that is going on, where the system is fluid and agile, responds to opportunities and threats immediately they arise and continuously enhances capability by networking learning throughout the organisation. Bulmers is busily making itself as flexible as possible to cope with a future which it cannot control or easily predict. With the energies of its people harnessed effectively, it has every chance of succeeding.

Cable & Wireless Communications

Cable & Wireless Communications is by far the UK's leading provider of integrated communications, information and entertainment services. It is also the ninth largest carrier of international traffic in the world. In 1997/98 its revenues amounted to £2.2 billion, up 12% on the previous year. It employs 10,000 people in the UK. The company is 53% owned by Cable & Wireless plc, one of the world's leading providers of international telecommunications services.

Scorecard:

Remuneration and benefits	★★★★
Progressive attitude	★★★★
Opportunity for promotion	★★★★
Training, development and education	★★★★
Working atmosphere and environment	★★★★

Biggest plus:
A new company which has already made huge leaps forward

Biggest minus:
Sailing in the uncharted waters of new technology

Cable & Wireless Communications plc
Watford Business Park
Caxton Way
Watford WD1 8XH
Tel: 0171 528 2000
website: www.cwcom.co.uk.

CABLE & WIRELESS

Cable & Wireless Communications

The Business

Cable & Wireless Communications came into existence in 1997 through a merger of Mercury with Nynex CableComms Group, Bell Cablemedia, and Videotron. It was the first UK company to offer multi-channel television and Internet services alongside the full range of telecommunications services. It is also strategically positioned to offer new products such as interactive digital services and multimedia products as they emerge.

The merger was widely hailed as a major move. *The Sunday Times* called Cable & Wireless Communications 'One of the biggest and most exciting companies to be formed in Britain for years'. The new company gave customers the best of telecommunications and the best of information and entertainment services from a single source. Cable & Wireless Communications is the only UK company to offer a combination of telecoms, broadband, data transmission, video shopping and Internet access.

The company has over 33,000 Internet customers, making it probably the fastest-growing Internet Service Provider in the UK. Its corporate customers include Fiat, Dixons, Hewlett-Packard, Tandem, Nortel and British Steel. Cable & Wireless Communications is currently spending £400 million on upgrading its national network. When complete, this will be one of the most advanced national telecommunications networks in the world.

The company's parent, Cable & Wireless plc, provides over 17 million customers in over 70 countries with a complete range of international, domestic and mobile communications. It is the world's third largest carrier of international traffic, provides mobile communications in 30 countries and operates the world's largest and most advanced cable ship fleet.

Company Culture and Style

The culture at Cable & Wireless Communications is one which encourages open and honest communication at all levels. Individuals are allowed to admit to their mistakes and are encouraged to learn from them. Line managers have an open management style which concentrates on finding a balance between the needs of the business and those of the employees.

Cable & Wireless Communications values employees for their personal strengths and skills, and always treats them as individuals. At the same time, no individual is bigger than the team he or she works in; teamwork is at the heart of the way the company works. It discriminates only on ability – not on sex, race, colour, ethnic origin, age, disability or any other factor. The company believes that every employee should have an equal opportunity to realise his or her full potential and contribute skills to the success of the business.

There is a strong emphasis on individual contribution. Russ Watling, of Cable & Wireless Communications: 'This is a fast-changing industry, and it is not possible to predict what we will look like in five years' time. That means a constant need to focus individuals on what they want to do, where they are going, and what skills they will need when they get there.'

The culture is one of constant innovation – not surprisingly, since telecommunications is the world's fastest growing industry. As a result, the company is unlikely to suit anyone looking for a quiet life. Conversely, individuals interested in being at the leading edge of a continuously changing and developing industry are likely to thrive at Cable & Wireless Communications.

Heather Robertson, a Modern History graduate, joined the company in September 1996. She comments: 'It's a young company so it isn't bureaucratic or stuffy. But you have to be prepared for change because we're working in a very competitive environment. And because it's such a large company, there's lots of scope for developing a career that really suits you.'

Human Resources

Cable & Wireless Communications is constantly seeking innovative approaches to manage and develop its people in a way which facilitates organisational change, enhances career planning for the individual, and contributes to the success of the group.

The approach of the company, and indeed throughout the Cable & Wireless group, is for the central HR function to provide a strong lead to the business on people-related issues. The aim is thereby to deploy top people in areas most suited to their skills and development.

There is a strong emphasis on 'performance management', an appraisal system which the company says 'allows individuals to put together career portfolios and get input from whatever source they need'. This means seeking feedback on their performance and style not only from their manager but from colleagues and subordinates.

Career Opportunity and Development

Encouraging employees to take responsibility for their own careers is fundamental to the nature of career development at Cable & Wireless Communications.

The company also invests heavily in training. The purpose-built Cable & Wireless College in Coventry is the main training establishment for the group, and is able to draw on academic expertise. It provides technical, sales and management training, develops the skills of a wide range of people from trainee engineers to senior directors, and its work also supports partners and other organisations worldwide. The company also has Open Learning facilities and a comprehensive library service available to all employees for private study.

The company has a graduate recruitment scheme, and will take on 28 graduate trainees in 1999. The scheme is made up of a number of streams, offering different training with some shared elements. In 1999, the streams are engineering, human resources, finance and marketing. Successful applicants to the scheme start with a two-week induction course at the Coventry College, followed by a series of placements which last from three to twelve months. Graduate trainees have a degree of choice in their placements, although some are fixed. The placement programme, which may last two years, leads on to the graduate's first role.

Career development is driven by a Personal Development Plan, which each individual creates through liaison with his or her line manager. This sets learning goals and provides a framework to fulfil those goals. This development may include considerable mobility, within the company or elsewhere within the Cable & Wireless group.

Remuneration

The company's remuneration philosophy is designed to attract, motivate, reward and retain the best employees. As a result, salaries are competitive. It has a performance culture in which employees can clearly link reward to their own individual performance and contribution. The system is flexible, allowing it to link remuneration to company success.

There is a comprehensive benefits package. This includes a pension, life cover, healthcare, dental insurance, and childcare vouchers. This package is also flexible, allowing employees to opt for credits instead of taking some of the benefits. They can then use the credits to improve other benefits – or take a cash alternative. Holidays are 23 days a year, rising to 25 days after two years' continuous service. This allowance too can be traded up to six weeks or down to four.

In addition, there is an Employee Assistance Line available 24 hours a day which employees can call for guidance and advice on legal issues, financial problems, consumer complaints and personal concerns.

The Future

Although the marketplace in which Cable & Wireless Communications operates is increasingly competitive, the company has a unique advantage: it offers customers local, national, international and data telecommunications, allows them to access a wide range of information services and enjoy the latest in multi-channel television services from a single provider.

It also has a strong customer base. One million homes use its telecommunication services and 600,000 people are connected to its cable television services. It has 75,000 small to medium-sized corporate customers and around 6,000 large corporate customers.

Telecommunications is not a cyclical business. Even in a recession, telecommunications can still raise a company's productivity. Being able to deliver integrated communications is increasingly seen as the best way forward, and this is precisely the strength of Cable & Wireless Communications.

Planned future developments from the company include 'telebusiness', corporate Internet services, online Internet access services and number portability, digital television products such as impulse pay-per-view, near video-on-demand and, ultimately, video-on-demand.

All this would suggest that Cable & Wireless Communications is in a good position to maximise the enormous potential of its industry while being able to shrug off its competitive nature.

Cadbury Schweppes

Cadbury Schweppes is one of the UK's best known and most respected corporations. It employs about 41,000 people around the world in its twin businesses – confectionery and beverages. The group invests heavily to maintain and expand its enviable portfolio of brands, including Cadbury's Dairy Milk, Wispa, Boost, Roses and Dr Pepper, which are on sale in some 200 countries. Cadbury Schweppes has embarked on a 'managing for value' programme to aid its pledge of increasing shareholder value.

Scorecard:

Remuneration and benefits	★★★★
Progressive attitude	★★★
Opportunity for promotion	★★★★
Training, development and education	★★★★★
Working atmosphere and environment	★★★★

Biggest plus:
The international spread of businesses gives great scope for employee experience

Biggest minus:
Cadbury has to be particularly fleet of foot to compete with giants such as Coca-Cola, Mars and Nestlé

Cadbury Schweppes plc
25, Berkeley Square
London W1X 6HT
Tel: 0171 409 1313
Fax: 0171 830 5200

Cadbury Schweppes

The Business

Cadbury Schweppes is one of the élite names of British business; respected, well known and highly regarded by its peers. Yet the group was formed only in comparatively modern times, when in 1969 Schweppes Beverages merged with Cadbury. Jacob Schweppe had founded the drinks arm of the business in the late 1780s with the manufacture of mineral waters. Fifty years later, John Cadbury established the roots of his empire by selling tea and coffee.

Today Cadbury Schweppes is a major global confectionery player with extensive soft drinks operations in the US. Sales topped £4.1 billion in 1997 and pre-tax profits reached £575 million. Comparisons are made difficult because of the decision to sell its 51% share of Coca-Cola & Schweppes Beverages and more recently to dispose of its non-US soft drinks operations.

Recently voted Britain's second best managed company after Tesco in a *Management Today* poll, Cadbury's 'Managing for Value' (MFV) programme is gaining momentum throughout the organisation and underlining the board's determination to boost earnings and shareholder returns.

Company Culture and Style

The group has traditionally enjoyed a reputation for paternalism and caring, for representing the highest values of business and for trying to 'play the game' fairly. This ethic has governed its internal behaviour towards staff and informed its external dealings in the marketplace.

All that is changing; not that the group intends to slough off any of its standards, more that the group chief executive, John Sunderland, knows: 'The markets in which we operate are brutally competitive. If we are to compete with the likes of Coke, Nestlé and Pepsi, our company and employees need to sharpen up.'

The informal and collegiate style which have been a hallmark of the group are likely to remain as is the very streamlined management

– there are only 150 executives and 8,000 managers in the entire group. The commitment to continuous education and training for employees will also continue.

But Cadbury Schweppes is an organisation in transition, it is clearly re-emphasising the confectionery part of the business and attempting to introduce a new dynamism. Mr Sunderland's MFV programme is designed to sharpen-up the whole organisation, to enhance the independence and risk-taking of employees and to empower its people to be bold, creative and challenging.

Human Resources

The current thrust of Cadbury's human resources team is concentrated on rolling out the MFV programme, the mantra for which is that 'managing for value is not just about financial management. It is 20% about the numbers and 80% about the people and culture, because people create value.'

The aim is that the organisation's thinking and motivation will have been overhauled within the next two to three years and that the programme will underpin all aspects of HR. The strategy is built on five key objectives:

1. Raising financial performance (earnings per share in double digits compared with an average of 6% in the early 1990s, greater free cash flow and doubled share value);
2. Sharpening the culture (employees are encouraged to be accountable, aggressive and adaptable);
3. Value-based management (the governing commercial and financial strategy);
4. Leadership capability (all of the 150 top executives are being reviewed and given new individual performance goals);
5. Rewards (share ownership among employees is being encouraged and different financial measures are being introduced as the basis for bonuses).

HR executives say this will mean looking at potential recruits differently – for their ability to challenge barriers and take a chance rather more than in the past. Those departments which have already been inducted in the new programme have adopted it enthusiastically. But, clearly, the company knows there will be some employees (it hopes not many) who will not want to make the change and may leave.

The MFV programme is expected to help the federation of group companies feel and function more like an integrated whole, talking the same HR language and able to share best practice globally.

Career Opportunity and Development

The company is now determined that senior managers must have had experience of other countries before they are allowed to take on top leadership.

An accelerated development programme offers 16 high flyers (usually in the 25–35 age bracket) the chance to be sent on an assignment to another country for a year. Edmund Ayeh, a shift manager with Cadbury in Ghana, said about his assignment in South Africa: 'The ADP exposes you to the unique culture of another country. From a business point of view, it increases your professional knowledge and understanding of how other businesses within the group operate within a manufacturing environment.'

For more mature managers, usually those most likely to become top executives, there is an international management development programme which involves a three-year assignment in a senior overseas role.

Cadbury Schweppes prides itself on the fact that its personnel development work means it almost never has to look outside for its top executives and is increasingly able to make the same claim at senior management level.

The group says it is now 'on track' in terms of the equal opportunities policy which was launched in 1994. Now the company is concentrating on reflecting the international nature of its business among its senior executives – it is much less of a UK-focused business. Cadbury Schweppes belongs to the Employers Forum on Age and attempts not to discriminate in terms of age.

Remuneration

The company regards its pay scales as towards the upper end of its peer group. Cadbury Schweppes offers a very well supported Share Save scheme which has recently been extended to additional regions in Europe, such as France, Spain and Portugal as well as North America. This scheme – awards for which tend to be made in September – provides participating staff with the full 20% discount on company shares and offers savings terms of three, five and seven years. Individuals are then able to roll the proceeds into a Cadbury PEP. More than half the entire workforce now owns shares.

Medical insurance schemes are provided for senior managers and cars are available for top executives, senior managers and sales staff. In addition, employees have a defined benefit pension scheme, discounted staff shops and leisure facilities. Bonuses based on company performance are common for most managerial and some administrative staff.

The Future

Cadbury Schweppes is going through a radical process of internal change while attempting not to abandon the traditions and values which have underpinned its history and for which it is admired. This could prove unsettling for some employees.

Chief executive Mr Sunderland sees no necessary conflict. The group, he says, still has a 'strategic credo of focusing on growth markets, building strong brands, growing by innovation and seeking value-enhancing acquisitions'. That has not changed. What is undergoing a shift, however, is the promise that these goals will be achieved at the same time as shareholder value is being driven forward. He has impressed the City audience with his determination – supported by early concrete evidence – that Cadbury can deliver on its fiscal promises.

In terms of group operations there could be some changes of emphasis as the managing for value searchlight ranges around the global portfolio – for example, Cadbury's Buttons and Fry's Turkish Delight have emerged as much more profitable than the group had thought while apparently attractive takeovers such as Snapple and Tropicana were turned down because they failed to match the new value criteria.

The disposal, for £1.1 billion, of the group's soft drinks business outside America – leaving its soft drinks operations centred on North America – underlines the company's determination to continue only with operations which meet its new demanding criteria. The deal could even see Schweppes disappear from the group's name.

But with the proceeds from that transaction and with debt reduced from the CCSB disposal, Cadbury will clearly start to look for a scale acquisition in the confectionery field in a bid to compete head-to-head with Nestlé and Mars.

Innovation, investment, imagination and internationalism look set to become increasingly important hallmarks of the group's development. But as the newly installed electronic share price display in the foyer of Cadbury's head office makes clear, all this will be predicated very firmly on providing returns for investors.

Christian Salvesen plc

Christian Salvesen is a major logistics business specialising in the strategic management of the outsourced supply chain. Christian Salvesen works in partnership with manufacturing and retailing customers to optimise inventory levels while ensuring that goods are available for the consumer precisely when required. Christian Salvesen has particular expertise – and a broad and prestigious customer base – in the food, consumer products and industrial sectors. It also has a food services division specialising in frozen food processing. Christian Salvesen has around 2,500 staff and 11,500 hourly-rated employees at 123 sites in the UK, Belgium, France, Germany, Holland, Italy, Portugal and Spain.

Scorecard:

Remuneration and benefits	★★★
Progressive attitude	★★★★
Opportunity for promotion	★★★★★
Training, development and education	★★★★
Working atmosphere and environment	★★★★

Biggest plus:
A newly-focused company – exciting times lie ahead

Biggest minus:
Geographically diverse locations, often requiring adoption of customers' identity

Christian Salvesen plc
500 Pavilion Drive
Brackmills
Northampton NN4 7YJ
Tel: 01604 662600
Fax: 01604 662605
website: www.salvesen.com

Christian Salvesen plc

The Business

Recent times have been highly eventful for Christian Salvesen. Once a 'mini Scottish conglomerate', in 1997 it de-merged Aggreko, its high-margin, mobile power generation business, which had absorbed much of the group's time and energy. Its corporate headquarters also relocated from Edinburgh, a poignant moment after a long association with that city, and many employees (including the directors) chose to remain in Scotland.

The relocation to Northampton, however – 'the logistics capital of the UK' – was a sensible and practical move which fused together the corporate level with the management of the logistics business. Christian Salvesen is now sharply focused – perhaps for the very first time – on the expansion of its rapidly evolving logistics business.

Christian Salvesen's core logistics business is organised into two principal activities and markets – Food and Consumer, and Industrial. Both operations concentrate on the most complex areas of the supply chain, where Christian Salvesen can use its management expertise, organisational ability and capacity to develop sophisticated IT and engineering systems to maximum advantage.

Customers who outsource their logistics management to Christian Salvesen include Marks & Spencer, Booker, Sainsbury's, House of Fraser, IKEA, British Airways, Vauxhall, Mercedes and Ford, Dupont, the *Daily Mail* and Dunlop. Christian Salvesen is very strong in the UK, and relatively so in Europe. It is looking to expand its operations in continental Europe to develop a pan-European network over the next four to five years.

Company Culture and Style

Despite its long and varied history, Christian Salvesen is effectively a new company, focused and energised on one specific business activity. Its own new culture is emerging, driven by the new management team established after the de-merger and by employees' skill, commitment and enthusiasm.

Virtually all senior management left with the Aggreko de-merger, or remained in Edinburgh. New chief executive Edward Roderick brought-in new management and moved the head office to Northampton. The dynamic Roderick constantly visits Christian Salvesen sites and customers, 'stirring the business up' according to John Paterson, group human resources director. 'How can we make more profit?', 'how can we improve?' 'we'll grow in Europe' and 'we need a better culture' may well feature in his vocabulary.

Under the 'old' Christian Salvesen empire, autonomous units evolved at different locations. While strong local cultures are not discouraged – and many sites have tremendous collective performance drives – management at the lean head office knows that it must install some overall identity and commonality of purpose and process.

This will not be easy, for many people are scattered far and wide, working on customers' sites in outsourced supply chain operations. And if you work at Safeway's distribution centre, you are effectively working for Safeway, which causes problems of identity. Many customers want the identity of Christian Salvesen (or any other service provider) kept quite low and inevitably, Christian Salvesen staff may become imbued with parts of customers' cultures. This is no bad thing when you look at the client list, but it is difficult to harmonise into a unique Christian Salvesen culture.

In response, a lot of effort has gone into internal communication. Christian Salvesen's revamped staff newspaper *Salvo* is now much more informative. It carries information on its European activities and people it never used to, and is translated into European languages. It's all about the 'coming together' of the business with the aim of getting people involved in the company.

At a recent group management conference (which included all European managers), four hourly-rated workers from different parts of the business were invited to share their thoughts on the company with the audience. The comments of warehousemen and lorry drivers proved enlightening, sparking a lively debate. Christian Salvesen is working hard to foster an open, communicative spirit.

Human Resources

Attention has swung, inevitably, to structures and procedures. 'Each location had grown its own peculiar set of employment practices,' says John Paterson. 'We had many policies, but few procedures attached to them – and they were not distributed widely.'

His task is to develop and install better processes and harmonise them across the organisation. The personnel and payroll system has come under the microscope, as has training.

'We're now saying, "let's not spend time re-inventing the wheel, but look instead at applying the best practices"' For example, training. Christian Salvesen does a lot of supervisor training, but it was performed differently in each business. It is now trying to do this on a group-wide basis so that it can transfer best practices, learn from experiences in different businesses and share common problems and goals.

Now with the right IT support, Christian Salvesen is better able to manage the payroll, monitor absenteeism, analyse data and get this information decentralised. The latter is important. 'We want, for example, individual operations to be able to hire drivers immediately (there's a current shortage). Before, they had to revert to the centre to request that a job offer was sent out,' recalls John Paterson. 'We want simple, fast, flexible processes owned by local management.'

Christian Salvesen is keen to build a management succession plan. It already has a performance culture based on results, operations and individual performances – many key parameters are measured – but it doesn't have a performance management culture. With European operations soon expected to contribute 50% of revenues, which will soak up people from the UK to start these operations, Christian Salvesen will need to identify its best people to fill the gaps.

'And then it's a matter of delivering the right training and development for these people. It must be business-focused so that they can take it back to the workplace,' adds John Paterson.

Career Opportunity and Development

Career opportunities are described as 'unlimited' and if the company is successful in its strategy of developing a pan-European distribution and logistics network, these opportunities should also become international in flavour.

Individuals have progressed a long way within Christian Salvesen. Jim McGeary, the general manager of Christian Salvesen's Bellshill distribution centre (one of its most important) began in the warehouse under the graduate training programme. To an extent, drivers work for themselves – and there is still a certain cachet in being 'a driver' – but in a business where you must understand transport there is scope to develop into other jobs. Christian Salvesen operates a Young Managers programme, which it expects to expand in 1999 and beyond. Managers from mainland Europe are involved in these programmes, and language tuition programmes are in place.

There is actually a surprising range of career types in Christian

Salvesen. Many professional people work on acquisitions, contract negotiations and bidding, sales and marketing and customer-facing roles. Christian Salvesen has a lot of sophisticated plant and mechanical handling systems to run. It is also building state-of-the-art warehouses for clients, involving construction design, logistics engineering and the computer systems that go with it. And many of its sites have personnel managers, finance and accounting and dedicated IT and systems specialists.

'Although in many of our operations, it's more your experience, knowledge and skill base that gets you through,' suggests John Paterson. 'It's not as professionally qualified as banking, or as technical as mechanical engineering. But that means there are no limits to what you can do. We have grown many people within the business and will continue to do so.'

Remuneration

Christian Salvesen regards itself as 'probably a median payer' and has little difficulty in recruiting people. It admits to a slightly paternalistic employer's view, perhaps born of its total commitment to health and safety. It offers harmonised life insurance, and pension schemes to hourly staff, but they have a low take-up ('we need more education,' suggests Paterson). The Share Save Scheme enjoys wider popularity, and a recent issue was heavily oversubscribed.

The company does not operate performance-related pay universally, but is currently looking at replacement reward structures. Individual depots and sites have local incentive arrangements and schemes on the shop-floor.

The Future

Christian Salvesen has embarked on a strategy which is rational, straightforward and clearly understood by managers. Edward Roderick says that it is 'ambitious in its targets for growth and value creation', but the trend towards outsourcing in supply chain management, and the relatively under-developed infrastructure and logistics industry in continental Europe, offers real opportunity.

As a new, energised management team sets about building a brand new business, Chris Smith, corporate development manager, says, 'We're quite excited about what we can do in Europe over the next three to four years. But we're realistic – particularly on managing the growth process.'

Christian Salvesen will continue to change traditional mindsets, developing 'people processes' that create productivity, manage and reward people appropriately. There's huge scope for change, and carrying staff with it will be vital. 'It's little things – like picking an extra customer order, taking an extra delivery on each vehicle run – that will make the difference,' says Roderick. And he's right.

Churchill Insurance Company

Churchill is the second largest direct response insurance company in the UK and one of the fastest-growing insurers in Europe. This £200 million business is wholly owned by Winterthur, part of the Credit Suisse Group. This association provides financial strength and support but Churchill retains its operational autonomy. The company employs 2,000 people in the UK and a further 40 in New Delhi, India.

Scorecard:

Remuneration and benefits	★★★★
Progressive attitude	★★★★★
Opportunity for promotion	★★★★
Training, development and education	★★★★★
Working atmosphere and environment	★★★★★

Biggest plus:
Great fun to work for

Biggest minus:
Difficult to join if you've already worked in insurance!

Churchill Insurance Company Limited
Churchill Court
Westmorland Road
Bromley
Kent BR1 1DP
Tel: 0181 313 3030
Fax: 0181 313 5361
website: www.churchill.co.uk

Churchill Insurance Company

The Business

Churchill is a great British success story. The company is the brainchild of chairman and chief executive Martin Long, whose experience with UK insurers convinced him that British customers would respond to excellent service. As a result, he asked Swiss insurance giant Winterthur to fund a new company. The name of the company embodies many of its attributes: Britishness, trust, strength and perseverance.

The company began life in June 1989 with 88 employees selling car insurance policies, and added home insurance products the following year. Today, Churchill has 1.1 million customers and 2,000 employees. Exceptional service underlies that growth rate. The company's vision is to deliver the unquestioned, publicly acknowledged, best customer service in the insurance industry worldwide. Martin Long believes that the company is already number one in Europe.

He is not alone in that opinion. A third of new business comes from recommendations and 85% of existing business is renewed. (Most competitors can only marvel at the renewal rate; the industry average is well below 60%.) Customers send in 150,000 comment forms a year without any incentive to do so – and over 99% of those customers are highly satisfied. Third-party endorsements are common. The Halifax chose Churchill to sell motor insurance after a rigorous evaluation of the top 20 such insurers in the UK. In their words, 'We felt that our customers deserved to have the highest standards of service.' Furthermore, companies such as Shell have studied Churchill's approach.

Company Culture and Style

The company is characterised by a flat and remarkably open structure. The attitude is one of continuous improvement, and everyone is encouraged to make suggestions. From January to mid October 1998 the tally was 70,000 suggestions and 1,808 quality ideas. This enthusiasm for improvement is partly due to the rewards on offer (anyone whose suggestion earns the company £500,000 will receive a free flat in Bromley!) but more to the fact that people feel empowered. The team spirit and sense of togetherness at Churchill is unusual and perhaps unique in its sector.

The company has a radical ideology: Say Yes Not No. Staff are not allowed to say no to a customer without permission – very different to many companies, especially insurers! That philosophy, and its resultant flexibility, has retained 18,000 policies since it became operational in March 1997. Perhaps even more arresting is the company's view of values and rules. As Martin Long says, 'Everyone in the company can break any of the rules – but no-one can compromise any of our values.' He also acknowledges that it is his staff, not he or his fellow directors, who decide the quality of the company's service; undeniable for a company which takes eight million phone calls annually.

The company has an impressive record of innovation. The firsts include service guarantees, wholly-owned garages to ensure the highest standards of repairs, courtesy cars for customers when their own are off the road, a customer loyalty programme, and much more. In a typical move, the company opened an IT software subsidiary in India in February 1996 linked to Britain by satellite. This supported Churchill's software (the best in the industry, capable of handling 18 million transactions a day); brought it a source of excellent, well-educated programmers; and allowed it to process development work around the clock. It also reduced costs substantially.

The company demands hard work and commitment from its people; but it is also highly supportive. It is both fun and rewarding to work for: long-service awards after three, five and ten years (which carries with it five days' extra holiday and a choice of all-expenses-paid trips), Top Dog awards for good performers, Star Performers and a Hall of Fame for outstanding performance (with rewards of weekend breaks), Silly Hat days and much more go to prove this point. Employees are actually exhorted to have fun and enjoy their work.

A striking aspect of the company's style is its openness, as seen for instance in its In-Touch days. Martin Long and his fellow executives such as HR director Michael Raywood will do other people's jobs for a day. As Michael says, 'This not only makes us more accessible, we learn a tremendous amount ourselves – and we can often make people's jobs easier as a result.' Clearly, Churchill is an unusual insurance company. It is also unusually successful. At a time when other insurers and brokerages are losing direction and being swallowed up, this company knows exactly where it's going – as its July 1998 acquisition of a telebroking operation in Ipswich demonstrates.

Human Resources

Martin Long: 'Most people have tremendous energy and talent – but they never use it at work. We try to harness this, so that people want to come to work. This is all about empowerment. Everyone is encouraged to develop and grow.'

In short, HR has high priority – and this attitude can be seen throughout Churchill's operations. After training, new recruits have mentors, people not in their chain of command, who can help them. Development centres for managers help keep them on top of HR issues. The company was the first UK insurer to have both Investors in People and ISO 9002 (the only recognised quality award for service companies).

Employees are regularly asked their opinions. The questions are often trenchant: What would you change about your job? What would you change about the company? Half-yearly questionnaires are supplemented by constant feedback and communication.

Career Opportunity and Development

Churchill staff are recruited on personality. Previous insurance expertise is almost a disadvantage in all but technical areas such as underwriting. Far more important are confidence, enthusiasm, intelligence and the ability to learn. Those who answer the company's recruitment adverts are given telephone interviews and the successful candidates invited for an array of intelligence, keyboard skills and personality tests. On average, one in three ends up joining Churchill.

Once on board, employees can expect excellent training – as recognised by its winning the 1998 HR Excellence Award as the best company in the UK for employee development, an annual award co-sponsored by *Human Resource* magazine and the Cranfield School of Management. For three weeks, recruits do nothing but absorb knowledge – and demonstrate their understanding through regular tests. They are then 'buddied' for perhaps four weeks, eased into full-time work through close contact and support from an experienced member of staff. Many other insurers put recruits to work almost immediately.

Development is ongoing after this initial period. Training and development contracts with each staff member identify the next step forward. Language training, MBAs, professional qualifications: the company will support people throughout extra training wherever appropriate.

Employees also develop through a multi-skills approach. Once competent in one skill, an employee can move on to learn another. Awards are given, rising from Bronze to Gold (and £500) for three-skill employees. This is great news for staff and also for customers, who are far less likely to be shunted around when phoning.

Remuneration

The company sees itself as an above-average payer for its sector. Pay rises are determined solely by performance, as measured by the review procedure. As a result of the reviews, pay rises can be from 0% to 15% – although zero would indicate serious performance problems. Pay can also be considerably enhanced through productivity. For instance, one employee has sold over 20,500 policies, earning herself a place in the Hall of Fame.

Benefits include an excellent money purchase pension scheme with company contributions as a percentage of salary rising from 5% to 10% with service (7% to 12% for managers). There is also a profit-related pay scheme. Other benefits are private medical cover, interest-free season ticket loans, a discount scheme, life cover, a car or cash alternative for managers, and great working conditions for everyone.

The Future

The first challenge for Churchill will be to maintain profitable growth in a mature, deregulated market. It will be aided by its powerful parent, but even more by its care for customers and staff. 'Quality of customer service represents the only long-term competitive advantage,' says Martin Long. 'Products, IT and strategy can all be copied, but outstanding customer service cannot be replicated overnight. We've worked hard since 1989 putting ours in place.' Of course, other companies will try to match Churchill's impressive customer service; but while they do so, Churchill will continue to innovate.

Although Churchill's marketplace will continue to remain highly competitive, the company has a genuine edge based on a radical vision, a deep commitment to customer care and staff development, and a refreshingly different way of operating. All these attributes make Churchill truly one of Britain's top employers.

Clifford Chance

Clifford Chance is an integrated multinational law firm providing a full range of financial and corporate legal services for the international business community. With a single equity partnership worldwide, Clifford Chance has over 1,800 lawyers based in 26 offices around the world, and some 4,000 people in all. Around 2,200 staff are based at the City of London office, but the proportion overseas is growing constantly. There are presently 332 partners.

Scorecard:

Remuneration and benefits	★★★★★
Progressive attitude	★★★
Opportunity for promotion	★★★★
Training, development and education	★★★★★
Working atmosphere and environment	★★★

Biggest plus:
A fiercely ambitious firm but with a refreshingly open culture

Biggest minus:
All successful lawyers work long hours

Clifford Chance
200 Aldersgate Street
London EC1A 4JJ
Tel: 0171 600 1000
Fax: 0171 600 5555
website: www.cliffordchance.com

CLIFFORD CHANCE

Clifford Chance

The Business

Ten years after the successful merger between the firms Clifford Turner and Coward Chance to create Clifford Chance, the firm has set out its vision for the next ten years. It is, quite simply, to be the world's premier law firm. It's already recognised as a leader – voted 'Best International Law Firm' in 1997 by *The Lawyer* and ranking number one in 29 categories of The Legal 500 clients' guide.

Clifford Chance is the largest firm within the UK legal profession and, with 26 offices, has the largest overseas network. This covers all the main European centres from Spain to Russia but also includes offices in America, the Middle East and the Far East. Clifford Chance's senior partners are credited with reading the trends in the 1980s and matching its firm to the globalisation of business.

Clifford Chance is a law firm – it does not aspire to be a multi-disciplinary consultancy, or provide accountancy or other professional services. Its lawyers operate internationally and domestically under both common law and civil law systems. They are trained to work in cross-practice, cross-border teams so that the firm can offer businesses an integrated, worldwide service from each office.

Innovation and the highest quality professional service characterise Clifford Chance's services to clients and its evolution into an international business. Clifford Chance was the first UK-origin law firm to establish a pan-European capability and to develop an international US securities law practice.

Company Culture and Style

Clifford Chance has a partnership spirit and the supportive, cohesive culture that goes with it. Its style is, of course, extremely professional. Yet it is unusually friendly and informal for a law firm. Openness, teamworking and good communications are the norm.

Although it is the largest City law firm and one of the most successful, Clifford Chance is keen to avoid complacency. Its reputation for dynamism, innovation and creativity is hard-earned and justified. Size is an issue, and certain cultural aspects of a large organisation can become formalised. But in the end, Clifford Chance is just like any other law firm – it has individuals, working for partners, in teams. It's just that Clifford Chance has more teams.

The firm has a series of 'Partner Goals' for how they are going to develop the business, with Managing Partner Tony Williams initially circulating his own goals to the rest of the firm. It's important that the senior partners live and breathe the core values of the firm, and they do. The first and foremost is total client orientation, but the second is strong relationships with their own people. The two form a virtuous circle – it's in the firm's self-interest to have motivated people earning fees from satisfied clients.

Because of the nature of its clients and their requirements, working for Clifford Chance can be demanding. The London office never closes, with shifts of secretaries working around the clock to support the lawyers at any given time. The lifestyle is nearer that of a merchant bank than a high street solicitor. Hard work is, however, offset by excellent rewards, outstanding facilities, absorbing career prospects and a strong sense of camaraderie.

Simon Davis, recruitment partner, sums up what it takes to flourish at the firm. 'There are certain qualities you must have to succeed here: dedication to the job, an imaginative approach to problem solving, the ability to get on with other people and masses of energy.' However, there is a great deal of support available as people learn the job and become more experienced. People are not criticised for making mistakes, but for not seeking guidance.

Human Resources

As Alistair Dawson, head of personnel, puts it, 'This organisation has only one real resource: its people. We succeed or fail by the quality and professionalism of our employees'. Not surprisingly, the firm is deeply committed to human resources and to the welfare and development of its individuals.

Clifford Chance is a serious employer, with a full range of jobs and activities. Half of the staff are lawyers, and the other half include other professional skills such as IT, personnel, finance and other support staff. The firm is now doing a lot more professional recruitment and direct entry.

It's going to need the people. The international arena will see a lot of activity and in 1999, Clifford Chance expects to have more employees outside the UK than in it. In early 1998, it had 500 lawyers in Europe; in three years' time it expects to have 1,000. Local nationals who once perceived they were joining a foreign firm now realise that they are joining an international firm which is at the same time equal to the best local firm.

Clifford Chance aims, of course, to be the employer of choice. Aware of the cliché, Clifford Chance scrutinises this in hard terms. It tracks its offer-to-acceptance ratio with the intention of moving it from 50:50 to nearer 70:30. Interpreting the 'declines' is not a sophisticated process, but Clifford Chance does ask them why they said no.

Career Opportunity and Development

Around 130 graduates join Clifford Chance in London as trainee lawyers each year, with another 50 worldwide. They receive an outstanding training package which includes considerable responsibility from the outset. The sheer quality of the training is recognised even by rival firms as being excellent. The two-year training period comprises four six-month periods or 'seats' spent in different areas within the firm, working with senior lawyers on a day-to-day basis. About 50% of trainees spend one of these seats abroad.

Once qualified (typically 95% of an intake are offered jobs with the firm on qualification), progress depends entirely on performance. Outstanding professional, client, personal and managerial skills will hold you in good stead. Some individuals have achieved partnership within six years of qualifying and by your mid-thirties, it is usually apparent whether or not you are likely to reach partner level. The ratio of lawyers and trainees to partners at Clifford Chance is 4:1

Keith Clark, Senior Partner, says, 'Clifford Chance on your CV is powerful. Some of you will make partner at Clifford Chance, others may become partners at other firms. But you will get good training and experience from us and it is up to you to use it.'

Remuneration

The firm regards itself as being towards the top of its marketplace in terms of remuneration. It also emphasises rewarding performance. Individual pay reviews are based on merit, and bonuses are paid for outstanding performance or unusually demanding work.

Benefits are all about the 'we expect a lot from you, and we give back in return' equation. The impressive list includes season ticket and staff loan facilities, private health insurance, a nurse on site and the firm's own doctor, a subsidised restaurant, life assurance and permanent health insurance. There is also a choice of final salary and money purchase pension schemes. Employees in the modern London office also enjoy a swimming pool, a gymnasium, squash courts and a fitness centre.

Performance is encouraged even before joining! Clifford Chance gives a prize of £600 to anyone who achieves an all-important first class honours degree after accepting an offer from the firm, and a similar prize for achieving an overall distinction in the Legal Practice Course.

The Future

There is nothing woolly about Clifford Chance's 'Vision'. It sets out some quite specific targets, including remaining the premier firm for finance practice and reaching the premier division (top three) for corporate work. In property, dispute resolution and tax, its aim is to be in the top three in London and in local European markets, to be equal to the best in the market.

Clifford Chance's international aspirations will also set the agenda. Management structures, personnel and training must continue to develop internationally, and with multinational clients expecting the same quality of service irrespective of location, Clifford Chance must ensure that it delivers these same consistent, professional standards worldwide.

The application of technology, to improve both client service and internal efficiency, will gather pace as increasing numbers of young people join the firm bringing with them computing familiarity and expertise. Clifford Chance's online 'NextLaw', which clients can access, is a totally different provision of legal service representing up-to-date advice available on the Internet.

There will be more international secondment across the Clifford Chance 'empire', recognising that London is not the centre of everything. Indeed, to make partnership at the firm, having worked in at least one other country will shift from the 'nice to have' to 'must have' category fairly soon.

Clifford Chance intends to push flexibility and change more and more, as it moves to shared responsibility in self-development. It is avoiding labelling this as a cultural 'change process' as some companies do, but just getting on with it. The message is that the firm will give you the opportunities and equip you to accommodate change, but increasingly it will be up to you to make it happen.

Davies Arnold Cooper

Davies Arnold Cooper (DAC) is a leading UK commercial law firm whose client base includes all sizes of British and international public and private companies in the manufacturing and service industries. It is particularly strong in insurance litigation, with a growing reputation in the pharmaceutical, construction & commercial property, technology and financial services sectors. Based in the City, DAC has other offices in Manchester, Newcastle and Madrid. DAC has 63 partners and a total staff of nearly 530.

Scorecard:

Remuneration and benefits	★★★★
Progressive attitude	★★★★★
Opportunity for promotion	★★★★
Training, development and education	★★★★
Working atmosphere and environment	★★★★★

Biggest plus:
An innovative law firm with a difference, a real meritocracy

Biggest minus:
Medium-sized, not yet one of the really big players

Davies Arnold Cooper
8 Bouverie Street
London EC4Y 8DD
Tel: 0171 936 2222
Fax: 0171 936 2020
e-mail: daclon@dac.co.uk

Davies Arnold Cooper

The Business

Davies Arnold Cooper (DAC) has built its professional reputation on a practical and commercial approach, but it is also a pioneering firm, setting the pace for others in its field. DAC distinguishes itself from its peers by its open culture, married to self-styled corporate values, in what is still largely a traditional profession. David McIntosh, the longest serving senior partner of any UK commercial law firm, believes that the 'legal profession is terrified of change. The biggest problem is seeing change as a threat.'

The formula is evidently successful. Davies Arnold Cooper has achieved strong organic growth throughout its 70-year history, and in the five years to 1998, fee income increased by 39%. The firm is very profitable.

Insurance litigation, where DAC is market leader, currently represents 75% of income. DAC is also a market leader in the pharmaceutical and healthcare, and construction and property sectors. Areas of future growth targeted by DAC include technology, financial services and retailing. DAC has worked on many prominent cases including Lloyds litigation, Piper Alpha, Hillsborough, pensions mis-selling, Opren and the Channel Tunnel rolling stock claim.

Company Culture and Style

DAC is refreshingly different from other law firms. It has an entrepreneurial, creative culture, and is determined to run itself like a business rather than a traditional firm of solicitors.

It sticks to some of the standard rules of commercial enterprises including reasonable prices, restraint in expanding staff numbers, efficient procedures and preserving unity within the organisation. It encourages non-solicitors to progress to the highest levels. It urges staff and partners to consider themselves first as business people seeking to make profit, second as lawyers.

In 1997, DAC initiated a major change programme called 'Action

Focus' to challenge for the premier spot as the provider of legal services to the UK insurance sector and to prepare for long-term growth in clients, income and profitability. Key aspects of the programme include a focus on core skills, the firm's client base, and emerging markets.

DAC first organised staff skills into a number of specialist resource groups, and then identified the business sectors for profitable growth. This dual focus has resulted in a fundamentally different, and effective, account management system.

The final, ongoing, stage of 'Action Focus' is a process of cultural change. Building upon the existing commercial principles, 'Action Focus' is intended to help DAC become better listeners, problem solvers, and to give and execute commercial advice beyond the expectations of normal legal services. The programme requires teamwork, and the firm's reward systems are geared towards assisting the selfless, not the selfish.

Key elements of DAC's 'Action Focus' culture are support not blame; profit not income; collaboration internally and externally with clients; and accountability. The programme has been well received by staff and clients alike.

'It's also about making everyone feel a part of running the business and having an impact on revenue streams, whatever their job title,' says David McIntosh. 'Everyone in the firm should be a leader.'

DAC also believes that being a lawyer should be fun. The many social activities engender self-confidence and pride in the firm

Human Resources

Human resources is an extremely important strategic management function at DAC, and has board representation. DAC's HR initiatives enjoy a high level and visible commitment from the managing partner and senior partner, David McIntosh, who considers that his main job is to motivate and enthuse others, although he is equally prominent in raising the overall profile of the firm.

Led by director Catherine Williams, the human resources team has a wide remit with many facets: bringing the right people into the firm; providing guidance and support in people management; coaching to improve partners' and managers' business management skills; practical delivery of policies supporting business strategy; and the team is used as an important source of ideas and initiatives for developing the people and the business.

The HR team is always at the heart of change programmes in DAC, in both leading and supporting roles. The department provides a wealth of management experience and offers the business practical advice. 'We work hard to build strong professional relationships with partners and managers. We recognise the importance of knowing our people, the business and our clients. Good working relationships are essential to ensure that the quality of our professional advice meets the business needs. Our aim is not only to articulate our principles and strategies but to align people's behaviour behind the rhetoric,' says Catherine Williams.

Career Opportunity and Development

DAC recruits people who are creative, commercially focused, who combine strong intellect with drive and enthusiasm. DAC offers real opportunities for all levels of staff. 'Our aim is to make everyone who joins successful,' says Catherine Williams

It avoids falling into the trap of selecting only academics, and attracts people with a diversity of talent and qualifications. The firm deliberately chooses people who respond positively to uncertainty, people who enter through non-traditional routes, people with business skills as much as legal qualifications, and who may well be more communicative with clients. Legal executives can thrive at DAC and the firm has five seniors who are treated on a par with partners.

'We've set the target that the Board is not necessarily the ultimate goal to aim for, nor that it constitutes the six best lawyers in the firm. It's just six people fulfilling Board functions,' according to David McIntosh.

Non-fee-earning staff – experts in their own field of marketing, IT, HR, facilities management and project management – are highly valued and genuinely treated as of equal status. This is only to be expected in a commercial business.

Opportunities for promotion and advancement are rich. In 1997 and 1998, DAC made no fewer than 115 promotions, including 26 lawyers qualifying with the firm. The fast-track system will move people quickly, but the firm is happy to accommodate those who don't wish to rise too far – it's more important that they embrace change.

Career development planning is a shared responsibility led by the individual, driven together with their manager, and supported and facilitated by HR. All staff have development plans and career opportunities and development structures that play to their strengths. The 'psychological contract' is extremely important in DAC, and is reflected in personal contracts where commitment to the values of the firm and its business goals are made at an individual level.

Skill development and learning, including formal and on-the-job training, represent a key area of investment at DAC – a hefty 7% of revenue is dedicated to learning and people development.

The development programme aims to give individuals good technical legal skills through case work, careful supervision, mentoring and formal training, in-house and externally. The variety of opportunity for continued education, learning and horizontal skills development is enormous, including external conferences, in-house seminars, technical workshops, Internet and Intranet, and business skills training, and the all-important interpersonal skills required by a client-facing business.

Variety is also a watchword for work experience. DAC has an exchange programme with Blackwell Sanders Peper Martin in the USA, and international placements with clients sometimes feature. DAC also has a training contract exchange with the legal department within a client insurance company.

Remuneration

DAC pays average and above-average market rates for fee earners in a profession not known for poverty. Market rates are monitored and formally reviewed twice-yearly, and all staff have at least one salary review each year.

Overall remuneration includes a bonus scheme, non-contributory pension scheme, health insurance, and a flexible benefits scheme being introduced in 1999.

The Future

With a better infrastructure and a re-focused client management structure, DAC could enjoy very rapid growth. Now is the time to translate ideas into action, with revenue providing the litmus test.

Technology is playing its part, whether in allowing 'virtual working', efficient client management through case conferencing or 'Extranet' information services, or Intranet communications. The judgement is what to embrace, what to spend and what on.

Change requires commitment and support and DAC goes well beyond organisational aspects, seeking actively to help individuals respond positively to change and to become more self-aware and self-managed. The pace of change only ever increases, and DAC must continue to respond quickly with new product, service and delivery ideas to meet clients' changing needs.

DAC is not afraid to explore, experiment and develop the firm so that in 5–10 years' time it may be unrecognisable. Here, people can really make a difference. The firm has flexibility as a core currency and is a pioneer – to its own advantage – in what is often a very traditional profession. The culture and mechanics are almost in place. Time will reveal just how far this spirited law firm can go.

Deloitte & Touche

Deloitte & Touche is the UK practice of the global accountancy and consultancy firm Deloitte Touche Tohmatsu. It is one of the 'Big Five' accountancy-based professional services firms, as a result of previous mergers. Last year total fees for the UK firm rose by more than a quarter to £563.2 million and the number of employees rose to just under 7,000. The international practice employs more than 72,000 people.

Scorecard:
Remuneration and benefits ★★★★
Progressive attitude ★★★★
Opportunity for promotion ★★★★
Training, development and education ★★★★★
Working atmosphere and environment ★★★★

Biggest plus:
Opportunity for rapid advancement

Biggest minus:
Constant client service focus puts heavy demands on staff

Deloitte & Touche
Hill House
1 Little New Street
London EC4A 3TR
Tel: 0171 936 3000
Fax: 0171 936 2346
website: www.deloitte.co.uk

Deloitte & Touche

Deloitte & Touche

The Business

Having joined the 'Big Five' accountancy-based professional services firms as a result of previous mergers, Deloitte & Touche distanced itself from the recent round of consolidations in the profession and is now focused on growing organically.

In common with other firms of its type, Deloitte & Touche has broadened the scope of its work so that, in the words of one manager, it is 'much more than an audit and accounting firm'. Depending upon the nature of the work, it can find itself competing with other Big Five practices, strategy consultancies such as McKinsey or significant information technology organisations, such as IBM or Sema. Consulting is becoming an increasingly important part of the business, with fees almost as high as those from tax advice.

Proud of an academic record that consistently puts its recruits ahead of the average in the Institute of Chartered Accountants' examinations, Deloitte is also keen to stress that, while always professional, it has a more relaxed and informal approach than some of its rivals.

Company Culture and Style

Led in the UK by senior partner and chief executive John Connolly, Deloitte sees this friendly and, by accountancy standards, informal style as critical in helping it attract the best recruits.

Though managers insist that there is not a Deloitte & Touche type as such, they agree that the usual qualities of intelligence, confidence, dynamism and creativity are not enough. Arrogance is frowned upon and recruits have to be able to work in teams, not just within the firm but also with clients.

This is important as the business moves away from the traditional arm's length advisory style to a more collaborative approach that involves working with clients on devising solutions for their business. One key result of this is that it means that employees have to arrive with the ability to learn at a fast pace and must also be able to build relationships with all sorts of people quickly.

One employee who has recently returned after a spell with a rival points to the fact that the firm is genuinely focused on serving clients rather than just expanding its business. However, there is still room for individuality, with people at all levels encouraged to come up with ideas.

Human Resources

In common with other professional firms, Deloitte & Touche puts great emphasis on training and development. Steve James, principal manager, human resources, explains that the focus on clients is inextricably linked with that on the firm's people. 'In order for us to be successful and to grow as a firm, we have to grow our people,' he adds.

Since HR managers are acutely aware of the costs of recruitment, a lot of effort is put into retaining people once they have been hired. The HR department puts this in terms of 'going for the long-term gain' with the secret being to get the psychological contract – the unwritten deal between the employer and the employee – right.

One of the areas that the department is working especially hard on is increasing the number of women who rise to the top of the organisation. As at other professional firms, women make up between a third and a half of the graduate intake, but there is a substantial drop-out rate as they move up the firm. Generous maternity packages and flexible working schemes are helping to slow the outflow and more women are reaching partner level, but the firm is looking to import some successful techniques from Deloitte in the United States in an effort to improve matters further.

Balancing the needs of employees with the demands of clients is a particular problem at professional services firms – and a clear contributing factor in the shortage of women at the top of them. But the HR department is taking steps to ensure that people do not become overwhelmed by work. It has carried out a survey which found that 62% felt that they had a good work–life balance, and has taken further steps to help people who have had difficulties in this area.

But Steve James acknowledges that not only do workloads vary from department to department, but also that individuals are all different in their attitudes to heavy workloads. 'For some people, it's not a problem,' he says.

Career Opportunity and Development

There is a clear career path in that the typical recruit arrives as a graduate and spends three years as a trainee chartered accountant. He or she then moves on into various areas of the firm, passing through various manager levels before becoming a senior manager and – after about 10 years in the firm – being considered for partnership.

However, in recent years a level of 'specialist' has been introduced between senior manager and partner. Though some of these specialists go on to become partners, there is a recognition that this is a way of providing a wider variety of career paths for those who may not wish to become partners, while continuing to offer their expertise to the practice.

The firm makes extensive use of 360-degree feedback and other appraisal techniques at all levels of the firm, including the partners. But perhaps the crucial elements are the development and assessment centres to which all would-be partners are sent. There, they are put in various role-play situations and given a lot of feedback about their performance in such areas as working with others, selling skills and presentation style.

Mentoring and coaching also play important roles at all levels of the organisation. Each student joining the firm is supported by four 'key people' – a staff partner, a counselling partner (whose role it is to take a broader view and deal with pastoral issues as well as work), a mentor who is a manager in the graduate's team, and an academic counsellor, who ensures that the graduate's studies are progressing satisfactorily. The idea is that they deal with 'the soft bits as well as the hard bits', says an HR executive.

Although this appears to be tightly structured, there are opportunities for rapid promotion and moves into different parts of the firm. Within four years of qualifying, recruits can expect to be senior managers with commensurate responsibilities.

The firm is making a conscious attempt to introduce younger employees to the broad range of opportunities available within the firm. One of the main elements in this is the holding of an internal careers fair for those recruits just coming up for qualification as accountants. Representatives from a variety of practice areas, including corporate finance, forensic accounting and corporate recovery, attend what is essentially another milk round so that newly-qualifieds are better able to make informed choices about the fields in which they wish to go on to specialise.

Remuneration

Like any other international professional services firm, Deloitte is intensely competitive in terms of pay and benefits. It is especially conscious that its competitors these days are not just other leading accountancy firms, but also merchant banks and specialist consultancy firms, such as McKinsey & Co.

In 1998 graduates started in the London office on about £19,000 a year, including 'settling-in allowances' and profit-related pay, and they can expect that to progress rapidly in salary terms so that on qualification they earn more than £30,000.

While partners are rewarded with a share of the profits, the nature of the organisation makes the use of other profit share arrangements more difficult, and reinforces the firm's focus on competitive salary packages.

Deloitte offers a range of benefits, including pension, health insurance, life cover and enhanced maternity leave, with individual entitlements often based on grade.

The Future

Having made its stand against 'mega-mergers' within the profession, Deloitte insists that it is 'comfortable' about its position in the marketplace on the grounds that it is a good place from which to focus on serving clients. However, it acknowledges that the 'whole agenda' is about the organisation's ability to respond to clients' global needs in a seamless fashion.

As a partnership it is confident that it has the flexibility and ability to deal with change quickly. 'Dealing with change is an everyday thing. It's built into the culture,' says one manager.

Diageo

Diageo is one of the world's leading consumer goods companies. Formed in December 1997 through the merger of GrandMet and Guinness, Diageo has an outstanding portfolio of world-famous food and drinks brands including Smirnoff, Johnnie Walker, J&B, Gordon's, Pillsbury, Häagen Dazs, Guinness and Burger King. Diageo sells its products in more than 200 countries, generating annual turnover of around £12 billion. It has 77,000 employees worldwide, 13,000 in the UK.

Scorecard:

Remuneration and benefits	★★★★
Progressive attitude	★★★★★
Opportunity for promotion	★★★★
Training, development and education	★★★★
Working atmosphere and environment	★★★★

Biggest plus:
Tremendous, expanded opportunity to work with some of the world's leading consumer brands

Biggest minus:
Cultural change will take time to settle down

Diageo plc
8 Henrietta Place
London W1M 9AG
Tel: 0171 927 5200
Fax: 0171 927 4600
website: www.diageo.com

DIAGEO

Diageo

The Business

The creation of Diageo through the merger of GrandMet and Guinness has taken it into the premier league of consumer goods companies. The fit between the two spirits businesses, geographically and by product, was excellent. And the merger was resolved with relative ease, with personalities proving no barrier to producing a balanced board.

'It's created a tremendous opportunity to grow our brands faster and more profitably,' says Tony Greener, chairman. And it has a stunning portfolio – its top 30 brands all hold the number one or number two position in growing markets.

What's in a name? Classics students will quickly tell you that *dia* is loosely based on the Latin word for 'day' and that *geo* means 'world' in Greek. It adds up to 'everyday, everywhere'. Eyebrows were raised at the name, of course, but it reveals global purpose.

Diageo manages its brands in four businesses: UDV, formed by the integration of IDV and UD (United Distillers), is the world's leading and most profitable spirits and wines company. Pillsbury is one of the world's leading food companies, with a portfolio of so-called 'megabrands'. Guinness is the world's leading stout brand, brewed in 50 countries and enjoyed in 150. Burger King is the world's second largest hamburger restaurant chain, with more than 10,000 restaurants in 53 countries.

The consumer lies at the heart of Diageo's business and marketing is the key to making great brands greater. Diageo intends to grow its brands through a combination of unmatched consumer understanding, outstanding brand support and excellent sales and operations execution.

Diageo, under chief executive John McGrath, is totally committed to shareholder value and using economic profit (EP) as the key financial measure. EP is a the income earned by a business after deducting a charge in the capital required to generate that income – it's an excellent measure because it brings together the profit and loss account and the balance sheet in one holistic measure to provide a true return on invested capital. Diageo applies this measure to each business and each individual brand – not just the corporation as a whole.

Company Culture and Style

'Managing for Value' is the company's core business philosophy. It helps Diageo develop strategies to build its brands looking some years ahead, covering strategic options, levels of investment and sales support, and which route will generate the most value. 'Everyone in the company can help to create value', says John McGrath.

A single culture of the newly merged businesses has been created quickly, although it is still early days and it will take some time to grow firm roots. But Diageo people will tell you that it feels different already.

A new set of visions and values has been introduced for the new company, to address what it is that binds together a diverse business. Diageo certainly has a commitment to brand management and marketing excellence – but the real challenge is to have people behaving differently.

'Passionate about consumers' lies at the heart of caring about brands. 'Be the best' urges continuous learning, setting high standards and delivering results by beating the competition. 'Proud of what we do' reveals Diageo's continued sense of integrity, sensitivity, diversity and social responsibility. 'Freedom to succeed' is all about creating an open, challenging culture based on teamwork and trust.

Diageo has gone through a tremendous development process and a unique learning experience. But people now have much more of a 'can do' mentality, as opposed to 'must try'.

Human Resources

Diageo recognises that the determining factor in superior performance is, ultimately, the quality of its people. 'When you have great brands, you've got to have great people to manage and grow them,' says John McGrath.

The demands made on the HR function are therefore high, particularly in a time of rapid change. Accordingly, HR has a high profile and good access to the key decision-makers. It has an executive member on each divisional board.

'We won't achieve our corporate goals if we don't change,' says Phil Radcliff, group organisation planning and development director. A major task is to ensure that people do not feel 'victims' of change, not helped by City references to the merger as 'big'. Various change programmes were set in motion to help Diageo people feel that could control their own destiny and make an impact. Organisational strategy is also essential

It was the spirits business UDV, which accounts for 55% of Diageo's operating profit, which has been predominantly affected by the merger.

A new structure was established specifically to grow its brands. Although Diageo did not choose the lowest cost option, it anticipates that the merger will reduce UDV and Diageo's cost base by £290 million in the year ending 30 June 2001. The £630 million cost of achieving synergy is a major investment, which includes headcount reductions, changing business locations, new systems and processes, and consequent asset write-offs.

'It took a huge amount of work from employees,' says Phil Radcliff. 'They really did live out our value of "be proud of what you do", even those who did not, unfortunately, have a long-term future with the new company. They remained committed to the end, even saying they would rather do something completely different afterwards rather than work for the competitor.' Consultants McKinsey said it was 'one of the best-managed mergers'.

Diageo is now well into the phase of making the merger work and deliver growth, cascading the values of the new business down the organisation.

Career Opportunity and Development

One attractive aspect that will make Diageo unique is the range of careers that it provides. Few companies can offer the same breadth of opportunity and experience in consumer goods covering foods, restaurants, beer and spirits.

Diageo realises that it won't achieve real change unless it sets high targets. All four businesses set 'stretch' targets, backed by a serious examination of how they can be achieved. This has unleashed a new lease of life and dynamism in the company, and staff have responded with vigour. The company is already working on developing better mechanisms to get movement across the businesses (which GrandMet had never really achieved).

With interesting loyalty issues raised – previously in spirits, people were trying to destroy each other's brands instead of building them up – Diageo has worked hard to give former Guinness and GrandMet people a sense of each other's business and brands. Pre-merger, 100 managers were taken to a retreat at the group-owned Gleneagles Hotel to be exposed to each other's brands. Pulling pints of Guinness was just one of the less arduous tasks!

Succession management is focusing on the extent to which people are living the new values. 'The matrix problem is where you have high performers not living the values, and non-performers who are living them,' points out Phil Radcliff. 'We obviously need the hybrid of high performers who are living the values. There's a lot of coaching to help people get there.'

The Senior Executive Development Programme and the Diageo

Management Development Programme (which targets around 200–300 high-potential people, typically in their late 20s/early 30s) have become major factors in the development approach. Diageo's core values are built into the programmes, backed by purpose-built workshops and heavy communication. 'Otherwise it becomes a soft initiative,' says Phil Radcliff.

Remuneration

Pay and benefits remain highly competitive, and Managing for Value allows Diageo to reward individuals according to their contribution. A new incentive structure is also being introduced to provide a direct link between the creation of value for shareholders and the way in which senior managers are rewarded.

The Future

Diageo's brands and financial measures are already top class, but the company still faces a huge task and the first three years' results after the merger will be the proof in the pudding. But the merger appears to be working, savings are ahead of timetable and everything seems to be going in the right direction.

The company is mindful of shifting away from the monoculture prevalent in the drinks industry and diversity figures highly on the agenda. 'How else can we reach new young consumers if our work force doesn't reflect their make-up?' asks Phil Radcliff.

And in the talent war, where every company is saying the same thing, Diageo wants to succeed in attracting and retaining the best talent. Linkages to educational establishments may be developed and fewer lines of supervision in the modern drinks business should help.

Employees are being surveyed at all levels of the organisation. Do they feel they have the freedom to succeed and is the organisation harnessing their creativity? Are they proud of what they are doing in the company? Are they passionate about understanding what consumers want, and about using that insight to build Diageo's brands? Are they achieving the very best work of their lives?

If and when the answers are 'yes' then Diageo will have harnessed real momentum towards becoming one of the very best consumer goods companies.

Dixons

Dixons Group plc is a retailing group specialising in the sale of high-technology consumer electronics, personal computers, photographic equipment, communication products and domestic appliances. The Group is divided into five retail chains – Dixons, Currys, PC World and The Link. It is also trialling @jakarta, a new games and PC software store, and has recently launched Freeserve, the UK's first fully featured free Internet service which now has over one million users. The group also operates Mastercare, the UK's premier after-sales service organisation.

Scorecard:

Remuneration and benefits	★★★★
Progressive attitude	★★★★
Opportunity for promotion	★★★
Training, development and education	★★★★
Working atmosphere and environment	★★★★

Biggest plus:
A range of career opportunities in all sectors due to the size and growth of the group

Biggest minus:
A fast moving business environment – only a negative for those who want an easy life!

Dixons Group plc
Maylands Avenue
Hemel Hempstead
Herts HP2 7TG
Tel: 01442 353000
Fax: 01442 233218
website: www.dixons-group-plc.co.uk

Dixons Group plc

Dixons

The Business

Dixons Group plc is a highly dynamic organisation, setting the pace for the electrical retailing industry. In this highly competitive marketplace, many major retailers have not survived the last recession but Dixons has maintained its edge and entered a period of strong growth to take advantage of the economic recovery.

The group's chief executive, John Clare describes the company as 'dynamic, fast-moving, competitive and ambitious'. Despite the group's success, David Mattinson, head of personnel at PC World, says the company is constantly striving to create new opportunities in the market. 'Dixons Group is always looking for a niche that's not being covered.'

In 1948, Dixons had an annual turnover of £5,460. Fifty years later, in 1998, it reported pre-tax profits of £218 million with an annual turnover of £2.8 billion.

The group is constantly exploring new retail formats to meet the changing face of retail. The most recent development is @jakarta, a specialist computer games and software store.

Freeserve is the group's hugely successful Internet Service Provider (ISP). Launched in 1998, it was the first fully featured free ISP and it has now become the UK's leading ISP with more than one million customers signed up.

Dixons Direct offers both Internet shopping via Dixons Online and home delivery over the telephone, while PC World Business Direct targets business customers.

The group operates PC Services – a national call centre in Nottingham, employing over 400 people who man the phones 24 hours a day, 365 days a year, solving customers' computer problems over the telephone.

Dixons also operates five tax and duty free stores at the major UK airports, including Heathrow, Gatwick, Birmingham and Manchester.

Company Culture and Style

Customer focus remains a driving force within the group. Dixons in-house campaign, 'My Customer, My Responsibility', is devoted to improving customer service. David Mattinson says, 'As a business, we are very good at designing stores, getting purchasing and the marketing of our product right, but MCMR, in terms of delivering excellence in customer service, is at the heart of our service proposition.'

Dixons is keen to ensure that the working environment is enjoyable. It encourages regular meetings at which staff have an opportunity to voice their thoughts, concerns and ideas.

Area sales manager for Currys South East Division Judy Sharkey says the emphasis in her role is on making contact with the company's employees. 'It's very much about discovering their strengths and weaknesses. I firmly believe that you only get successful sales if you develop people properly. It's the staff in the stores who are doing the selling and they need to have the desire to succeed and be given the support to do so.'

The group's devotion to customer service is very important for its employees. Mastercare field service engineer Ian Baston says, 'You are the company as far as customers are concerned and it's important that you build up a good relationship with them. I get good back-up from colleagues in Customer Services and the workshop and that's important.'

Human Resources

Dixons places great importance on customer service and providing training for its staff. Over the years the internal courses and schemes have changed but they retain the same focus – to provide staff with the skills they need to succeed in their field.

Chairman Sir Stanley Kalms says, 'Sales increasingly depend on high quality staff understanding the complexities of our ever-widening range and being able to assess and demonstrate the best product to meet each customer's needs. Last year we served some two million customers every month, all of them people on whom our reputation depends. Our training programmes place particular emphasis on customer service and product knowledge and every store has exacting targets and incentives to ensure that we deliver increasingly high levels of customer satisfaction.'

Over the next two years the group aims to get all of its head office managers on to a management development programme which will help them to develop their people management skills.

In addition, all front line managers are given regular training to help them develop the skills they need to use in the workplace.

Career Opportunity and Development

Recently Dixons has placed a greater emphasis on its management trainee programme, aiming to recruit both graduates and A-level students. David Mattinson says that it is vital that the group maintains its strong focus on the quality of its new employees. With the emphasis now firmly on recruitment he says that they aim to get new employees to their first management position within a year.

New employees are always being recruited from a variety of different paths. Amy Burnett recently transferred to the Oxford Street branch of The Link with a background in photography. 'I started with the group at the newly launched store in Bedford. It's really exciting to be in at the beginning. Working in a team which starts together creates a strong working relationship.'

Chairman Sir Stanley Kalms says, 'The growth of the group's retailing business has created many opportunities, enabling us to double our workforce over the past five years. We have recently welcomed our first New Deal trainees and intend to recruit a further 100 over the next year. Our commitment to all our people is to provide the training and the opportunities to develop their skills and harness their abilities so that they enjoy long and fulfilling careers.'

All new sales staff joining the company are sent on a residential course known as Career Start. There are seven Career Start centres around the country. Training is not just for the newly arrived however. Dixons carries out a lot of training throughout the year to reinforce its commitment to customer service excellence, both for existing staff and new staff joining the company.

Remuneration

The emphasis is on the success of the group and the role of each individual. David Mattinson says the group recognises a need to reward sales staff as well as management grades. 'A lot of our sales staff are career sales people and it's important not only to train them but to reward them.' He claims few other retail groups can offer the same fast-track career opportunities as the Dixons group.

Dave Mattinson says the group is currently trialling a new commission based pay structure guaranteeing its staff a minimum level of commission in their first year in the business. 'It's aimed at helping us recruit and retain staff but it also gives staff a safety net in their first year.'

Pay levels throughout the group are reviewed regularly and the group recognises the need to have a good overall salary package to attract and motivate staff.

All staff are eligible to join the company's pension scheme as well as a Save As You Earn share scheme. They are also entitled to discounts on insurance policies and a range of other benefits including length of service-based share option schemes.

The Future

The half-yearly results for 1998/99 indicate that it should be another positive year for the group. This optimism is reflected in the proposed new store openings programme scheduled for 1999. Over 50 new stores throughout the UK and Republic of Ireland are due to open during this period, creating 2,000 new jobs for enthusiastic and customer service oriented staff. Over 400 positions will be based in Scotland, 200 in the Republic of Ireland and 100 in Northern Ireland. Included in these openings are the expansion of @jakarta, the new high street software chain aimed at PC and games enthusiasts. Jobs will also be created at the head office in Hemel Hempstead and at Mastercare, the group's after-sales service organisation.

As well as new store openings, new and innovative products will allow the group to introduce the latest technology to the mass market through the various chains.

The group continues to grow market share and to invest at record levels in improving its existing store portfolio, in new space, in new businesses, in its infrastructure and in its people. The group's sales are expected to continue to grow in all major product categories, with domestic appliances, photography, mobile phones, computer software, accessories and digital technology all expected to be successful.

The launch of Freeserve has revolutionised the UK Internet market, becoming the UK's largest Internet service provider within three months of launch. Growing numbers of Freeserve and PC users will continue to receive an excellent back-up service from PC Services staff now trained in all aspects of the Internet. A dedicated management team has been established to ensure that Dixons takes full advantage of the opportunities generated by the success of Freeserve.

Eli Lilly

Eli Lilly is a global leader in the pharmaceutical industry. It employs 31,000 people worldwide, 2,000 of whom work in the UK. The company markets its products in over 150 countries.

Scorecard:

Remuneration and benefits	★★★★★
Progressive attitude	★★★★★
Opportunity for promotion	★★★★
Training, development and education	★★★★
Working atmosphere and environment	★★★★★

Biggest plus:
An innovative company where people are really valued

Biggest minus:
Developing new drugs is costly and time-consuming

Eli Lilly and Company Limited
Dextra Court
Chapel Hill
Basingstoke
Hampshire RG21 5SY
Tel: 01256 315000
Fax: 01256 315858
website: www.lilly.com

Eli Lilly

The Business

Eli Lilly is a global research-based pharmaceutical corporation dedicated to creating and delivering innovative healthcare solutions that enable people to live longer, healthier and more active lives. It was founded by Colonel Eli Lilly in 1876 in Indianapolis, USA. The company was one of the first to initiate a research programme in the 1880s. In the 1920s, Eli Lilly introduced the world's first insulin product. It was also one of the first companies to mass-produce penicillin in the 1940s. Today, the company concentrates on five vital therapeutic categories: neuroscience, infectious diseases, endocrinology/diabetes, cardiology and oncology.

Over the last five years, the company has refocused on its core business of creating innovative molecules. Eli Lilly prides itself on its innovation and creativity. It is one of the world's largest research and development companies, and in 1998 spent over £1 billion on investigating and developing new medicines. The average length of time from discovering a new drug to making it available to patients is 15 years, and the average cost of discovery and development is from $350 to $500 million. However, the company is working hard to bring both measures down.

Eli Lilly operates in over 30 European countries, with its regional HQ in London. In 1999, the company celebrated 60 years of UK manufacturing, and its Basingstoke operation remains a cornerstone for Lilly manufacturing throughout the world. Basingstoke produces, packages and warehouses several of the company's best-selling medicines for supply to the UK National Health Service and for export. Also in the UK is the company's largest bulk manufacturing facility for animal and human health products at Speke, Merseyside.

Company Culture and Style

The culture of the company is underpinned by its three long-established core values: respect for people, integrity and excellence. These values are constantly re-examined and interpreted so as to be relevant to contemporary society. Stephen Fry, HR director: 'These values are so much a part of everything we do that they become engrained in everyone who works for us and affect the way they make decisions.'

Refreshingly in today's world, Eli Lilly still seeks to employ people for a career, not hire them to do a job. The emphasis is on building a career that will allow people to develop; that often includes their doing a number of different jobs within the organisation. The company is also built on relationships. This has been at the root of much of its success in the past. Eli Lilly acknowledges that this must now be balanced with more formal work processes, but at the same time, wishes to retain the benefits of relationship working.

Not only does Eli Lilly offer excellent career development, the type of work it does makes a positive difference to society. In recent years, for instance, the company has brought to market several important new drugs for the treatment of cancer, diabetes, depression, schizophrenia and cardiovascular complications, and a preventative therapy for osteoporosis. It has also made a substantial commitment to women's health.

Working for the company is also rewarding in another sense. In 1993, all employees were granted share stock options (where the local culture allowed this; otherwise, a cash alternative was given). A second set of options came in 1995, and more may follow. The result of this is that employees now feel a far greater sense of ownership. For instance, people are keen to identify ways to save money, to make process improvements, and so on.

The company looks to take on people who are keen to learn and have the capacity to do so; it wants strong individuals who are good at working in teams, are innovative and have good ideas – but do not need to reinvent the wheel at every stage; and for men and women who get results. It also looks for people with the highest ethical standards.

People can be empowered early on, depending on their ability and commitment. Stephen Fry: 'If people can show they are making a contribution, fulfilling their responsibilities and influencing others within and outside their job descriptions, the opportunities are endless. If you need pushing every day, you probably won't succeed here. But most of our people aren't like that; they want to succeed and as a rule have significant long-term career aspirations.'

Internal communications have improved significantly in recent years. Communications channels now include magazines such as *Focus*, *In Touch* and *The Edge*; e-mail, voicemail, and global TV broadcasts by the chairman and senior executives.

Human Resources

HR management is vital for the company, as borne out by the chairman's set of priorities for 1999. The opening priority was: 'The first job of management is the development of our people.'

The company sees the function as one of reciprocity between itself and its employees. For instance, the company has the responsibility to create and develop a strategy, to communicate its vision, and to reward and recognise its people. The employees have the responsibility to continue to grow their skills, to perform to the best of their ability at all times, and to work together effectively.

Every two years, Eli Lilly conducts a 'voice of the Employee' survey to measure opinions across a range of key areas. It is also a member of the Mayflower Consortium. This organisation provides questions which can be compared across a given business culture. For instance, 17 questions relate to employee satisfaction, and Eli Lilly was above the industry average for all 17 in the UK.

Career Opportunity and Development

The key to career opportunity at Eli Lilly is that it is very much the responsibility of the individual – with the company providing all the support needed. As a result, the sky really is the limit when it comes to career development. The only restrictions are the individual's talent, commitment and determination to succeed.

Since 1995, the company has operated a system it calls Performance Management. Stephen Fry: 'This is not just another name for an appraisal. Instead, it's a sophisticated system whereby people sit down with their managers and plan their objectives for the coming year. At least twice a year, those objectives are revisited and changed if necessary. Everyone has his or her own development plan, which links into the pay review cycle.'

Cross-functional moves are very much a part of the way Eli Lilly likes to develop people, at all levels. This ties in well with employee aspirations: people want to learn, want to experience new challenges. There are also a number of opportunities to work overseas, with around 350–400 people working outside their own country at any one time. In particular, the UK operation farms out a lot of its talent abroad, and also takes some in from outside. The company provides considerable support for people moving to an overseas appointment, including help for the family.

The company has always been seen as very good for training and employee development. Any relevant skill can be acquired, either internally or outside (with the aid of company support). If needs are sufficiently widespread, previously externally sited training will be brought in-house. Eli Lilly has a number of links with universities; for instance Speke has a link with Manchester University. There are also tie-ups with a series of MBA programmes.

Remuneration

The global stock option programme is a key element of remuneration. As to salary, the company sees itself as a very good payer. It benchmarks itself against other top companies and pays accordingly.

It operates a similar policy in its portfolio of non-cash benefits. These include everything expected from a blue-chip employer: a defined benefit pension plan, cars where these are needed for the job or at certain management levels, life assurance, private healthcare cover, and a social club which organises a range of sports and social events.

The Future

The future looks very bright for Eli Lilly. It has a strong pipeline of products which will serve it well into the next millennium. It also believes it has the innovative ability to fuel more growth.

Challenges for the company are primarily two-fold. Stephen Fry: 'The first challenge is continuing to find the right calibre of people. The top individuals will really be a commodity in the future: I foresee a war for talent. I believe we will compete well for that talent, but we cannot afford to relax our efforts here. The second challenge, dependent on the first, is to keep the new products coming. Here too there will be hard work ahead, but I remain convinced we are well placed for the future.'

Ericsson Limited

Ericsson Limited is one of the major operations in the Ericsson Group. Ericsson is the leading provider in the new telecoms world, with communications solutions that combine telecom and datacom technologies with freedom of mobility for the user. With over 100,000 employees in 140 countries and annual turnover in excess of 167 billion Swedish Kroner, Ericsson simplifies communications for its customers – network operators, service providers, enterprises and consumers – the world over.

Scorecard:

Remuneration and benefits	★★★★
Progressive attitude	★★★★★
Opportunity for promotion	★★★★
Training, development and education	★★★★
Working atmosphere and environment	★★★★★

Biggest plus:
Dynamic, fast-moving, exciting – and lots of opportunities

Biggest minus:
Only for those who embrace change!

Ericsson Limited
Telecommunications Centre
Ericsson Way
Burgess Hill
West Sussex RH15 9UB
Tel: 01444 234567
Fax: 01483 305503
website: www.ericsson.co.uk

ERICSSON

Ericsson Limited

The Business

Ericsson was founded in Sweden in 1876 and began selling telephone sets in the UK through an agent in 1880. By 1897, Britain accounted for 28% of the company's telephone sales, so it was a logical move to set up its own office in London in 1898. Today, Ericsson is one of the largest telecommunications suppliers in the UK, with established public network operators, fixed and mobile, as customers along with businesses of all sizes. The UK is Ericsson's third largest market after the USA and China.

Impressive though this progress was, the 1990s have seen even more rapid growth for Ericsson Limited thanks to deregulation and liberalisation of telecoms markets, and to Ericsson's own substantial global investment in research and development: 16% of turnover goes on R&D. Ericsson now leads the market in the wireless office environment, its mobile phones are available for all cellular standards and all networks in the UK, and its enterprise networking technology is in service with businesses, local governments and universities.

Growth has been particularly strong over the last five years; no less than 60% of Ericsson's turnover in 1997 came from products not even available three years ago. Net sales in the UK in 1997 were £1 billion.

Company Culture and Style

Ericsson Limited's group HR director Margaret Brooks: 'The pace of change just gets faster all the time. As a result, we need to keep up with this change as a company – which means attracting and retaining the right people.' To thrive, those people must be highly competent, flexible and creative. They need to deliver results, be customer-focused, responsive, technically literate and open-minded. Team players and those with a global mindset do well, but above all they need to welcome change, to see it as an opportunity.

The culture at Ericsson is open, stretching and challenging, an environment where individual contributions are expected – but also recognised. This is definitely not an organisation where managers take credit for the achievements of their staff, nor is it hierarchical or bureaucratic. Rather, Ericsson has an unusual degree of consensus in its operations.

At the heart of the culture is customer service. Pushing standards forward and producing results which go beyond customer expectations can be demanding; but Ericsson people tend to relish the opportunity to work with leading-edge technology. The feel of the company is dynamic; 50% of the workforce are aged 35 or younger, and 40% are graduates. It is also truly global. There are over 3,000 Ericsson expatriates in more than 80 countries.

Ericsson's group chief executive officer Sven-Christer Nilsson launched a new organisational structure in October 1998. This was in direct response to the changing world of telecommunications, and Ericsson's market focus is now even more geared to making it easier for the customer. In typical Ericsson style, this major change was superbly handled. The top 400 managers in the group were assembled in San Diego for the launch, and it was then cascaded throughout the organisation in great detail by local briefings supported by the global newspaper and Intranet facilities. These also allowed question and answer sessions.

Internal communications at Ericsson Limited include an excellent company magazine (20 pages, full colour throughout), divisional newsheets, an Ericsson Group newspaper, a highly professional Ericsson Group glossy magazine, posters, News Screens, Wide Angle View, communication days, lunchtime addresses and Intranet communication. Suffice it to say that no-one is ever in the dark at this company!

Human Resources

Ericsson's aim is to be an excellent employer. Margaret Brooks: 'We want to ensure that people are both excited and challenged by their jobs. It's a demanding environment. I believe we can all meet that challenge.' HR policies are worked out for the group as a whole, but – in line with the attribute of flexibility – local companies work within this framework and develop their own initiatives.

There is a very strong commitment to HR in Ericsson: and its importance was re-emphasised in the recent restructuring. The objectives are to offer all staff excellent training, facilities and scope for development. An excellent appraisal system is in place. There is also an emphasis on developing future managers, with the company continually striving to improve model management techniques.

There are regular employee opinion surveys on a wide range of themes, including a worldwide employee opinion survey called 'Compass' which in the UK is run every two years. Each country has the opportunity to add its own questions. Response rates are regularly above 80%. Each UK unit has its own results, which in turn are fed back to staff through management briefings. Smaller-scale surveys are also used, to focus on issues arising in local areas.

Career Opportunity and Development

The reasons for joining Ericsson are clear-cut. The company offers its people the chance to work with state-of-the-art technology, to enjoy stimulating challenges, to be a valued part of a team in an open, non-bureaucratic culture, and to work overseas. Lots of work is project-based, giving employees the satisfaction of seeing work through from inception to implementation.

Graduates can expect first-class training and early responsibility. Once on board, career development can be rapid. Given the global nature of the group, development is often overseas for those with the right skills and commitment. All vacancies are advertised internally, and 200 Ericsson Limited employees are currently working abroad. This would typically be a 2–5 year contract, but there are also a number of shorter assignments for 6–9 months. Wherever employees work within the group, they remain supported by the common social welfare package.

There is clearly a feeling that there is always something new to do; fresh challenges are the norm, not the exception. Ericsson is a complex organisation with a wide range of sophisticated and fast-changing technology. Matrix management encourages people to develop new skills as their careers progress. As a result, turnover is low at Ericsson. Furthermore, a number of those who do move outside the group find themselves returning!

Competence development is a high priority at the company. Because of the rapid pace of change in the marketplace, employees need to be willing to learn new skills throughout their careers. Indeed, the company maintains a multi-skill environment. These new skills can come through a range of ways: web-based learning, an open learning centre, courses tailored to the needs of the individual, and the Ericsson Training Centre which opened in 1997. Although primarily for customers, the centre is also used for internal training. Courses include around 50 non-technical subjects and an almost limitless number of technical topics. Technicians are regularly upskilled, keeping their abilities in line with the continual evolution of the technology.

Remuneration

Ericsson sees itself as a good payer in the median of its market range overall, but can and does pay especially well for particular scarce skills. Annual pay reviews are related to individual performance and merit. The use of incentive schemes is being extended. The company sets objectives for itself and its units, which in turn are cascaded down to individual targets each year.

Benefits include flexible working hours at most locations (except for managers and certain staff), subsidised meals at all sites, healthcare schemes, maternity provision (including support for childcare), a final salary pension scheme, cars for managers, sales force and essential users with a cash alternative and a trade up or down facility – and a range of events at each site such as a formal ball or a beach barbecue.

The Future

Ericsson's profile has improved in the 1990s, and the name is increasingly well known – aided by marketing, advertising and even an appearance by the company's products in the James Bond blockbuster *Tomorrow Never Dies*! Even so, the rapidly changing marketplace means that the company cannot be complacent or stand still. Margaret Brooks: 'Our biggest challenge is to ensure we are flexible, adaptive and responsive given that the business is evolving so rapidly. We do our best to predict those trends, but surprises are inevitable! As a result, we need to help people feel confident about this environment and help them see changes not as threats but as opportunities.'

The company looks well placed to handle whatever the future of telecommunications may bring, aided by its ability to restructure itself when needed. As Sven-Christer Nilsson put it: 'Our task is to understand our customers' opportunities and needs and to provide communication solutions that are better than our competitors . . . it's a matter of identifying and investing in those areas offering the best growth. And assuming the role of being our customers' guide in the new world.' This type of thinking is typical of a forward-looking, dynamic and fast-growing group at the forefront of cutting-edge technology.

Ernst & Young

Ernst & Young is one of the world's leading professional services firms and one of the 'Big Five' in the UK. Its core activities are audit and assurance, tax, corporate finance, corporate recovery and management consultancy. In 1998 it acted as auditor to one in five of the world's top 1000 companies. It is one of the world's largest tax practices and also the world's fourth largest management consultancy. Ernst & Young has 85,000 people based in 675 offices in some 132 countries. The UK business, which is the second largest in the worldwide organisation, has 7,800 staff and 470 partners operating from 24 offices. UK gross fee income was £633 million in 1998 with an average profit per partner of around £308,000.

Scorecard:

Remuneration and benefits	★★★★★
Progressive attitude	★★★
Opportunity for promotion	★★★★★
Training, development and education	★★★★
Working atmosphere and environment	★★★

Biggest plus:
Looks like a winning team in a growing range of management disciplines

Biggest minus:
The inevitable tensions that arise from rapid growth

Ernst & Young
Becket House
1 Lambeth Palace Road
London SE1 7EU
Tel: 0171 928 2000
Fax: 0171 928 1345
website: www.eyuk.com

⊒⫼ ERNST & YOUNG

Ernst & Young

The Business

Ernst & Young's business is thriving and it has the credentials to match. In the UK, Ernst & Young is extremely ambitious – its target is to double its revenues to £1 billion by the end of 2001. 'The firm's success is driven by the flexibility, teamwork and professionalism of our people, and has seen a fundamental change in the nature of the organisation,' says Nick Land, Chairman.

Ernst & Young is currently in the process of integrating its worldwide practices and in 1998 tripled its number of international vice chairmen to nine.

Ernst & Young's offices outside London are now grouped into four regions. This structure creates greater flexibility and a strong consistent industry focus to spearhead the sales and marketing effort and client delivery. It gives Ernst & Young clients three important service qualities: local capability, 'best in class' teams and specialist industry knowledge. It also helps the firm's own people develop strong functional skills and in-depth industry knowledge.

Company Culture and Style

'Rigorous but fun.' Ernst & Young has a genuinely open culture and style of working. People enjoy their work and enjoy working for the firm. An informal, first-name environment encourages all employees to contribute and to voice their opinions openly. It's also a sharing firm, a tone which is set by the partners who are 'what you see is what you get' in style. In turn, Ernst & Young is increasingly basing its reward and progression, including career moves, on achievement rather than time served.

New employees after one day with the firm are asked the question: 'What impressions of Ernst & Young have you formed to date?' The answers show a high level of consistency – an informal, open environment, the supportive nature of the culture, a desire for people to make a difference, a high level of professionalism, big and global. Words like 'challenging', 'stretching', 'reaching', 'hungry', and 'restless' are mentioned quite often.

But the debate that people have is also challenging and intense. When individual opinions on a subject are probed and elicited no-one is trying to 'find someone out' – people really want these views. A lot of listening goes on. 'People often say that the executives at Ernst & Young have bigger ears than mouths,' says Geoffrey Pye, head of HR operations.

The 'Living our Vision' initiative, with the goal of being recognised as the leading firm which contributes most to its clients' success, is designed to gain competitive advantage by involving all of its people in the development of Ernst & Young through empowerment and continuous improvement.

Ernst & Young people are bright, 'regular' people with intellectual rigour – otherwise they will not survive. That means being independently minded and confident in their own view, but at the same time collegiate and team-oriented. A commercial mind is important. For graduates, that might translate into an awareness of what's happening in the world and a rounded interest in business. Fast and flexible are other key characteristics – graduates will be expected to get there quickly, and then change again once they have got there. Movement can be frantic. 'Not so much a hot desk as a hot carpet,' suggest Geoffrey Pye.

Human Resources

Human resources is taken very seriously at Ernst & Young, and has shifted from the 'enthusiastic amateur' leadership often associated with partnerships to a professional, strategic function working closely with the executive.

One core concept is to demonstrate value to its people (after demonstrating value to its clients) and to align the employment relationship between firm and employee. The expression 'We treat our people and our clients the same, and our clients come first' might summarise this.

The HR team is responding to 'the growth challenge', and recruitment is necessarily a major activity. In the area of graduate recruitment, Ernst & Young is at the forefront of best practice. It recruits over 500 people each year in the UK alone. Elsewhere, Ernst & Young is making its recruitment and selection processes more professional and slicker, particularly in hiring experienced people and direct entry partners. 'In the industry as a whole, the pool has tended to be each other,' says John Cornish, national recruitment director. 'This has got to change.'

Career Opportunity and Development

Ernst & Young has so much to offer. There are countless opportunities for those who seek them, across a wide range of disciplines in a host of different countries. In addition to audit and tax, the firm is enjoying impressive growth in newer areas, such as business risk consulting, information systems advisory and assurance, corporate finance and management consulting. Fast-tracking is a real opportunity.

'There are now some eleven different entry points for graduates compared to the previous three for accountancy,' says Sarah Prosser, manager, national graduate recruitment. Many people joining Ernst & Young do not need to take professional qualifications. All-round development is just as important, acquiring transferable skills that can be used in different parts of the firm.

All trainees are allocated a counselling manager who works in partnership with the individual to ensure a balanced, relevant and successful start to their career. This pattern of co-developed work and career objectives is continued throughout a career with Ernst & Young, including partners.

The culture has changed elsewhere – the executive is looking to HR to inject a fresh rigour to partner development. Becoming a partner should no longer be seen as the pinnacle of a career, but the beginning of another. Looking constantly at what you are doing, keeping up-to-date and pushing forward are all expected of an Ernst & Young partner.

The firm has invested heavily in a raft of learning and development opportunities. Development workshops, involving 2–3 days away, cover all levels in the firm and are designed to help self-reliant people work out where they want their career to go and how to get there themselves. There is a wide selection of management, technical and specialist training programmes to help everyone develop their personal and managerial skills base, and a link to the Henley Centre for a 'Virtual Business School'. The whole process is enhanced by on-the-job training, personal mentoring and coaching.

Some 90% of all employees receive a formal assessment rating each year, involving a discussion and a conclusion. Ernst & Young is working hard to maximise the quality of this assessment process, by setting clear objectives and ensuring that the discussions are open, honest, and constructive with a big emphasis on development.

Remuneration

Attaining partnership is still a valuable goal for every professional in the firm. And it is possible to reach this as early as 31 years old, with a salary package of £135,000 (£185,000 in London) to spur you on. That Ernst & Young talks about ages and salaries in connection with partnerships is indicative of the openness of the firm – it is one of only two of the top five firms which publishes this information in its annual report.

Pay philosophy at Ernst & Young is to reward individual effort through base salary, not bonuses. It believes strongly that individual bonus payments can cut across the teamwork concept and become counter-productive.

The Future

There is a big agenda for Ernst & Young's future. Globalisation will be a main driver, with increasingly global clients wanting global solutions. That will create a lot of international movement between the firms in the Ernst & Young federation, and the appointment of Lewis Ting, as Ernst & Young International vice-chairman–human resources, demonstrates the intent. As Geoff Pye puts it, 'We want to be the international employer of choice – for those we choose.'

The firm also wants to be clear on the value proposition of what Ernst & Young means to its clients and its people, and a major branding exercise is underway. As Ernst & Young expands, growing pains and tensions are inevitable, and the firm will have to work hard to avoid diluting its strong and successful culture as it necessarily brings in new faces from outside.

Ernst & Young is a huge depository of knowledge, which can be accessed from anywhere within the firm. Exploiting this resource effectively through IT is a major challenge for Ernst & Young, which it is taking seriously by establishing a Knowledge Management Network.

Meanwhile the work/life balance issue is bubbling to the top of many people's agenda. Ernst & Young acknowledges that in retaining female employees, its record needs to be better (as it is recognised generally in all professional services). It knows that it is to its own commercial advantage to tap all people resources and so is looking at flexible working patterns, while recognising the difficulties when client needs override lifestyle choices.

Indeed, young people increasingly want to pick and choose how their life is organised and take more, rather than less, control over their work. That Ernst & Young is actively addressing these contemporary ideas shows that the firm is in hot pursuit of the commercial 'win/win' situation.

Federal Express Europe

Federal Express (FedEx) is the world's largest express shipping company. It delivers around 3 million packages every day, to 211 countries representing 99% of the global economy. FedEx's fleet of 596 aircraft operates between 366 airports worldwide, and FedEx has no fewer than 42,500 vehicles on the ground. During the fiscal year ending 31 May 1998, FedEx reported revenues of $13.3 billion. FedEx has 145,000 employees worldwide, and around 1,500 in the UK and Ireland. FedEx UK and Ireland is part of the Europe, Middle East & Africa (EMEA) region, whose headquarters are in Brussels. FedEx's UK hub is at Stansted Airport, and it also has ground operations and offices throughout the country.

Scorecard:
Remuneration and benefits	★★★
Progressive attitude	★★★★
Opportunity for promotion	★★★
Training, development and education	★★★★★
Working atmosphere and environment	★★★★

Biggest plus:
People always come first

Biggest minus:
A fairly unique style and culture, in which not everyone excels

Federal Express Europe, Inc.
FedEx House
Bondgate
Nuneaton
Warwickshire CV11 4AL
Tel: 01203 343333
Fax: 01203 381559
Website: www.fedex.com

Federal Express

Federal Express Europe

The Business

The original idea of an overnight express delivery business was conceived by Frederick W. Smith while an undergraduate at Yale University. He founded Federal Express Corporation in 1973 and has never looked back since. Ten years after start-up, Federal Express (known universally as FedEx) reached $1 billion in revenues. That figure today is in excess of $13 billion. Smith stands as an American business legend, and as chairman and chief executive, now heads up the FDX Corporation.

The nerve centre of the unrivalled FedEx international network is the 'SuperHub' at Memphis, Tennessee, which is also FedEx's worldwide headquarters. FedEx is expanding its network of operations in the UK, with offices in Nuneaton, High Wycombe and Coventry as well as operational stations throughout the UK.

International express shipping is forecast to grow by 15–20% until 2005, and FedEx is well positioned to profit from that growth.

FedEx invests over $1 billion annually in advanced technology: in its complex management system of vehicles, packages, routes and even weather forecasting, to the vital customer interface. More than 550,000 automated customers already use products such as FedEx World™ Shipping Software or FedEx interNetShip™ to speed up the shipping process. Electronic commerce and supply chain management are increasingly important areas of business.

Company Culture and Style

There are many descriptions of the special FedEx culture – people-oriented, supportive, diverse, dedicated to open communications, energised, accessible top management, and a 'do' rather than 'say' attitude. It is certainly an open culture where each individual feels involved and is encouraged to excel.

From the outset, Fred Smith set about creating a model workplace, putting in place progressive personnel policies. 'From its inception,

FedEx has put its people first because it is the right thing to do and is good business as well. Our company philosophy is People–Service–Profit.'

Everything that FedEx attempts and accomplishes is premised by People–Service–Profit (P–S–P), contending that if it takes care of its employees, they will in turn deliver impeccable service to customers, who will reward the company with the profitability necessary to secure its future. The key word here is 'commitment – FedEx expects commitment from its staff, but gives it in return and is always willing to 'go the extra mile'.

FedEx has a very flat structure. There is a maximum of five layers of management between the CEO and any employee, and team-working is absolutely fundamental. Flat structures mean that even more effort is put into forums to get people talking together.

People who enjoy working for FedEx, and who succeed, are likely to be committed, very customer-focused, and prepared to air their own views. Increasingly, they need to be comfortable with technology. There are frequent remarks about people having 'purple and orange blood' (referring to FedEx's corporate colours), and those who show the right commitment are rewarded well.

Human Resources

Central to FedEx HR policy is delivering on its P–S–P philosophy. Much effort goes into resourcing, development, employee participation and remuneration. FedEx aims to give fair and equitable treatment for all, reward achievement and performance, and ensure that everyone can fully develop and utilise their talents.

Underpinning these objectives is a drive towards defining what differentiates exceptional performers. FedEx's HR team has been working closely with employees and managers to establish the competencies required for specific roles and job families, and to translate these into development initiatives and performance management.

In recruitment, FedEx is increasingly using leading-edge selection techniques, particularly where the company needs high-quality recruits for line management, finance, marketing and IT.

Long before many organisations introduced upward appraisal systems or 360-degree feedback, FedEx was utilising Survey, Feedback, Action, or SFA. Effectively, SFA is an upward appraisal process for managers by their employees. In the survey each year, employees can make constructive suggestions towards improving the business without fear of retribution. Feedback is usually positive – FedEx managers are very accessible, first-name terms are the norm, and individuals are encouraged to say whatever they think. And to complete the process, managers must produce an action plan which is clear, achievable and recorded.

Helen Hutchins, personnel manager, UK and Ireland says: 'Although completion of the survey is voluntary, the company has enjoyed a 98% employee participation rate; in my opinion this underpins the importance and high regard that employees place on this process. SFA is very beneficial and supports our "people first" policy.'

FedEx proliferates in open communication. FX TV broadcasts worldwide to every station. VPs and MDs are encouraged to visit each station in their district regularly. Team briefing sessions are held monthly, weekly or even daily in some locations in order to discuss current issues, re-emphasise operational plans, set future objectives, and get feedback from the team.

The European Works Council Directive has allowed FedEx to review the ways in which it consults and communicates with its staff on both a local and European basis. A new European Employees Consultative Forum has emerged (one of the few companies to do this), where elected employee representatives have a chance to meet and discuss issues with senior company executives. FedEx's open communications culture is *highly* successful. So much so that no formal union recognition agreements are needed in the UK business.

Career Opportunity and Development

FedEx is at the forefront of management and operational best practice which provides the grounding for an excellent career. You can achieve a lot at FedEx as there are few shackles, and if you have ideas, the company will listen and implement the good ones.

Six-monthly or annual performance reviews encourage a frank and open discussion between manager and employee and also provide a platform for personal development plans. All vacancies are advertised internally on a Bulletin Board via e-mail.

With an increasing emphasis on management development, FedEx has evolved the way it recruits and develops its leaders.

The training schedule at FedEx is best described as comprehensive, featuring both knowledge and skills training internally complemented by more specialised interventions from outside. Each job function is supported by training of some sort. FedEx managers attend the Leadership Institute in Memphis within three months of their appointment, but with the EMEA region growing so fast, there is a drive for FedEx to deliver more management training within its own region.

Within the EMEA region, movement, development and promotion is active, as it is one business unit. There is encouragement for people to think about an international career with FedEx, and the company would like to do more. Practicalities (often relating to visas and local regulations) mean that this is more likely at senior level, but FedEx will work hard to overcome obstacles when it wants to move its people around.

Remuneration

FedEx is competitive on remuneration packages with a combination of basic and variable pay, plus relevant benefits which might include company cars, pension scheme, and various health programmes.

Rewards for exceptional individual or group performance are important at FedEx, and *Bravo Zulu, Star, Superstar, Golden Falcon, Five Star* and *President's Club* are creative recognition programmes.

The Future

FedEx operates in a growing, but extremely competitive marketplace, where there is absolutely no room for complacency. The company is all-powerful in the US, and strong in the Far East, but it has a lot further to go in Europe. It knows that it has to improve the visibility of its brand in the UK, that of a global company and not a US company in Europe, but that brings the excitement of changing things from afresh.

Technology has allowed FedEx to embrace and cultivate different ways of working, valuing the flexibility practices such as teleworking, home-working and other mobility improvements.

FedEx is constantly challenged to maintain its open, communicative culture, which is why it needs a continuous supply of good leaders. The company wants its managers to be inspirational, have excellent judgement, and care at the individual level. It seems to succeed.

FI Group

FI Group is a business technology services company, leading the market in applications management and outsourcing – two of the fastest growing sectors of the IT industry. Its portfolio of services also includes managed services, recruitment and business change expertise. Founded as one of the UK's first computing services and training companies in 1962, FI was floated on the London Stock Exchange in April 1996. FI is a success story, having grown by more than 40% every year between 1995 and 1998. It has nearly doubled its number of full-time employees since 1996 to 2,000, bringing the total workforce of the group to over 4,000.

Scorecard:
Remuneration and benefits ★★★★
Progressive attitude ★★★★★
Opportunity for promotion ★★★★
Training, development and education ★★★★★
Working atmosphere and environment ★★★

Biggest plus:
Become an owner in a fast-growth company

Biggest minus:
Like many consultancies, a lot of work is done away from the office

FI Group plc
Campus 300
Marylands Avenue
Hemel Hempstead
Herts HP2 7TQ
Tel: 01442 233339
Fax: 01442 238400
website: figroup.co.uk

F·I·GROUP PLC

FI Group

The Business

FI Group manages 'business critical' systems for predominantly blue-chip customers, including Barclays, BT, Bank of Scotland, Sainsbury's, Thames Water, Eagle Star, Esso, and Whitbread. FI builds long-term, interdependent partnerships with its customers, sharing strategic risk and reward.

'FI has long since innovated in strategic partnering, and the trend toward outsourcing is ideal for customers who exploit information technology as an enabler of business change,' says Hilary Cropper, chief executive.

Founded as one of the UK's first computing services and training companies in 1962, it became a pioneer of the distributed office concept and telecommuting. This commitment to flexible working still holds sway today – of its total workforce of 4,000, some 1,000 are freelance contractors. FI also supplies freelance and contract staff to clients, and IT Recruitment and IT training now form integral parts of the business.

FI is a real champion of employee share ownership. From the original employee buyout in 1991, 40% of the shares are still owned by employees. The company has no doubts that employee share ownership contributes significantly to its success, and is a really important motivator.

Company Culture and Style

FI has one of the most distinctive cultures of any UK company. 'What differentiates FI is the dual commitment to customer service and group performance that comes from collective ownership,' says Cropper.

Flexible working is now formalised in the Flexible Employment Contract, and it's something which FI is very proud of. It believes that offering people a range of contractual relationships with FI Group is a 'win-win' situation. Flexible working allows FI to keep high calibre people whom it might otherwise lose (it admits that it cannot find enough good people) and also retain important flexibility; for the individual, it allows them to balance important work/lifestyle/family issues.

This is a young company, and a well-balanced one at that. Six out of the eleven executive board members are women, and this equality is maintained at all levels of the organisation with the possible exception of recent graduate intakes.

Curiously, some of the best people coming through the ranks have studied music. 'Most musicians are highly numerate and make excellent IT people,' observes Mike Harling, Group HR director.

Add to numeracy some other important qualities found in people who succeed at FI: dedication, 'stickability', discipline, excellent communications and interpersonal skills and, of course, flexibility.

Human Resources

FI takes around 100 graduates a year – male or female, and with IT or non-IT related disciplines. Interviews are conducted 'properly', involving aptitude testing, an interview, an evening get-together, and group sessions. Degree disciplines are largely irrelevent. FI is looking very much for strong interpersonal skills; it's not just about sitting behind a PC – meeting the customer is where it starts.

FI has become very slick at recruitment and put a lot more effort into training and career development despite already being very good at it. Last year, FI Group received Investors in People re-accreditation, with IiP 'amazed' not only at how much the company had grown, but how it had improved from its original assessment three years before.

'We aim to give everyone in the company the freedom and support to reach their full potential, by recognising individuals' needs at the same time as fulfilling the company's objectives,' says Mike Harling. 'To improve our communications and create clearer career opportunities we have established an Intranet, a new face-to-face communications programme, a company-wide career framework and performance management process, and enhanced induction for our many new recruits.'

With the growth in outsourcing, FI has become expert at transfer of undertakings, bringing people into the company, integrating them quickly and moving them on in the organisation.

Direct entry occurs at all levels. Because of the competitive market, FI exploits virtually every means of recruitment – advertising, headhunters, careers fairs, there is even an incentive scheme (with £2,000 reward) for employees to recommend people. FI often receives speculative applications after its financial results are reported in the press. 'People like successful companies,' suggests Rosie Symons.

Career Opportunity and Development

FI affords a host of career opportunities in its four main career streams – technical, business consultancy, management and professional – and there is a common career framework for all employees.

A competencies framework has been established showing skills required for each job, and individuals discuss with line managers and with HR what they need to do to turn their skills and experience into action. Personal development plans are integral to the feedback and performance management process.

Graduate entrants enter a formal two-year programme of training, including interpersonal skills and the 'MBA in One Week'. The aim is for all to reach the same standard of technical and professional competence before making the decision which direction to pursue.

'FI becomes a big target for recruitment companies because of the quality of our training and the calibre of the graduates we recruit,' notes Mike Harling. 'But if we don't convince them that their best career is here, then we deserve to lose them.'

Many of the best graduates recruited are 'first bouncers', who have been trained elsewhere and might include late developers making a radical career change. FI observes that because they already have other business skills, they move quickly even though they start at the same level as fresh graduates.

FI must be one of the few UK companies to have acquired an Indian IT company, but that is what it has done and has 1,000 employees there. With its offshoots in the US and Singapore, FI can offer a wider range of skills and experience to its customers. And it has one very attractive customer base. As opposed to joining an IT department of a company, working for FI means you can work for many high quality companies in diverse sectors such as retail, telecommunications, finance and pubic utilities. International customers frequently invite FI teams to go with them overseas.

Remuneration

Remuneration philosophy is based on recognition and reward, correlating to salary plus benefits, bonuses, and then a web of share schemes. Rewards are competitive and performance-based, but it is the range of share schemes and flexible benefits packages which distinguish FI.

Profit-sharing becomes more advantageous when taken in shares instead of cash; the share option scheme is leveraged to the amount you put in; and there is an attractive Save-As-You-Earn scheme. Put the three together and individuals can build up a sizeable stake in the company equal to several times their salary. In 1997, 96% of the funds set aside for profit-sharing were taken in shares by employees rather than cash.

Two trusts – the Qualifying Employee Share Ownership Trust (QUEST) and the FI GROUP Shareholders' Trust – ensure that there is a supply of shares for future employees and together own 22% of the group. In total, the workforce and its associated trusts own 40% of the equity. FI believes that the size of employee share ownership must be significant to have any real impact. Some 95% of employees own shares in FI – a real investment in its success.

Flexible benefits were introduced because FI recognised that people make intelligent choices as to what means most at a particular point in their lives. Popular choices include type of pension, company cars (can flex up or down or take cash), and selling your holidays back to the company or buying extra days. It's not easy and there is a cost, but FI reckons it's worth it. 'Flexible benefits are not for the faint hearted HR Director,' suggests Harling. But recruiters think that the flexible benefits scheme is a 'big plus' in selling FI to prospective employees.

The Future

FI is certainly going to need more people. And with more IT services now provided to businesses rather than IT departments, FI people must really understand their customers' businesses. That puts an onus on sustaining the quality of recruitment and development, competing with all the other hungry IT and business service companies for sometimes limited talent.

Communication within a growth company is a big challenge, particularly when so many staff are located on customer sites. A bond needs to be formed. It's why the Intranet is important, but FI is working on an array of team and cascade programmes to make everyone really feel a part of FI.

FI could have become one of those computer services companies that promised a lot but didn't deliver. FI has delivered. It's going to be tough to keep its growth rate going, but it seems to have got absolutely the right relationship with two out of the three of the virtuous triangle – employees and customers – and the third, shareholders, consist of many of the former. The City seems to think that ambitious FI has the capability to do great things – now it has to go and do it.

Fitch plc

Fitch is one of the world's largest business and design consultancies, with over 30 years of experience helping clients achieve competitive advantage. Fitch plc is quoted on the London Stock Exchange. It has offices in Columbus, Boston, Detroit, San Francisco, Osaka and Singapore, and also owns the French international consumer style and trend forecasting agency Peclers. Fitch generated total revenue of £22 million in 1997 and currently works with over 200 clients in 24 countries. There are some 350 full-time Fitch associates worldwide, 120 of them in London.

Scorecard:

Remuneration and benefits	★★★
Progressive attitude	★★★★★
Opportunity for promotion	★★★★★
Training, development and education	★★★
Working atmosphere and environment	★★★★

Biggest plus:
Progressive, highly creative company, at the forefront of business design consultancy

Biggest minus:
Relatively little structure to career development

Fitch plc
10 Lindsey Street
Smithfield Market
London EC1A 9ZZ
Tel. 0171 509 5000
Fax: 0171 509 0100
website: www.fitch.com

Fitch plc

The Business

Fitch is a leading international design business, with the London office at its heart. In 1988 it acquired RichardsonSmith, a successful US agency, in a move which accelerated its business development in the States. Fitch also has a joint venture Polymer Solutions Inc. with GE Plastics, focused on product commercialisation. Fitch's international reach includes Peclers, an office in Osaka, Japan, and a worldwide network of other associates.

Fitch's stated business purpose is 'helping manufacturers, retailers and service providers achieve and sustain a long-term competitive advantage', according to Martin Beck, chairman and chief executive.

Fitch has four core competencies – brand development (developing new brands and rejuvenating existing ones by integrating market research, brand strategy, graphic design, information design, interactive media design and production; consumer environments (redefining and reshaping both the shopping and entertainment experiences); new media (a user-centred approach to interaction design); and product development (including market research, product planning, industrial design, ergonomics and engineering).

Company Culture and Style

Fitch is becoming a so-called 'Third Generation Consultancy', a hybrid advisory business somewhere between traditional management consultancy and design, offering clients 'informed intuition' on the question 'What's Next?'. Having identified this niche for itself, Fitch exhibits a lot of corporate self-confidence. Fitch remains very creatively-oriented, but adopts a highly strategic consultancy approach to prove the hard-core effectiveness of design in business. 'Design makes logic surprising,' suggests senior director Zuilmah Wallis.

In drawing upon both the analytical skills of management consultants, and the more creative, intuitive skills of designers, Fitch's strategy has forced a culture change. It feels that this makes it unique. Fitch has had to work hard on integrating two very different but complementary sets of skills, and on changing its working methods in order to integrate.

The design business always appears to be glamorous and fun. Fitch is certainly no exception. But it is also about very hard work. 'We have good fun working hard,' suggests Felicity Thomas, business development co-ordinator. Fitch remains outward-focused, concentrating almost entirely on its clients and on consumers and their fickle trends. Its chosen business is always changing, almost always for the better. Necessarily, Fitch is 'not afraid to make mistakes' nor is it risk-averse.

Fitch is a very young-minded company and offers a great working environment. It has a very open culture, without having a clear team structure. There is a huge flow of ideas involving everyone in the business, and people are rarely pigeon-holed. Individuals can move very quickly up the ladder – and or to other ladders – and there are many examples of high achievers in rapid time.

So what is 'Fitchness'? Fitch people have, or are expected to have 'a natural sense of curiosity about the world', says Zuilmah Wallis, 'and be prepared to share ideas'. There is a big team spirit at Fitch. In some businesses, knowledge is power. At Fitch, people want to share.

Fitch's trendy new offices in the old Smithfield (meat) Market building in the City of London once attracted the unwanted and undeserved attention of animal rights activists. But they make for a fabulous place to work – open plan, busy, interactive, predictably stylish and colourful. The Dome Room has redefined the standard for meeting rooms.

Human Resources

Fitch invests heavily in recruiting and retaining people, especially those who have real knowledge of the world, common sense, and are innovative. 'I'm not sure that the educational system is helping us in this regard,' says Zuilmah Wallis. 'At least that's how it sometimes appears in the design industry. People are often not taught the fundamental disciplines of work.'

That means a lot of on-the-job training, especially for graduates fresh out of design training college. Fitch will certainly take people with lots of initiative and entrepreneurial instincts, but not with large egos. 'And they must have a good sense of humour,' adds Felicity Thomas. The team-based approach, pressures of work, and not least clients, demand it.

Interaction at work is positively encouraged, although much is spontaneous anyway. 'Cre8' is a forum held every couple of months, when Fitch associates discuss and present their work to each other so that cross-fertilisation of ideas and best practices are realised. With 150 associates in London working on 70–80 clients, there's much to talk about.

'Down the Market' talks allow people to raise any issue, anonymously, which the management team will answer as openly and honestly as possible at company meetings.

Fitch harnesses all of its creative work at an annual Creativity Day. This is an 'awayday' event, where a hall, studio, warehouse or other suitable location is taken over completely, and is a great focus for the business. Both the London and US companies hold them.

The Creativity Day serves both as a get-together where achievements can be reflected upon, and also as an opportunity to think about the future. It's where Fitch's famous 'Trends Walls' are conceived and produced. Staff are invited to brainstorm future scenarios in a very open way on a brief based on future trends. Last year the theme was 'the Five Senses', with each member of staff having to decide what from the 1990s they felt each sense epitomised. The previous year it was '50p – what can you make for it and why?'. People go to a lot of trouble on these tasks and engage in considerable lateral thought. The role-playing nature of Creativity Day also gives junior staff a good practice run ahead of client exposure.

Career Opportunity and Development

You will surely enjoy the work at Fitch. That's due to the quality and variety of clients the consultancy sets out to win, and that the Fitch brand attracts. Clients range from the largest bluechips to small entrepreneurial start-ups.

You may also need your passport. Around 40% of the London office's business is outside the UK, so someone has to travel. Designers find themselves jumping on planes to far-flung destinations, planners adapting design solutions to foreign cultures. Many people cross the Atlantic (and other seas) on a project basis, and there is presently a whole team from the UK helping build retail design expertise in Fitch's US business.

If you want the company to plan your career progression, though, you'll hate it at Fitch. Flexibility is the watchword, and Fitch people are expected to have a large input into defining their own roles and charting their own career path. But if you are good, and take the initiative, you can achieve a lot.

Remuneration

Fitch is highly competitive among its peer group (on remuneration, in line with its aspirations to attract the best people in the business. Partners (the equivalent of associate director and above) also participate in a bonus scheme, which could add up to 12% of salary depending on performance.

The 'City Jet' scheme is open to everyone. Two people each month are chosen on the basis of outstanding contributions and given £500 to go away to a European city. The only condition is that they return and deliver an evening slide or picture show, with drinks, for the whole company. Enthusiastic Fitch employees often cannot help taking a busman's holiday, studying retail design and consumer products in their destination city!

Fitch grants a week's paternity leave, and offers a comprehensive maternity package which recognises women in the workplace and encourages them back after they have had children. In addition to the statutory government scheme, Fitch offers 50% salary for the additional time which is paid on their return to work with a proviso that employees must stay for a minimum of one year. A shrewd move in an industry that typically employs as many women as men.

The Future

Fitch will relentlessly pursue its ambitions, while making itself as recession-proof as possible. If it makes quick acquisitions, Fitch may struggle to recruit senior management at the same pace, and the company recognises that integration of new companies may consequently take longer to complete.

Indeed, finding great people to recruit seems to be a constant problem. They should exist, the company is looking for them, but finding them is very hard. Growing people from within, in a changing culture but with client service, strategic planning and creativity as constant values, is one thing. But finding people outside is harder.

Fitch must continue to perform well financially. Earnings growth of 20% year-on-year represents high expectation, and as a quoted company owned by shareholders, Fitch is expected to deliver.

Fitch has invested in technology – some £1 million spent in three years is a lot for a company with a turnover of £22 million – and it must find a way to blend 'hard' information with the traditional 'soft' information that nurtures creative businesses. Indeed, it has to harness all knowledge that exists within the company. Marrying structure to creativity and being profitable is quite a challenge, but Fitch is more than ready to face it.

Friends Provident

Friends Provident is one of the UK's leading providers of insurance and investment services. It has more than three million policies in force and assets under management exceed £29 billion. Friends Provident's 5,500 employees are located in six major offices and a number of branches throughout the UK. Friends Provident is also a member of the Eureko Alliance in Europe.

Scorecard:

Remuneration and benefits	★★★★
Progressive attitude	★★★
Opportunity for promotion	★★★★★
Training, development and education	★★★★
Working atmosphere and environment	★★★

Biggest plus:
A real hands-on, 'just do it' business

Biggest minus:
Regulation and consolidation in the financial services industry dictates frequent change

Friends Provident
Pixham End
Dorking
Surrey RH4 1QA
Tel: 01306 740123
Fax: 01306 740150

FRIENDS PROVIDENT

Friends Provident

The Business

With proud Quaker traditions dating back to 1832, and publicly committed to remaining a mutual company, Friends Provident has inbred business values of integrity, ethics and fair play. Treating the customer fairly is uppermost in mind, requiring a careful balance between the interests of customers, employees and other stakeholders. These values look like serving the company well as the financial services industry races through unprecedented change.

Friends Provident (FP) is certainly fast-growing. And it's no slouch when it comes to acquisitions and mergers. Having bought fund management group Ivory & Sime (re-christened Friends Ivory Sime and now run as the group's separate investment business) early in 1998 and acquired the sales force of United Friendly, FP bid successfully for Exeter-based life insurance company London & Manchester towards the end of the year. A 'sleepy old mutual' certainly not. This one is hungry for growth and very business-oriented.

It has rushed into nothing though. Looking around at the key business drivers, the Marketing Effectiveness Project was devised in conjunction with management consultants. From this process emerged a new organisational structure which, cleverly, was appropriate to FP whether or not it acquired London & Manchester and indeed, other organisations. Effectively, FP now has two main business streams – retail business and asset management.

Chief executive Keith Satchell is quick to point out that FP's success 'is based on continuing to ensure that, in all areas of the group, we keep in mind the need to deliver the promise we make to our customers when they join us: continually meeting their needs through high quality service, professional advice and products which are value for money'.

Company Culture and Style

Many companies claim 'integrity' high among their values, but at Friends Provident it's central, standing as a signpost through everything the company does. For example, Friends Provident was the first company to create an ethical fund for investors to allocate their funds.

It has other values too, of course. Like valuing people and treating them fairly. In its annual report, Friends states that 'The Group is committed to its policy of encouraging employee involvement at all levels.' It assists this through briefings and discussions through the management chain, a full range of employee publications, a staff forum, and by establishing effective working relationships with staff and line management representative bodies. There is a corporate commitment to achieve Investors in People recognition, and within this, the British Quality Foundation which is concerned more with business processes.

In acquiring companies such as Ivory & Sime, FP has no intention of eliminating 135 years of culture. There is no sheep dip, and FP is happy to accommodate a diversity of cultures. In fact, it is rather good at integrating people, and has learned to look deliberately at the way its new charges do things, ready and willing to absorb the better ways into its own.

Insurance companies are often risk averse, but not Friends Provident. People here are results-oriented. Chief executive Keith Satchell encourages people to take risks *and* responsibilities, and not to be scared of making mistakes. Not a new idea at FP, but a new emphasis. As a company, it places greater value on management ability as well as technical (actuarial) ability. There are prominent retail and marketing people as well as actuaries; there are actuaries no longer behaving as actuaries (although they are, as ever, smart in the numbers, believing that they have identified and can unlock value in acquired companies that analysts cannot even see!).

Sensibly, the company observes rather than creates cultural values, and reacts to them accordingly. This is a tenet of a very practical organisation, one that looks forward, continually identifying opportunities, but possessing few frills. If others have more razzmatazz, Friends Provident has a 'just do it' attitude, which reveals the 'we trust you' factor that exists between people in the company.

Human Resources

The personnel function at Friends Provident takes a clear and important view – it is the line that runs the company. Sales directors, customer services, business operators are the people who sell and provide service – personnel's function is to act as a support mechanism to help the line functions get the best out of their people. That means identifying the right people, paying them properly, and developing them against a template of personal and performance development programmes.

FP believes quite firmly that individuals run their own career. 'You can count on us, but don't rely on us,' says David Bebo, director of personnel. Employees are considered to be best placed to judge, identify and manage their own aspirations and development requirements. This is fundamental to FP's development philosophy, and translates right across all training.

FP has a long-standing tradition of supporting its people in developing their business skills and professional qualifications. It also runs the Personal Development Scheme to show support to staff who wish to develop other skills or knowledge in their free time. This might be cooking, sailing, painting – any activity in fact. It represents an extension of the 'running your own career' concept, trusting staff to translate intellectual issues to physical results and then import values back into their working lives.

An encouraging feature of the recent Staff Opinion Survey was that the 'most satisfied' responses related to issues of real value to the business, as opposed to personal ones. 'It made us realise that perhaps we're not as bad as we thought,' said David Bebo.

Career Opportunity and Development

Graduates are recruited to specific roles in actuarial, investment, sales, IT and other professional and support functions. Responsibility will come early on and people can expect to be moved around the organisation. All work is regarded as a development opportunity. Managers are encouraged to get their people to work differently, better, improving 'at the edges' and make themselves suitable candidates for promotion. Promotion is on the basis of performance in the role.

An important clue is that most of the company's top managers are 'FP people' through and through, who have grown their careers within FP. With so many financial services companies looking for 'a man on a white charger' to come in from an external industry and provide a miracle transformation, Friends Provident asks a valid question: 'Do the people at the top come from your own organisation, or were they pulled in from outside?'

That Friends is a growing organisation provides opportunities in itself, for staff at all levels and all disciplines. There is nothing like success. If you can do it and deliver results, you will certainly get on at FP. And you will always be given the opportunity to do more.

Remuneration

In a competitive industry, Friends Provident is very focused on market rates. It is building a remuneration system which allows the company to recruit and retain high calibre people, still emphasising that it is willing to pay people for what they do or can do rather than what that person thinks he or she *might* be capable of doing. FP also believes that people must see that the way in which pay is allocated is fair. This puts the onus on the pay system to be well structured and openly understood.

If anything, Friends Provident has moved away from a paternalistic remuneration structure (packages including loans, mortgages etc. and other benefits which are allocated to certain categories of people, such as help with accommodation). It regards this as running contrary to the 'own career responsibility' notion, and so is to a more commercial basis. Remuneration policy is now more about base pay plus appropriate benefits and a variety of incentive arrangements depending on the role (sales jobs inevitably include higher levels of commission).

There are notable exceptions. The paternalistic view still remains in the provision of a company pension, recognising that this may have less appeal when recruiting younger people, but good for retention of people over 40 (it's a final salary scheme).

The Future

The overriding dynamic in the financial services industry is consolidation of companies. 'Acquire or be acquired' is an often-used adage. The company itself cannot see this trend stopping for a long time. Friends Provident intends to be one of the winners, aiming for a top five position among insurance companies. One of the company's strengths is the range of different channels through which it sells its products. The company is in the vanguard of the trend towards 'stakeholder pensions'. Watch out for more acquisitions.

Friends Provident will be putting a lot of effort into enabling flexible careers and making people more mobile within the organisation with broader skills. Its remuneration structure, which is being adapted to include more 'broadbanding', will underpin this.

The company also aims to help more with people's development, tapping into their capacity to add value. At the same time, it wants to ensure that people have a life outside the office, recognising that the culture in the UK often expects people to put everything into their work leaving little for their personal lives.

Gavin Anderson & Company

Gavin Anderson & Company is an international communications consultancy, specialising in financial and corporate public relations, and public affairs. It was formed in 1991 when Gavin Anderson acquired the business of Valin Pollen; Gavin Anderson & Company is wholly owned by Omnicom. The Gavin Anderson international network includes offices in Sydney, Melbourne, Canberra, Singapore, Tokyo, Hong Kong, New York, Paris, Frankfurt and London. The London office, close to Liverpool Street in the heart of the financial centre, concentrates on financial and corporate PR, investor relations, and has a particularly strong reputation for transactional work. Some 50 staff work in the London office, 200 worldwide.

Scorecard:

Remuneration and benefits	★★★★★
Progressive attitude	★★★★
Opportunity for promotion	★★★★★
Training, development and education	★★★
Working atmosphere and environment	★★★★★

Biggest plus:
Great working lifestyle in a friendly, successful PR consultancy

Biggest minus:
Relatively unstructured, like most consultancies – people must be self-reliant

Gavin Anderson & Company
New Liverpool House
15–17 Eldon Street
London EC2M 7LD
Tel: 0171 457 2345
Fax: 0171 457 2330
website: www.gavinanderson.com
e-mail: gavinfo@gavinanderson.co.uk

GAVIN ANDERSON & COMPANY

Gavin Anderson & Company

The Business

Richard Constant, chief executive of Gavin Anderson & Company's London office, believes there are two types of public relations firm: 'There are the gunslingers, characterised by people who tell clients what to do on the basis of their own experiences and gut feel. Or there are those which are more rigorous in their research, analysis and planning, and like to be regarded as a thoughtful firm.'

Gavin Anderson's aspiration is to own the reputation for being the best-qualified international firm in its three sectors of business: financial communications, corporate communications and public affairs. Gavin Anderson declines to participate in industry surveys which rank consultancies by size, but worldwide, Gavin Anderson & Company is probably the largest firm by revenues in corporate and financial work and its consultancies are usually in the top three in their markets.

But Gavin Anderson's philosophy is to be the best, not the largest. Despite being small and lean, Gavin Anderson is extremely international. The senior management team at Gavin Anderson is a small, cohesive group that has built a high degree of trust working across boundaries. Many large 'supermarket' firms fight internecine disputes over budgets and territories – time that Gavin Anderson considers is better spent looking after clients.

With a strong reputation for transactional work including mergers and acquisitions, stock market listings and buy-outs, Gavin Anderson's UK client list includes Reuters, British Energy, SmithKline Beecham, Trinity, Unigate, Johnson Matthey and Misys.

Company Culture and Style

It should come as no surprise that clients come first, above all else, and Gavin Anderson is committed to providing a first class, quality advisory service.

You cannot be an effective consultant unless your advice is worth having (although this does not deter some people). The work is taken very seriously, and Gavin Anderson consultants strive to make sure that their knowledge and skills are well honed, facts researched and checked, in order to establish and maintain credibility with clients.

The people who work for Gavin Anderson are bright graduates, usually with some City experience, and almost inevitably with lots of character and personality. They tend to thrive on working in a client-driven, lively, hectic and often pressurised environment. Understanding clients' needs and being available to service these needs whatever the time of day (and sometimes night) are paramount. Tenacity and commercial awareness are vital.

This spills over into a mutually supportive environment where real team players are held in much higher esteem than individual hotshots. There is a 'buzz' at Gavin Anderson, and it can often be frantic and frenetic, with something 'different and striking' about many individuals.

'Friendly' is a word that crops up all the time when Gavin Anderson people (past as well as present) describe their colleagues and the prevailing office atmosphere. Gavin Anderson nurtures its special culture very carefully. Much effort goes into the interview process because it is important that people will fit in and work well together. 'Successful candidates have often met most of our people before they start – that's how key it is,' adds Fiona Harrison, personnel director.

The firm reinvests considerably in a couple of energetic parties annually. So many firms claim a 'work hard, play hard' culture; financial PR agencies like Gavin Anderson define it. You don't need to be a party animal, but you mustn't be shocked by those who are.

Human Resources

'Our management style is fairly hands-on,' says Richard Constant, 'but we do not over-manage our staff – they are encouraged to develop their own style and flair.' Gavin Anderson, happily, is a relatively unstructured environment where individuals are trusted to control their own work.

Gavin Anderson dislikes terms such as 'human resources' or 'the science of people', which smack of big corporates, preferring to deal with people as personalities rather than with policies. The firm really cares about its people and this shows in its personnel style. If it's possible in a mostly open plan office, everything is 'open door'.

Personnel is key to the operation of the business and management functions – it does, after all, manage the resource which ensures that clients receive the best service from the highest calibre people available.

Whereas personality might have once got you a job in public relations, at Gavin Anderson, qualifications are more important. Candidates must take various tests (written, not psychometric) and the firm looks for different City or professional backgrounds, including invest-ment banking, stockbroking, legal, accounting and journalism.

All staff have personal managers who are encouraged to take this role seriously and actively. Without the account group structure some-times found in other agencies, a personal manager is not a line manager – typically it will be a director selected only for his or her empathy with people.

Is Gavin Anderson a sexist company? Some 68% of its employees in London are female. In pursuit of a flexible workforce, the firm takes a flexible and 'family friendly' approach. Several individuals are now working part-time, staff are encouraged and supported during further education, and the firm even claims to be flexible about directors' time! 'Because we're smaller, we can be flexible in terms of the policies we develop,' says Fiona Harrison. 'We look to what the workforce will be like in five years time and how we will attract it.'

Career Opportunity and Development

If you gain the respect of your work colleagues, you can map out your career very quickly at Gavin Anderson. This is a lean company with a very flat structure and you can really 'go for it'. But you must be self-motivated and self-promoting – not in an arrogant way, rather that it is smart to draw attention to excellent work.

Levels range from executive through senior executive, associate director, director to managing director. Beyond lies the Gavin Ander-son international network and the Omnicom empire and inter-company transfers and overseas postings may well feature more in the future.

Secretaries are still called secretaries, but with Gavin Anderson's inclination to promote from within, they are encouraged to take on responsibility and to progress. Some have made it through to executive and risen to the challenges of account handling.

Performance reviews and promotions follow a democratic process of peer group consensus. This enlightened approach ensures that indi-viduals receive well-rounded references and their career does not rest in the hands of one person.

For a small company, training and development is taken seriously and budgeted for. The menu of training activities includes writing skills, financial and regulatory issues, IT applications and language skills. The in-house lunchtime seminars run by Richard Constant are very popular.

Remuneration

Gavin Anderson is very competitive on salaries – it is prepared to go for the best and pay for the best. Bonuses and profit-share will reflect the vagaries of the business which, with a high proportion of remunerative transactional work, will vary from year to year. Directors can command good salaries, particularly if they also bring in new business. The overall package of benefits is very attractive.

The Future

Clients are becoming more sophisticated, accelerating a trend towards polarisation in Gavin Anderson's areas of public relations consultancy, with the best quality work increasingly going to fewer firms. Gavin Anderson intends to be one of these firms. Gavin Anderson enjoys domestic strength on the base of an international network that specialises and works. Many competitors just cannot match this.

The trend of major international companies restructuring is driving mergers and acquisitions in Gavin Anderson's financial practise area, which in turn stimulates the need for corporate and employee communications. Increasing regulation of highly competitive businesses is raising demand for public affairs work. Gavin Anderson therefore sees strong growth opportunities in all three areas.

Working for high quality companies, Gavin Anderson's biggest challenge is to continue to find and develop people into high-level consulting positions. Recognising that high calibre people will often find work in other sectors, Gavin Anderson emphasises its proposition of 'quality people, quality clients, quality work'. Certainly this friendly and dedicated firm can offer excellent job satisfaction and rewards to match in a top public relations consultancy.

Gemini Consulting

Gemini Consulting is a global management consulting firm dedicated to helping clients design and implement strategic change. Gemini Consulting is a distinct, wholly-owned subsidiary of the Cap Gemini Group, which also includes Cap Gemini, one of the largest IT consulting firms in the world. Gemini Consulting has more than 20 offices on five continents, working with clients in virtually every industry, anywhere in the world, across the traditional barriers of language, culture and custom. Gemini Consulting is organised into four regions: the Americas, France, Central Europe, and Northern Europe (including Asia/South Africa). In 1997 the consultancy revenue for the group was $900 million. The firm employs 2,300 people worldwide, 340 in the UK.

Scorecard:
Remuneration and benefits	★★★★★
Progressive attitude	★★★★★
Opportunity for promotion	★★★★
Training, development and education	★★★★★
Working atmosphere and environment	★★★★

Biggest plus:
Highly stimulating work, a very progressive company to work for

Biggest minus:
Much of the work is on-site at client companies

Gemini Consulting
One Knightsbridge
London SW1X 7LX
Tel: 0171 340 3000
Fax: 0171 340 3400
website: www.gemcon.com

GEMINI CONSULTING
A Cap Gemini Group Company

Gemini Consulting

The Business

Gemini Consulting has earned its unique reputation through a simple but powerful belief: people matter. Gemini believes that the best consulting solutions are those that the people of an organisation can wholeheartedly embrace. When everyone in a client organisation is fully committed, innovative ideas become operational reality.

Through the power of people, Gemini aims to help leading companies around the world and across industries achieve faster, more sustainable results and create a more deeply rooted foundation for new opportunities. One in three of *Fortune*'s Global Top 100 companies are Gemini clients.

Gemini Consulting is a very young firm, but with a 35-year heritage. It was formed in 1991 by the integration of five consulting firms: the MAC Group (strategy formulation), United Research (business improvement and change management), Gamma International (organisation and information systems strategy), and strategy firms IKO (Norway) and Asia Advisory Service (Japan). Nearly a dozen firms have joined the organisation since 1991, most notably GTP in Germany and Bossard Consultants, expanding Gemini's services and geographic spread.

Company Culture and Style

Gemini was founded consciously as a different type of consultancy, one that would make a difference and leave a legacy, and place people at the centre of everything that it does.

'Being a people-oriented business requires a particular type of consultant', according to Steve Beck, managing director of Gemini Consulting's Northern Europe region. 'When they meet our clients, they must be able to manage the political and emotional dimensions, as well as the rational ones.'

With strategy frequently devised at the top and implemented at lower levels of an organisation, it is the middle management layer that may feel it has everything to lose and nothing to gain. Not always perceived as 'the good guys', consultants must have the ability to work at board, front-line and middle management levels, communicate strongly and work closely in teams.

Strongly results-driven, Gemini is absolutely committed to implementing its recommendations – it doesn't just make them and then leave.

In recruiting people, Gemini is therefore looking for a 'fit' with its culture and values. 'Intellectual and analytical rigour we regard as a minimum entry ticket,' says Steve Beck. 'But then we look for people-orientation, emotional literacy, the ability to convince and persuade, and teamwork.' Therefore Gemini talks openly about values – enthusiasm, mastery, trust, even fun, words which are absolutely fundamental to Gemini because without them, it cannot deliver its promises to clients.

Gemini is also a very friendly, happy and human organisation. Friday sees most consultants return to its offices from client sites and this is a prompt for a 'fun' day of informal dress, socialising and a chance to catch up with colleagues. The two set-piece social events, the family summer picnic and Christmas party, used to be three but the (employees') kids party has been replaced by a donation to a children's charity. Gemini also helps in UK schools by sponsoring and mentoring head teachers. Knowledgeable employees – and 40 put their names forward – selected the art collection which adorns the Knightsbridge office walls. And if consultants are late in completing time sheets they are fined, with all proceeds given to charity!

Human Resources

Gemini's HR function is absolutely essential to the success of the firm and is staffed by professionals many of whom, like Laura Agostini, head of Global HR, started life as a management consultant. Recruitment, career development, competencies, remuneration all fall under its remit.

Gemini recruits from a number of sources – graduates, MBAs, direct hires, occasionally from other consultancies. Gemini's proposal to individuals is that they can make a difference, to the firm and to clients, as well as building their own skills. Gemini's global team of consulting professionals is drawn from among the best business minds available, with a heavy emphasis on significant practical experience in their areas of specialisation.

Upon joining Gemini everyone – and that means everyone – enters the two-week Gemini Skills Workshop. Working through real client cases, the fortnight includes the chance to learn and practice required analytical, personal and process skills. It's also an excellent opportunity for early networking.

Before leaving the workshop, each person is assigned a mentor within the firm, who is a career coach to the consultant. You can also change your mentor. It's all designed to fit people quickly and comfortably into the organisation.

Career Opportunity and Development

There are five levels of professional at Gemini: consultant, senior consultant, managing consultant, principal and officer, although titles don't appear on business cards.

Consultants who begin their career at Gemini are challenged with responsibility early in their careers, the chance to make an impact from their first day on the job, and the satisfaction of knowing that they are contributing to the resolution of major business issues that affect markets, economies and – most importantly – people.

'The Shop' is an office-based 'hothouse' for Gemini's entry-level consultant population. The Shop performs discrete research and analytical pieces of work for clients and helps prepare proposals.

The other way in which people get real training and development is working on real projects. People are deliberately moved around between projects to gain a breadth of experience, which might involve working abroad.

Everyone has two performance reviews each year, including critical (but supportive) feedback of the 360-degree variety. Reviews are tied to developing competencies and in turn, your career. Also biannually, the officers and principals discuss and review everyone in the firm. The focus is again on development, to enhance the individual's and the firm's capabilities with the added benefits of identifying people for promotion. Another huge investment in terms of time, but again critical to the firm.

The Gemini (virtual) University is run six to eight times a year and everyone in the firm is budgeted for and expected to attend courses.

Individuals work for a specific region, but international moves reflect individual aspirations as well as the needs of the business. Staffing is carried out at local and global levels, and recruitment of MBAs and other searches are undertaken globally; industry hires are usually made at the local country level. But by managing Consultant level you will be expected to have worked outside your country and supported projects beyond your own specific area of expertise. 'It's always what you contribute to our clients and to Gemini globally that counts,' says Laura Agostini.

Gemini remains a happy company, which wants to give everyone a chance to do brilliant work.

Remuneration

To remain competitive on salary Gemini carries out global surveys on its peer group, skewed more towards the strategy consulting 'boutiques', although it believes it is absolutely right not to be the very highest payer. While salary is hardly ever decisive, its consultants are paid well nonetheless. The basic package comprises salary, bonus and benefits (flexible and self-managed). Gemini is perhaps more bonus-driven than its competitors, based on what you have contributed to clients and to the firm (this will include mentoring and enhancing the capability and development of the firm – a recurring theme).

The Future

Gemini believes (indeed, has researched globally) that employees' needs and attitudes are changing. Increasingly, people are valuing a balance between work and lifestyle. Gemini has seized this opportunity to re-design continually its approach to managing people and in so doing, maintain the special Gemini philosophy and the way it works.

Gemini is a prime mover in this postmodern trend. FlexForce has been in place for five years and will be fundamental to the way the firm looks at contracting and compensation. 'We understand that people want to flex their working time, perhaps spend more time with their families,' says Laura Agostini. 'So we've said, let's formalise it in a contract, be open and clear about the options, and get it accepted across the whole company.' Two options already in place are the sabbatical (12 weeks away on half pay every four years) and a nine-month reduced work schedule or 'school year' to allow staff to spend more time with their families.

Management consultancy has evolved from executive coaching in the 1960s/70s (clients effectively hired gurus), direction-setting and insights (1980s) and the results/bottom line approach that Gemini pioneered in the 1990s. The challenge now is adapting to and meeting the next wave, which Steve Beck sees as 'building capability' – a much softer notion which recognises that much will still centre around processes and technology, but more will be about building the individual and corporate capabilities of clients' people.

The technical dimension will become increasingly important, with clients seeking advice on how to apply IT to run their business better and how to implement these changes. Gemini Consulting's relationship with its sister companies in Cap Gemini provides the firm with strong capabilities to meet this need.

But the real war in the consulting industry is for people, and the winners will be those which construct and deliver the best value proposition. Gemini appears to be right at the front.

Glaxo Wellcome

Glaxo Wellcome is one of the world's leading healthcare companies, and one of the UK's largest companies. It is a leading manufacturer of treatments for asthma, epilepsy, migraine, herpes, HIV/AIDS, cancer and skin conditions. Its annual sales are approximately £8 billion and it invests over £1.15 billion each year in research and development. It has operating companies in 76 countries and supplies products to 150 countries. Glaxo Wellcome employs around 54,000 people worldwide, and 13,000 in the UK.

Scorecard:

Remuneration and benefits	★★★★
Progressive attitude	★★★★
Opportunity for promotion	★★★★
Training, development and education	★★★★★
Working atmosphere and environment	★★★★

Biggest plus:
A great achiever in a rewarding industry

Biggest minus:
The pace of change is frenetic

Glaxo Wellcome plc
Berkeley Avenue
Greenford
Middlesex UB6 0NN
Tel: 0181 493 4060
Fax: 0181 966 8330
website www.glaxowellcome.co.uk

GlaxoWellcome

Glaxo Wellcome

The Business

Glaxo Wellcome is a research-based company whose people are committed to fighting disease by bringing innovative medicines and services to patients throughout the world and to the healthcare providers who serve them. Its goal is to be the leading global company in fighting disease and improving health. Glaxo Wellcome has a keen eye for commercial opportunity to maximise the potential of products coming to the market.

Founded over 100 years ago, Glaxo grew continuously and, in 1995, joined with Wellcome in a high-profile merger where the fit between the two companies was a good one. Pharmaceuticals remains a global industry so large that even the giants do not have large market share compared to other industries.

Glaxo catapulted itself to prominence in the early 1980s through the phenomenal success of its anti-ulcer drug, Zantac – the world's first $1 billion dollar drug and the biggest selling pharmaceutical of all time. In 1997, its main patents for Zantac expired but this impact has been absorbed. That the company's pipeline of new medicines is one of the most comprehensive in the pharmaceutical industry is testimony to Glaxo Wellcome maintaining its leading position at the cutting edge of medical science. It has set itself the tough challenge of introducing three new medicines every year from the year 2000.

Company Culture and Style

As an employer, Glaxo Wellcome is often described by recently-joined graduates as 'totally unstuffy', 'non-hierarchical' and 'an employer which has exceeded my expectations'. Selective phrases no, because Glaxo Wellcome offers one of the best training placement programmes available.

Glaxo Wellcome is a group of young, dynamic, very bright people. Within the company there is a respect for an individual adding value over and above what is expected from their basic work. The environment is such that all people have always been encouraged to do things in a different, better way. Possibly because the company has an R&D dominance, people who are attracted to Glaxo Wellcome are looking for change.

'I have visited every site and am always impressed by people enjoying and being stimulated by their work and finding ways of doing it better,' says John Raywood, HR manager. 'Most are also shareholders in the company and are anxious for the company to do well, knowing that they play a real part in it'.

The issue of culture change relating to the merger of Glaxo and Wellcome is now in the past. While two or three years ago it was possible to identify easily 'Glaxo' or 'Wellcome' people, it is now almost seamless. Everyone now thinks 'Glaxo Wellcome'.

Glaxo Wellcome is more often than not the biggest employer in locations where its facilities are found – both an advantage and a disadvantage. And its manufacturing locations across the UK are not necessarily in the main population centres. Head office staff have had to swap the glamour and convenience of offices in Berkeley Square in Central London for life at a research and development facility in the suburbs. But all Glaxo Wellcome locations are well appointed with excellent, self-contained facilities including restaurants and sports.

One thing that staff at Glaxo Wellcome share is a genuine sense of doing some good in the world, and healthcare can provide a tangible sense of purpose less evident in other careers. But the laughs do not stop once you begin work, and the company positively encourages 'life after work'.

As a good corporate citizen, Glaxo Wellcome sponsors an array of events in art, music and theatre, and supports work and projects undertaken in the community by its employees.

Human Resources

The board regards human resources as an integral part of its business strategy. 'We are putting enormous emphasis on valuing and demonstrating commitment to our people,' says Dr David Findley, director, human resources. 'We recognise the need to promote a collaborative approach to the career development of everyone and it is important to communicate this.'

In a decentralised business, HR tries as far as it can to apply common standards in a structure that is often far from uniform. 'People need to feel they are being treated fairly,' adds David Findley. Of course, expediency will sometimes take precedence.

Glaxo Wellcome is a leader in many HR best practices. For example, there is a range of programmes to support women in the workplace, including childcare facilities, enhanced maternity leave, and 'phase back' arrangements. Glaxo Wellcome is also proud of its record in diversity, in terms of employment of cultural, ethnic or disability groups. Glaxo Wellcome believes strongly in the Investors in People standard.

Glaxo Wellcome recruits around 130 graduates each year in the UK. Due to the nature of its business, it also hires a substantial number of postgraduates and direct-entry professionals.

Career Opportunity and Development

There are excellent opportunities for stimulating, rewarding careers throughout Glaxo Wellcome. The general style of the company is to stretch people as far as they can, and the pace of change is such that there is constant movement in levels of responsibility. Often you don't need to change position to climb the hierarchy – you can also do this if you are seen to have 'grown the job'.

Glaxo Wellcome is shifting to a more flexible way of working and an implied re-negotiation of the unwritten contract between employer and employee. Individuals are increasingly responsible for determining their own career paths, but between mentors, managers, HR and fellow colleagues, all the support and guidance needed is still there.

Glaxo Wellcome believes in devolved businesses, and each of the group companies operates autonomously in many respects, including recruitment. Each country also constitutes a different market and is therefore responsible for its own activities. In the UK, Glaxo Wellcome has four main sectors of activity – head office, research and development, manufacturing and supply, and Glaxo Wellcome UK Limited (covering marketing and sales). They may often be sitting cheek-by-jowl, however, with different functions occupying the same site, and there is a great deal of interchange.

The company encourages its top talent to move internationally to benefit their careers, recognising that it is also in the company's interests for this to happen, and to facilitate this has recently appointed a worldwide human resources director.

Remuneration

Glaxo Wellcome knows that to attract and retain the best people, remuneration is important. It goes to great lengths to benchmark all aspects of remuneration so that it can stay at the top end of the scale among its peer group.

Pay, benefits and conditions have been harmonised (after much work) into a single system following the merger of Glaxo and Wellcome. One example is the amount of time and effort spent launching and communicating the new UK company pension scheme, described as 'leading edge' due to its flexibility and portability. Keen that everyone joined the scheme because it is highly beneficial, Glaxo Wellcome gave each individual the opportunity to meet one-to-one with an independent financial advisor. The sign-up by staff was 100%.

Staff are actively encouraged to become shareholders in their company. Glaxo Wellcome runs an attractive Share Save Scheme, while many people are eligible for share options.

The Future

The pharmaceutical industry continues to undergo rapid, sometimes bewildering, change. People accept the potentiality of more mergers within the industry, and it is a fact of life that any rumours of link-ups with other companies will inevitably generate a lot of internal talking. But staff at Glaxo Wellcome are working for one of the largest companies, and so have the confidence that people would be 'coming to you' rather than the other way around.

Glaxo Wellcome has moved quickly and positively to replace the revenue streams that its 'wonder drug' Zantac delivered for so long. Sir Richard Sykes, chairman, says, 'Rapid and profound advances in technology and scientific knowledge are creating opportunities that are greater than ever before. Our scientists are developing new skills which are driven by genetics and genomics, state-of-the-art technologies, new partnerships and the sophisticated use of information. Shareholders can be assured that Glaxo Wellcome is at the forefront of the application of these new approaches which have the potential to change fundamentally the provision and the practice of medicine.' Inevitably, a new approach which brings new products to the market quicker is going to put pressure on all parts of the organisation.

Recognising that there is more scope (and desire) for people to move around the business, Glaxo Wellcome wants to improve the provision of international careers. This means removing barriers and making sure that there is a more collaborative approach to managing its businesses and sharing best practices.

Glaxo Wellcome is a much-admired company, showing great vitality and business focus for such a large organisation. A constant theme – the business of fighting diseases – adds a rewarding dimension to work and achievement in a company that has a superb track record of research and commercial success.

Goldman Sachs International

Goldman Sachs is a leading investment banking, securities and asset management firm serving corporations, governments, institutions and individuals in markets around the world. Goldman Sachs is guided by its Business Principles emphasising commitment to clients, excellence in service, teamwork, integrity and creativity. Over a quarter of the firm's assets and its people are outside the USA, a trend likely to increase. Goldman Sachs employs approximately 16,000 people worldwide, of which 4,000 are in Europe and 3,500 in London.

Scorecard:

Remuneration and benefits	★★★★
Progressive attitude	★★★★★
Opportunity for promotion	★★★★
Training, development and education	★★★★
Working atmosphere and environment	★★★★★

Biggest plus:
The premier global investment banking and securities firm, with an open, honest culture

Biggest minus:
Must be able to handle the pressure and responsibility

Goldman Sachs International
Peterborough Court
133 Fleet Street
London EC4A 2BB
Tel: 0171 774 1000
Fax: 0171 774 4477
website: www.gs.com

Goldman Sachs International

The Business

Goldman Sachs has few peers in investment banking, and is one of the most successful, highly respected businesses in the world. It consistently receives external accolades, while from the inside, employees believe that the firm's premier reputation is based on several key factors – a flat structure, a distinct Goldman Sachs culture, a heavy emphasis on teamwork, a proud 130-year history, and offices in 23 countries.

'We are not a US firm operating overseas,' says Peter Sutherland, chairman of Goldman Sachs International in London. 'We are a global investment banking firm.'

Goldman Sachs is a diverse, far-reaching business. It is active throughout the world, maintaining a high profile in every major financial centre. The services it provides help shape the activities and performance of governments, large multinational corporations, financial institutions, fast-growth emerging companies, institutional investors and wealthy individuals.

Goldman Sachs applies its high value-added, integrated skills to complex, challenging and demanding corporate and investment situations, providing advisory services, financing, sales and trading, and asset management.

Company Culture and Style

Goldman Sachs is an organisation in which nationalities, cultures and languages mix freely – a sum of entrepreneurial individuals following a powerful team ethic to achieve their objectives. This strong culture is one where people understand and support the desire to be the best. At Goldman Sachs, excellence is a way of life. Staff will experience the 'Wow!' factor when they answer who they work for. The name definitely has *élan*.

Goldman Sachs is guided by its Business Principles – of which it articulates 14 – and it only does business consistent with these principles. Most importantly, clients' interests always come first.

There is an enormous, collective will to produce high quality work – which must come from yourself. It goes with the challenge of the job. Goldman Sachs staff find themselves with a lot of responsibility, access to senior managing directors, access to clients. You are putting yourself in a very challenging environment and people often receive more responsibility than they ever imagined.

Qualities valued at Goldman Sachs include integrity, high motivation, intelligence, creativity, and commercial sensitivity, with an emphasis on building long-term relationships rather than completing immediate transactions. Goldman Sachs executives must feel comfortable relating to and counselling clients; they must establish credibility, honesty and trust, and sometimes disagree. Often the best advice is just don't do the deal.

Goldman Sachs is a flat organisation, with very little in the way of hierarchy. Team-building is fundamental across all of the businesses. This is *one* firm. Goldman Sachs cultivates an open environment, where it can encourage people not to be afraid to make 'the right kind of mistakes'. Indeed, there is a high degree of 'what do you think?'. It is no mistake that its recruitment strapline is 'Minds Wide Open'.

Goldman Sachs is a collaborative firm where *camaraderie* is spontaneous and genuine, and where people think of each other as friends as much as business colleagues. There is also a strong sense of justice; if people ever feel they have not been dealt with fairly, the chairman's door is open. Indeed, all MDs offices are open, and they never ask beforehand why you want to see them.

Human Resources

The HR activity at Goldman Sachs goes to great lengths to recruit, develop and motivate exceptional people capable of delivering excellent service at international levels for the next five, ten, and fifteen years.

Goldman Sachs Business Principle No. 6 says: 'We make an unusual effort to identify and recruit the very best person for every job. Although our activities are measured in billions of dollars, we select our people one by one. In a service business, we know that without the best people, we cannot be the best firm.'

It is regarded as a business imperative to recruit its workforce from diverse backgrounds, and the firm can boast considerable success. There are already 52 different nationalities working in London alone. Goldman Sachs knows this is a strength, and intends to emphasise and encourage it more.

There are many supporting initiatives for employees in place. Keen to attract a more diverse workforce to develop longer careers, Goldman Sachs will bend over backwards to help all staff, addressing working family type issues and providing, for example, childcare facilities.

'We also encourage our people to keep fit and healthy,' says Alison Bott, head of human resources in Europe. 'The emphasis is on helping employees look after themselves. We value their contribution and the "wellness" factor is an holistic approach all about balancing life's needs.' The firm provides health services including a GP on site, educational programmes, nutritional guides and legal counselling, and has recently sanctioned a 20,000 square foot gym in London.

Goldman Sachs has done relatively well in retaining its people, obviously made easier by the tremendous success of the firm. Goldman Sachs people will always be attractive to poachers who value their experience, but the firm avoids competing in the 'spot market', preferring instead to emphasise the tremendous long-term career opportunities it offers. 'The better you do, the further you go' is one of the great attractions of Goldman Sachs to individuals.

Career Opportunity and Development

'An exceptional place to pursue a career' is how Goldman Sachs has been described. The sheer scale of Goldman Sachs's business allows it to offer an outstanding range of world-class careers to talented individuals.

Moving people around – between divisions and internationally – is something that Goldman Sachs does as well as anyone. 'There are many pretenders to being a global firm, but only if you have people with genuine international experience and a global mindset are you really able to make that claim,' says Alison Bott.

In promoting career mobility, the firm thinks very broadly about the right person for the right job, and personal skills are just as important as technical expertise. The 'Goldman Sachs experience' is always valued, and by sending experienced staff abroad, the so-called 'culture carriers' ensure that the values of Goldman Sachs are exported.

There is a huge training focus to give people all the personal, technical and managerial skills that they need. A new training facility in London has recently been approved to match the massive training centre in the US. Training and development methods are state-of-the-art, using interactive techniques and the latest technology to underpin the firm's global resourcing challenges.

An individual's review process is very thorough, and 360-degree career performance management is fundamental to the teamwork concept. Themes from 360-degrees percolate directly into compensation and into personal development plans.

Remuneration

Pay is essentially performance-based. Goldman Sachs pays very well, starting at graduate level. It wants the best people and pays at the top level, but where there are 'spikes' in the competitive market, Goldman Sachs tries not to get drawn into bidding situations. It prefers instead to emphasise the substantial benefits of long-term career ambition. Successful people at Goldman Sachs will nearly always find themselves at the top of any pay scale offered by competitors.

The Future

Goldman Sachs expects the key drivers of global integration – political liberalisation, rapid advances in technology and communications, and demographic shift – to continue. While pursuing 'the art of the possible' with its clients in this context, Goldman Sachs will continue to look for new areas of opportunity and risk to provide its high value-added services. The firm has been implementing an emerging markets strategy, and is also placing increasing emphasis on its asset management activities.

Being first or second in almost everything it does, Goldman Sachs is only too aware of the dangers of complacency. The firm intends to avoid any 'institutionalisation of success', and recognises that communication will be vital, particularly between 'seniors' who lead the firm and formulate strategy, and the young professionals who are inevitably closer to the markets and are the sensors of the firm.

As the firm extends its global reach, maintaining the Goldman Sachs culture and its way of doing things will be as important as ever in navigating its course, especially in countries with strong local cultures and different business practices, although this is probably less of an issue than it could be.

The possible flotation of Goldman Sachs, which was put on hold in 1998, was well publicised. Going public would obviously have many ramifications for the firm – on its structure, accountability, on human resources. But whatever the future, the firm remains committed to maintaining its culture of putting clients' interests first and enhancing its assets – its people, capital and reputation.

Goldman Sachs people regard the firm as being 'something special', and want to work hard to leave behind something better. With this in-built commitment to the highest standards, and a culture that values everyone in the firm as being important, people are rightly proud to say that they are professionals at Goldman Sachs.

Gossard

Gossard is the biggest branded lingerie producer in the UK with its two brands, Gossard and Berlei. It also has good-sized businesses in the US and Europe and operates in a further 50 countries through a series of distributors and agents. Gossard is part of Courtaulds Textiles plc, which is among the top five European textile firms. It is an integrated company, covering manufacturing, distribution, marketing and sales of quality lingerie, with an annual turnover of £50–60 million. Gossard employs around 2,200 people worldwide, 900 in the UK.

Scorecard:

Remuneration and benefits	★★★
Progressive attitude	★★★★
Opportunity for promotion	★★★★★
Training, development and education	★★★★
Working atmosphere and environment	★★★★★

Biggest plus:
Putting more than the 'buzz' into Leighton Buzzard

Biggest minus:
Intensive pace of work dictated by the fashion industry

Gossard
Grovebury Road
Leighton Buzzard
Bedfordshire LU7 8SN
Tel: 01525 851122
Fax: 01525 850038
e-mail: Paul.Bishop@Courtaulds-Textiles.com

Gossard

The Business

'I'm not like most men,' suggests chief executive Mark Pilkington with a glint in his eye. 'I'm actually trying to put bras on to women.'

Lingerie outfit Gossard represents one of the 'sexier' parts of the Courtaulds Textiles business.

Gossard has two principal brand labels. The Berlei range emphasises 'well-being' and technically based design benefits, such as sports bras, including its 'Shock Absorber' brand promoted by British athlete Sally Gunnell. Meanwhile the Gossard range is sexy, fashionable, backed by a 'fun' style of communication and marketing. Gossard has achieved fame for its 'push-up' bras, including the Ultrabra, and people like Sophie Anderton – 'the Gossard Girl' – have become household names, or at least faces.

Gossard is very much about quality and its lingerie has won the Queens Award for Export twice, and five first prizes from the British Clothing & Knitwear Export Council – no other company has won more.

The lingerie market is heavily influenced by fashion trends, with outerwear trends translating into underwear. As Christian Dior once said, 'Underwear is the foundation of fashion'. When Madonna was strutting her stuff in the 1980s, there was a huge boom in push-up bras; in the 1990s, the minimalist trend has meant that many lycra items are sold. 'And Gossard has to follow these trends,' says Mark Pilkington. 'We must produce lingerie that is both appealing and appropriate, and we follow the catwalk closely.'

Company Culture and Style

Rather than being a textiles company, Gossard aspires to be a consumer goods company that happens to make bras. And there, you could say, the gauntlet has been laid down.

Gossard is trying to get leading edge values infused into the company. It's actually referred to as 'EDGE' (Exceptional people; Desirable products; Great advertising; Excellent service). The company knows that it is not quite there yet, but everyone in the company is encouraged to be aware of these values.

A 'work hard, play hard' culture is emerging. 'If you do this as part of a team, and you're winning, it can be one of the most exhilarating experiences,' says Mark Pilkington. It may mean long hours, also smarter working, and it certainly means having the desire and motivation to become the leading fashion player in the European lingerie market in the next five years.

Successful brands are all about momentum, and if you get on a roll, everyone wants to be part of it. But the toughest part of being a rolling stone is getting to the top of the hill. That is why enthusiasm is perhaps the most highly valued quality in Gossard.

And many people are pursuing Gossard's aspirational goals with great enthusiasm. 'Giving that little bit extra means different things to different people,' says Mark Pilkington. 'We want everyone to do that little bit more than the competition. Every person can make a difference.'

Gossard is moving its production to a teamworking system, like other Courtaulds Textiles businesses, though it is not standard in the textiles industry. People have been genuinely incentivised by the team's overall performance, taking pride in the whole process and the finished product. Teamworking also generates more sociable work dynamics: it's less lonely trainees can be integrated quickly into a team culture, and it exposes those 'not pulling their weight'.

'The great thing about Gossard is the number of people who say they love working there,' says Paul Bishop, logistics director, responsible for human resources. 'There's a real pride in the company: people get a buzz out of seeing their company's advertisements on TV; partners love coming to company do's because everyone gets on well together; it's a first-name business; everyone eats in the same staff canteen.'

Gossard is also a fun company. People socialise together frequently, the managing director complaining that the last round in the pub cost him in excess of £200. The informal, self-confident style is evident at packed sales conferences, where pantomimes and comedy revues often feature.

Human Resources

In labour intensive businesses, human resources is usually a busy function and Gossard is no exception. Paul Bishop sits on the board, and all Gossard's directors are very people- and team-oriented.

Paul Bishop says, 'Training is extremely focused rather than of the "nice to have" variety. It's integral to the appraisal system and management by objectives. If we want people to be performance-driven, we have to equip them with the right tools.'

Gossard has hired leading edge people externally in certain areas –

for example, supply chain, IT and sales and marketing experts from leaders like Unilever, Johnson & Johnson and Colgate Palmolive. These people work alongside the company's many excellent long-term contributors, mixing new ideas with experience. Some of the strongest areas of the company are led by people who have worked at Gossard for many years.

Managing and communicating this change has been vital. The company takes the time to explain why and how the latest developments and technologies have moved on, whether they be in supply chain, IT or sales training. 'If you bring in new expertise and skill levels, people in the business are entitled to have things explained to them,' says Paul Bishop.

If there have sometimes been mixed feelings, Gossard employees have responded well to change – particularly when they see the results and performance improvements. 'In many areas we are already excellent,' says Mark Pilkington, 'and in all areas we have excellent people.'

Career Opportunity and Development

Seven of the nine current directors were managers in the business, evidence enough of the opportunities at Gossard.

Gossard believes, with some justification, that it can offer the same levels of professionalism and excellence as large businesses do. Gossard is one of around thirty businesses in Courtaulds Textiles, and being a smaller company means a greater sense of ownership, less bureaucracy and the ability to take quick decisions. It also gives early opportunity at a young age to get into responsible line management positions.

There is also movement within the Courtaulds Textiles group – across businesses and across disciplines – and there are international opportunities within Gossard itself. People in finance, production and general management have worked abroad on short and longer term assignments.

Marketing at Gossard has a proper front-end link to the consumer and, given the fashionable nature of its products, provides for very interesting work. In marketing, professionals are expected to come from outside. 'We need fresh skills, fresh ideas,' says Paul Bishop. 'It's not an area which requires 20 or 30 years' experience in the industry.'

Remuneration

The textiles industry has traditionally been low-paying, which has challenged Gossard as it shifts to becoming more of a consumer goods company. Staff turnover is low for the industry, suggesting that pay is not a decisive factor. To recruit experts from outside, remuneration has had to become more competitive and Gossard is now looking at levels internally. Professional staff at Gossard increasingly have earnings related to performance.

Supervisors and managers also follow an eight-weekly 'management by objectives' process. The review process allows management to clarify what they want people to do, praise them when they succeed, and identify development needs when they do not.

'The process helps us to get there quite quickly,' says Mark Pilkington. 'It's usually a question of commitment and it helps sort that out too.'

The Future

The lingerie industry is globalising and consolidating very quickly. While smaller companies are expected to disappear, new entrants are expected in the form of designer labels such as Calvin Klein and Armani.

Gossard expects the Internet to make a big impact, with catalogue home shopping already representing 15% of all lingerie sold in Europe. Meanwhile advances in technology could allow the bespoke manufacture of individual 'celebrity branded' bras to order, rather than a 34B or 36A which Mark Pilkington describes as 'a simplification of reality'.

First, Gossard wants excellence in the basics – improved reliability, delivery on time, ensuring that products are always well researched and markets segmented, supported by good communications, advertising and operating procedures. Gossard regards this as 'the catching-up phase', with the fast-moving consumer goods companies as the pacesetters. Once achieved, Mark Pilkington expects the company to 'address some of the bigger issues and become leading edge'.

Gossard believes that people want personal growth, in the form of continuous learning. They want their managers to be visionary, leading edge in their discipline, using state-of-the-art tools. They also want the right type of training – not training for training's sake.

After learning comes earning opportunity. Hence Gossard's 'Dash for Growth'. This will create many opportunities – perhaps to develop a business, acquire a company, introduce and launch a new product range, or exploit new media such as the Internet. It does not want people to get 'stuck'

Colleagues credit Mark Pilkington with having brought pace and passion to Gossard. 'It's challenging but rewarding,' says Paul Bishop. 'We know we have to run to keep up, but his energy rubs-off.' Gossard has a tremendous amount still to achieve, but there's a real buzz about the business that people love.

GWR Group

GWR is one of the largest local radio groups in the UK. Since its formation in 1985 it has grown quickly and in 1999 had revenues of around £75 million. The GWR broadcasting group now has 35 local radio licences, broadcasting to a potential audience of 12 million listeners across a wide area of southern and South-west England, the Midlands and East Anglia. GWR also owns Classic FM, Orchard Media (acquired in 1999), and stations in Bulgaria, Austria, and Poland. The group is the majority shareholder in Digital One, which holds the licence to broadcast 10 digital radio stations across the UK using the new Digital Audio Broadcasting system. GWR has around 750 full-time employees, plus another 150 freelance employees, including presenters.

Scorecard:
Remuneration and benefits	★★★
Progressive attitude	★★★★
Opportunity for promotion	★★★★
Training, development and education	★★★★
Working atmosphere and environment	★★★★★

Biggest plus:
Successful, purposeful, local and exciting media business

Biggest minus:
Very decentralised, not at all like working for a corporation

GWR Group plc
PO Box 2345
3B2 Westlea
Swindon SN5 7HF
Tel: 0118 9284314
Fax: 0118 9284310

G W R group plc

GWR Group

The Business

Group chief executive Ralph Bernard's strategy has been to grow GWR quickly through acquisition, to reach the critical mass necessary to have clout. Having got there, restrictions on ownership of licences imposed by the radio authorities in the UK have prompted GWR to concentrate instead on the quality of its portfolio of licences, the performance of individual stations and the move into digital broadcasting – the future of radio.

Radio continues to be the fastest-growing sector of the UK media, having increased from 45 stations a decade ago to nearer 200 today. Commercial radio's share of the listening population has increased at the expense of the BBC and its share of total display advertising has risen from 3.6% in 1994 to 5.3% in 1998.

Importantly, GWR's audience is 'the right type'. Around four million adults listen each week to GWR's local stations, and Classic FM alone attracts 5.1 million listeners, while the proportion of younger listeners in the 18–24 age group – the one of predominant interest to advertisers – has risen over recent years.

Company Culture and Style

The radio business is characterised by youthfulness, fun and immediacy, and these attributes are found at all of GWR stations. A young people's business, the average age of GWR staff is around 32. This business has to be fun if radio is to be successful in attracting advertisers.

Because commercial radio transmits almost every minute, 24 hours a day, the need for immediacy is obvious. Local radio is often about what is happening in the local community, today, now. Being sensitive to very local factors – people, incidents, sports events, traffic, even the weather – requires a special kind type of attitude and personality. And nothing contrived – people must be genuinely interested in the subjects they are reporting. Ralph Bernard says: 'Local commercial radio's key strength is its freedom to respond to local concerns.'

With a large number of stations, structure is increasingly important to GWR. Stations or companies bought by GWR will, to a certain extent, be subsumed into the culture of the group. But GWR always recognises the importance of the close interaction that individual stations have with their local communities and seeks to preserve local cultures within the environment of the overall group culture. GWR has spent a great deal of time standardising its systems in such areas as finance, broadcasting and sales, in order to achieve a common platform of performance across the group.

GWR carefully follows a balanced approach to its different stakeholders: employees, listeners, advertisers, and equity shareholders. Deputy chief executive Patrick Taylor suggests, 'We regard employees as the first stakeholder group, but the shareholders as the ultimate stakeholders. Any media business is best served by first getting the motivation of its employees right.' Although many companies talk about 'putting the customer first', he is absolutely right. Without motivated people providing informative, creative entertainment, there will be no listeners, and no advertisers, and no financial returns for shareholders. The virtual circle is, again, a reality.

GWR is somewhat different for a radio operator in that it actively researches its audiences to find out exactly what music they are interested in. Classic FM in particular spends a lot of time on detailed research, and this is regarded as a key factor in its success.

Human Resources

Patrick Taylor believes that a caring attitude can be particularly beneficial in the radio business. Motivating employees does not just involve areas such as pay, but means providing decent working conditions, fostering team spirit, managing well, and telling employees when they – and the business – are doing well.

GWR's human resources activity is carried out principally through line management. While values and cultural direction come from GWR's central management team, individual station managing directors – who meet regularly – are responsible for communicating news, ideas and company information to their own staff.

GWR believes strongly that the company will benefit if it succeeds in harnessing the creativity and ideas of all people in the organisation. It continues to examine and explore ways in which employees and management can communicate together effectively, to the ultimate benefit of the company.

Across the group, GWR has standardised the checklist of things that 'a good employer' does – employment contracts, performance and appraisal processes, training, pension arrangements, exit interviews, and incentive schemes.

Career Opportunity and Development

There are many careers to be had within GWR, but the two main ones are in programming and advertising sales. Careers in programming will progress through presenting, planning and production. In sales, the route begins at sales assistant, through executive, manager to director. In addition, GWR offers the professional specialisations of finance, IT, engineering, HR and administration.

One enlightening aspect of GWR is its approach to succession management, which provides a clue to how GWR has been able to fuel its expansion plans successfully. The original GWR companies have been quick to identify a successor to a manager about to move on so that, when Chiltern Radio was acquired for example, GWR was able to transfer to it some of its key managers while allowing the stations they were taken from to function normally.

You do not have to be a programmer or sales executive to move into general management at GWR. Many station managing directors have come from a news environment, and even from accountancy. This is all part of GWR's culture – the company will develop any talented person with the right intrinsic qualities for management. Group chief executive Ralph Bernard himself comes from a journalistic background.

GWR has three divisions: Classic FM, UK Local Radio, and Overseas. People do move between local radio stations, but – by virtue of the word 'local' – not often overseas. All vacancies are advertised internally.

As GWR grows, it is increasing the emphasis on more general training, and communication skills are considered as important as any. The group has also pioneered training in coaching techniques to enable managers to help staff perform at their best.

The sales force is trained specifically, so that they are fully aware of the GWR product, what it stands for, and how the local dimension is all-important. Collective training courses deliver valuable spin-off benefits, in that people network informally with colleagues around the group, build team spirit and revitalise team efforts.

With the goal of harnessing the ideas and creativity of all of its people, GWR trains its managers to help individuals develop, convert and apply original ideas which can benefit the overall business. GWR recognises that a blame culture is rarely an innovative one, and therefore stresses that people should not be scared of failure, only be willing to try things out and learn from experience.

Remuneration

Basic pay at GWR is generally quite good – maybe even slightly above market rates – and working conditions vary from location to location. Flexibility is a prerequisite, and staff expect variety in their working life.

Pay policies and benefits, including profit-related pay, pensions and company cars, are standardised across the group, depending on the size of the station.

The Future

With the acquisition of Classic FM and Orchard Media, GWR is at the limit of the number of allowable listening population 'points' under current regulations. The company must concentrate instead on improving the quality of its licences. That might mean a continual trading of its portfolio, or 'Playing a game of monopoly', as Patrick Taylor puts it. GWR is likely to stay on the look-out for more overseas radio opportunities. At home, digital radio will offer exciting opportunities.

Within the UK, GWR is exploring novel ways to build new enterprises from its relationships with listeners, in areas that go beyond straightforward broadcasting. Unlikely to rush, GWR will assess its best options, those that explore the wider relationship with its listeners, and seek to leverage the corporate or individual station's brand name across different products and services. Locally that should mean a deeper involvement with the community, while the Classic FM magazine, which is already a market leader, highlights the potential nationally.

The shareholder structure and director profile of GWR is interesting. GWR shares are quoted on the London Stock Exchange, but half are held in non-institutional hands. The Classic FM deal brought-in both entrepreneur Sir Peter Michael and EMI as shareholders. With a highly entrepreneurial bunch of people managing the business, backed by experienced shareholders including the *Daily Mail* and General Trust, GWR is likely to remain a growing company doing exciting things.

Halifax

As the UK's biggest mortgage lender and a substantial player across the full range of personal financial services (including savings and investments, share dealing and insurance), Halifax boasts over 20 million customers. Formerly the world's largest building society, the bank's ambition is to be the UK's leading provider of personal financial services. It has acquired Clerical Medical Investment Group and is in the process of acquiring the Birmingham Midshires Building Society. In 1997, pre-tax profits stood at £1.6 billion. The company employs 37,000 people and, in addition to its central sites in Halifax and Leeds, has 820 branches and over 600 estate agency outlets.

Scorecard:

Remuneration and benefits	★★★★
Progressive attitude	★★★★★
Opportunity for promotion	★★★★
Training, development and education	★★★★
Working atmosphere and environment	★★★

Biggest plus:
The Halifax brand is the best known and best regarded in financial services

Biggest minus:
Change is the only constant in this market

Halifax plc
Trinity Road
Halifax
West Yorkshire HX1 2RG
Tel: 01422 333333
Fax: 01422 333000
website: www.halifax.co.uk

Halifax

The Business

Halifax plc is a broad-based financial services giant that has made the leap from being the world's largest mutually owned building society to become one of the country's largest public companies. The stock market flotation in 1997 was a huge success, creating millions of so-called 'windfall' shareholders, many of them employees. The private shareholder base is now estimated at nearly four million.

The traditional strengths of mortgage lending and deposit taking have, in recent years, been supplemented by diversification into general insurance, share dealing and investments and pensions, including the acquisition of the Clerical Medical Investment Group. The planned acquisition of the Birmingham Midshires Building Society will expand the company's customer base even further, strengthening its claim to be the premier provider of personal financial services on the high street. There is also a banking subsidiary in Spain.

Company Culture and Style

As a stalwart of the building society movement, Halifax was at the epicentre of the debate over whether such mutual organisations could survive and prosper in the contemporary financial services arena. While conscious of the need to respect its origins and traditions, the directors decided the financial realities were such that they needed to achieve a stock market listing. Thus, the ownership of the business transferred from members to shareholders.

Critics of demutualisation have suggested that the disappearance of institutions such as building societies destroys a unique culture, where the welfare of customers and staff takes priority over the crude pursuit of profit. The opposing view is that a public listing acts like a breath of fresh air, invigorating the business and allowing modern practices to sweep away outmoded structures and concepts. Halifax has certainly acted swiftly to introduce contemporary performance management and reward programmes. These move away from the established grading hierarchy and are designed 'to encourage staff to respond better to the needs of our customers'.

At the heart of the company's approach is 'The Halifax Way', which has three components: Delight the Customer, Support Each Other, and Do It Superbly. The focus is clearly on the consumer and staff who are able to develop their customer service skills will clearly flourish. And this does not apply simply to external customers in branches and on the telephone; staff regard each other as suppliers or customers and are therefore encouraged to work in such a way as to delight each other – which paints a rather charming picture.

Jon Foulds, chairman, attributes the uninterrupted progress of the business through the conversion process to the efforts of staff: 'Conversion to plc status was a true milestone, accomplished by staff who rose magnificently to all the huge challenges involved.' His thoughts are echoed by John Lee, group personnel and communications director: 'Halifax plc will only be as good as the people who work for it.' Implicit in these statements is a recognition that, as a financial services company, Halifax deals in complex products rather than physical goods; this means the quality of the service provided is all-important, since it is the most immediate yardstick by which customers can judge the organisation.

Halifax acknowledges its mutual society roots by retaining close links with the communities in which it operates. It is an enthusiastic sponsor of the arts and supporter of both local and national charities. Its Community Development Circles are designed to get staff involved and it will match funds raised by staff for agreed charitable projects.

Human Resources

Halifax's human resources philosophy has been developed internally and remains constantly under review. As befits such a large organisation with several discrete businesses, different areas have their own personnel functions, with the group personnel facility serving as a centre of best practice.

Some degree of group co-ordination remains important because Halifax wants to provide a 'uniform customer proposition'. This means that, whether the customer is dealing with someone in a branch or over the telephone, borrowing to buy a house or trading in shares, they should receive consistently high levels of service and be delighted with their experience of the Halifax brand. One of the roles of human resources is therefore to support management in their objective to get staff to focus on the Halifax customer (not just on their individual area of operation).

For this reason, Halifax deliberately encourages its staff to plan their careers with reference to the entire organisation, rather than a particular segment of it. It believes that this approach will build links within the business which will support the overall brand. It also means that senior managers will have knowledge and experience of a variety of functions and thus be able to enjoy a broad perspective of the group's overall operations.

Career Opportunity and Development

Self-development is to the fore at the Halifax, with staff encouraged to take professional examinations wherever possible, be it in banking, marketing, personnel management or business administration. There are no barriers to movement within the company; indeed, this is welcomed, helping to increase the options for succession planning, which ensures that the organisation is not vulnerable to the loss of any particular individual.

Considerable effort is devoted to personal development planning and performance measurement. Each member of staff has agreed objectives and is given management assistance to help develop the skills required to make the business a success. An annual performance appraisal provides an assessment of progress, although regular reviews and coaching sessions should ensure that there are no major surprises. Strong links have been established between performance and reward to stimulate staff further.

In its previous guise as a building society, Halifax saw many of its staff progress in linear fashion, remaining within a relatively narrow area of competence. As a modern bank with a range of financial services businesses, it is keen to see people moving horizontally into new areas. It believes that this will benefit them by broadening their range of experience and benefit the business by making the best use of the knowledge and skills available.

Remuneration

As a mass provider of financial services, Halifax competes for staff with a large number of banks, building societies and other providers. This necessarily obliges it to offer competitive salaries for its branch staff and those who work in its administrative centres.

Further up the management scale, Halifax regards itself in competition not only with the cream of the financial services market but also with blue-chip industrial institutions such as ICL and IBM. It attracts quality staff through the provision of benefits such as concessionary mortgages, car-leasing arrangements and private healthcare. All Halifax staff can participate in a share save scheme.

As might be expected with an organisation of this size and complexity, a sophisticated banding system has been introduced to create a clear and consistent remuneration structure throughout the business. However, given the emphasis on rewarding individual excellence, individuals are able to advance their earnings either through promotion or in recognition of performance. An annual business-related bonus is currently being developed to replace profit-related pay, the tax advantages of which are being phased out by the government.

The Future

In a fast-moving world, the financial services market is undergoing particularly rapid change. There have been a number of high-profile mergers and takeovers, and few believe that the demutualisation activity of recent years (of which Halifax was such a prominent part) has run its course. The organisations which remain are jostling for position and are looking to high-quality staff to deliver the required superior performance.

One of the issues Halifax is obliged to confront is the change from a building society to a bank. Whereas the society could afford to be largely conservative in outlook, the bank faces the more urgent pressures associated with keeping its shareholders satisfied. This inevitably increases the emphasis on achieving targets and meeting expectations.

What is more, the old 'job for life' attitude associated with the society is disappearing. Not, it should be stated, because the bank does not look for long-term commitment from its employees; it is more a case of today's employees recognising that career progression is often achieved by moving from one firm to another, perhaps a number of times over the course of the years. So Halifax must be prepared to accommodate a changing workforce.

One of the ways it is coping with this situation is by training people to work in several disciplines. As a multi-faceted business embracing mortgages, insurance, investments and share-dealing, it needs a flexible workforce that is able to respond to the rapidly changing needs of the organisation.

Hewlett-Packard Company

Hewlett-Packard is among the global leaders in the manufacture of printers, computing, communications and measurement products. It began as a maker of scientific and technical measuring instruments, but entered the computer market in the 1960s. It is now market leader in printers and a growing proportion of turnover comes from PCs, servers and workstations. By the end of 1998, it employed 127,200 people around the world, with 5,500 of them in the UK.

Scorecard:

Remuneration and benefits	★★★★
Progressive attitude	★★★★★
Opportunity for promotion	★★★★
Training, development and education	★★★★★
Working atmosphere and environment	★★★★★

Biggest plus:
The HP Way continues to unite us

Biggest minus:
The HP Way can demand even more

Hewlett-Packard
Cain Road
Bracknell
Berks RG12 1HN
Tel: 01344 360000
Fax: 01344 363344
website: www.hp.com

Hewlett-Packard Company

The Business

Once dismissed as a test-equipment company that dabbled in PCs, Hewlett-Packard (HP) is now one of the leading companies in this highly competitive sector. Though becoming big has slowed overall growth after a spell in which revenues doubled over a five-year period, HP is still expanding and in 1998 had total revenues of $48 billion. It also retains the respect of those it comes up against. From the start, the company has been noted for its innovation and had an inclusive view of business as a force for good.

Founded in 1939 by two engineers – Bill Hewlett and Dave Packard – in Palo Alto, California, HP produced the world's first desktop scientific computer in 1968 and the first scientific pocket calculator in 1972. But until the late 1980s, its growth was solid rather than spectacular, leading the *Wall Street Journal* to describe the company in 1990 as 'a torpid dinosaur among fleet-footed little predators'.

Two years later, HP closed some of its PC factories, moved more quickly than its rivals into client-server networks, and consolidated its lead in ink-jet printers so that by 1995 it had a third of the market. This helped the company build a strong position in distribution and marketing, essential for success when introducing such products as a low-priced multi-media PC.

The result was a 26% rise in net revenues in 1995 alone, while net earnings increased by 52% and net earnings per share grew 51%. The number of employees, which had not gone up for three years, rose to 102,300. 'Our ability to innovate and adapt has fuelled these results during a time of real industry upheaval,' the company said.

Joel Birnbaum, senior vice-president of research and development, added: 'HP's success will depend more and more on newly emerging technologies.' With this in mind, the company has stepped up spending on basic 'blue-sky', as well as applied, research.

In the PC business, the company has been especially successful in reducing not just costs but also production cycle times, or how long it takes from the customer placing an order to switching on.

Company Culture and Style

Given that it is as well known for its management style and philosophy, HP is better placed than just about any organisation to have coined the term 'corporate culture'. Co-founder Bill Hewlett described the 'HP Way' as 'policies and actions that flow from the belief that men and women want to do a good job, a creative job, and if provided with the proper environment, they will do so. Closely coupled with this is the HP tradition of treating each individual with consideration and respect, and recognising individual achievements.'

There is an emphasis on an inner core of shared values: trust, total integrity, teamwork in achieving common objectives, flexibility and innovation in responding to challenges. HP introduced 'management by objectives' in the 1950s, working on the principle that day-to-day decisions are best made by those closest to the action – a view that many big corporations are only just coming around to.

At the same time, it pre-empted the development of the stakeholder concept by formalising the corporate objectives that outlined goals in terms of not just profit but also such areas as customers, fields of interest, growth, people, management and citizenship.

In the 1980s the group introduced a then little-known concept called Total Quality Management in a joint venture in Japan. It led to a dramatic turnaround and was quickly spread across the whole company to great effect.

The HP tradition of first name informality goes back to the company's origins, while the company-wide profit-sharing plan dating from 1962 has its roots in a production bonus established at the outset.

Grass-roots creativity is encouraged at HP Labs, the central research organisation that has a key site in Bristol and provides selected scientists with the funds to investigate their own ideas.

Human Resources

HP is noted for its enlightened attitude to human resources. In the beginning, it decided not to take on large contracts that could lead to 'hire and fire' employment instability. And in 1970, when the deteriorating economy led to a sharp fall in orders, it introduced a nine-day fortnight, with a 10% cut in work and pay for all managers, in order to avoid the need for enforced redundancies. Furthermore, the founders rejected offers for the company because they did not want employees exposed to new employers' unknown motives and decisions.

When times have been hard management has always chosen to reduce costs in as many ways as possible, but to accelerate training and development in anticipation of the upturn.

The 1995 rise in net earnings of more than 50% was achieved with just a 4% increase in the workforce. 'That's a real tribute to HP's people, who continued to show tremendous skill, energy and resource-fulness in anticipating and responding to customer needs,' said chief executive Lew Platt.

But such a performance also raises issues of productivity, fairness and reward. 'Productivity in the 1990s requires more than laptop com-puters and voicemail,' says the company. 'It means enabling employees to stay creative and motivated by providing support and tools that help people balance the demands of work, family and other commitments.'

The company has pioneered the concept of flexible working hours, and in 1995, after analysing the results of 14 trials involving more than 500 employees, HP implemented variable work schedules as an option available at all US sites. By the end of 1998 the proportion of the worldwide workforce using variable working arrangements, such as telecommuting, had reached about 20%.

HP has also joined the American Business Collaboration for Quality Dependent Care, a group that sponsors projects aimed at improving facilities for children and senior citizens in the communities where it operates.

In recent years, the company has become a powerful proponent of workforce diversity. In 1995 it set up the Diversity Leadership Council, a team of high-level managers from across business sectors, with the aim of strengthening its commitment to benefit from the ideas of women and of people of all nationalities, races and lifestyles. Such initiatives continue as a result of the senior management's conviction that 'diversity will provide the company with a strong competitive advantage'.

Career Opportunity and Development

HP regularly features among surveys of ideal employers as well as the lists of most admired companies. But the company insists that such showings will not lull it into complacency. 'We're obsoleting our own products by replacing them with better ones before competitors can, and we're asking basic questions about priorities and processes throughout the company. We know the formula for success in the future will be different from what it is today,' it says. But such changes are supported by the HP Way, which ensures that personal evolution, through continual training and development, will continue to be the engine of growth.

In the UK, HP recruits graduates for all of its main sites, including the sales headquarters in Bracknell, the Telecoms, Microwave and Systems facility at South Queensferry, near Edinburgh, the recently expanded Labs and Computer Peripherals operation, both based in Bristol, and the components operation in Ipswich. And it has demonstrated its commitment in this area by establishing graduate recruitment organisations for the UK and Europe.

Insiders talk eagerly of the chances to move from one part of the company to another as their careers progress as being a key factor in encouraging them to stay.

Remuneration

HP is highly competitive in pay and benefits, with a particular attraction being the profit share awarded across the company in the same proportions every six months. Since the scheme began in 1962 workers with at least six months' service have received an average of 6.75% of earnings through the bonus. In 1998, it accounted for just under 4% of the total pay bill.

The Future

In early 1998 Lew Platt coined a new 'big phrase' – 'The Power of One and the Best of Many' – to convey the idea that the company contained many diverse divisions covering a variety of businesses. Though each of these would be free to operate in different ways, and the way the business as a whole was run would always evolve, the HP brand meant that there must be certain shared values and processes. And that is the enduring power of the HP Way.

Homebase

Homebase is a market leader in DIY and garden centres. It is part of the J Sainsbury Group. Homebase sales in 1998 amounted to £1.2 billion, with operating profits at £55.5 million. Homebase employs 5,800 people full time, 11,160 part time.

Scorecard:

Remuneration and benefits	★★★★
Progressive attitude	★★★★
Opportunity for promotion	★★★★
Training, development and education	★★★★
Working atmosphere and environment	★★★★

Biggest plus:
A warm and friendly company in touch with market trends

Biggest minus:
Operates in a market changing faster than ever before

Homebase Limited
Beddington House
Railway Approach
Wallington
Surrey SM6 OHB
Tel: 0181 784 7200
Fax: 0181 784 7755
website: www.homebase.co.uk

Homebase

The Business

Homebase was founded 17 years ago by J Sainsbury plc, with the aim of applying the skills of supermarket retailing to DIY. From modest beginnings – one store in Croydon – Homebase expanded rapidly to hold the position of equal fourth in the DIY sector.

Four years ago, Homebase had the opportunity to buy Texas Home-care: an unusual opportunity, since Texas was the larger company. Homebase seized this opening, and for the last three years has focused on integrating the Texas business into its operations. Today, the combined organisation has a nationwide network of nearly 300 stores from Truro to Elgin and holds about a 27% share of the home improvement and garden products superstore market.

In recent years, the DIY market has changed dramatically, fuelled (or reflected) by TV programmes such as *Better Homes* and *Changing Rooms*. Home refurbishment is now a far more acceptable and widespread hobby than in the past. People are redecorating on average every three years instead of every eight years, as was the case when Homebase was founded. Fashions and trends are more apparent, and the pace of change is increasing all the time. Homebase, centred on the decorative end of the business, is well positioned to maximise these changes.

Company Culture and Style

Homebase has a reputation for being a very friendly company. Judith Evans came from Sainsbury's to join the company as its new HR director. 'I found it very warm and welcoming from day one. The people here genuinely seem to want to help make your job work.'

The company is not hierarchical, and indeed is quite relaxed in terms of status. Clothing is smart rather than stiff or formal. Perhaps the dominant cultural element is that Homebase is a 'can do' organisation. Many new recruits are surprised at how much they can achieve; that's because they are empowered early in their careers and don't need to wait for permission to take decisions.

The integration of Texas has led to some cultural changes. But Homebase has managed these well, being determined to retain its small company feel within what is now a large organisation. That feel includes rapid response, quick lines of decision-making and the desire to treat its people as individuals.

Homebase is of course a retail organisation, and this drives its culture. Judith Evans: 'We need people who are practical, and who like to get things done. This is a fast-moving and competitive market. But we also want people who are innovative and prepared to change things where necessary.'

People certainly seem to enjoy working at Homebase. Being part of a Homebase store typically means working with anything from 40 to 120 others and contributing to the team spirit. The working atmosphere is excellent. Many of the people who work for Homebase are also passionate about DIY, and clearly relish being able to work in such an environment.

The style of Homebase is constantly changing as the market changes. Lots of work was done in 1998, for instance, to manage change. This included initiatives such as staff councils called 'News and Views' whereby every department, office and depot was represented, and employees were encouraged to raise issues which could improve the business. This produced a lot of positive feedback. In addition, the company is introducing a new business planning process, designed to continually align overall business objectives with personal objectives.

Human Resources

The importance of HR within Homebase was recognised in 1998 with the appointment of its first board-level HR director. Indeed, of its three key corporate objectives, one is about the importance of its people. Clearly, HR has a high priority at Homebase.

Within the people objective, Homebase strives to put in place an effective infrastructure for coping with change. It has invested considerably in training. For instance, within the garden centres, the horticultural training is first class, allowing the staff to give customers outstanding advice whenever they need it. Training programmes also run right through from the shop floor to the highest levels of management.

The ethos for such substantial investment in training is simple: Homebase believes that high-performance people produce a high-performance company.

Career Opportunity and Development

There are significant opportunities for both promotion and personal development within Homebase. Within almost every store there are people who began as part-timers and have moved on to the highest levels. The company is always looking for people who are prepared to grow and develop. There are also opportunities for store staff to move to the head office, or elsewhere within the J Sainsbury Group.

DIY and garden centres have a strong seasonal bias, which explains the large number of part-time staff employed by the company. But it also takes on many A-level school leavers and a number of graduates as retail managers in training. The early days will combine getting a feel for retailing with substantial training – not surprising when one considers that the average Homebase store has 20,000 products. Garden centre recruits attend courses at Hadlow College, leading to a nationally recognised qualification. However, the future trend at Homebase will be to ensure that new recruits learn about all elements, providing more rounded individuals, multi-skilled in all areas of the business.

Everyone within the company has an annual appraisal: and anyone with drive and who develops commercial acumen will get on. Ability and of course ambition are the only requirements for career development. The appraisal includes a career development section which allows employees to state how they wish their careers to progress. With the business continuing to expand, there are naturally more opportunities for everyone.

Katharine Darley is a garden centre manager in Penge. 'My background is in marketing, but I switched to Homebase to combine my business and leisure interests (plants and gardens), and never looked back. The real fun comes in the bedding season in April, when trolleys full of plants practically fly out of the door. But all year long you see the results of good ordering, displays and maintenance. Your takings and growth percentages are an accurate reflection of how well you're doing on all these fronts, and I find that very satisfying.'

Paul Durrant is deputy DIY manager at Kingston. 'What I like most about the job is developing staff who have little or no retail or DIY knowledge, and helping them grow in confidence and ability. A lot of it isn't direct training, it's communication. For example, we have "walk and talk" sessions where I focus on a certain product and discuss what you'd use it for, what the most common questions are, and so on.'

Training is competence-based, so anyone with any weaknesses can correct them. The DIY stores run a programme with Manchester Open Learning, their equivalent of the Hadlow courses. Homebase has also participated in the Sainsbury's MBA programme. Training is both in-house and external.

Remuneration

Homebase offers a competitive salary package which is benchmarked against other DIY stores and against other retailers.

There is also an excellent set of benefits. This includes profit-sharing for all permanent staff after one year's service; a pension scheme (and the opportunity to make AVCs) for all permanent staff after five years' service; a SAYE scheme; a 10% Discount Card for use at Homebase, J Sainsbury and Savacentre; holiday allowance rising to 27 days a year; sickness benefit; health maintenance plans; personal insurance; a discount on private medical insurance; legal expenses insurance; professional fee reimbursement; paternity leave; pre-retirement courses; and sports and social facilities. Many store managers get a company car, and managers of larger stores can earn a bonus based on company performance.

The Future

This is undoubtedly an exciting time to work for Homebase. The market is lively and there is a great deal happening on both the DIY and garden centre fronts. The challenge for the company is to be able to keep pace with the rapid changes in its marketplaces; however, its record to date, and especially over the last few years, suggests that it should be able to take this challenge in its stride.

Huxley Associates

Huxley Associates is a specialist IT recruitment consultancy with annual turnover in excess of £13 million. Huxley Associates employs highly experienced consultants working in specialist teams covering specific business and technical/IT areas. It is particularly strong in banking and finance. The head office is in the City, but it is extending its UK coverage all the time and has recently opened offices in Manchester and Reading. The growing size of Huxley Associates' workforce currently numbers around 125 people.

Scorecard:

Remuneration and benefits	★★★★★
Progressive attitude	★★★★
Opportunity for promotion	★★★★★
Training, development and education	★★★★
Working atmosphere and environment	★★★★

Biggest plus:
Tremendous opportunities. Sometimes like being self-employed, but within the supportive framework of a growing business

Biggest minus:
Targets. Pressure. Targets. Pressure

Huxley Associates
America House
2 America Square
London EC3N 2AH
Tel: 0171 335 0005
Fax: 0171 335 0008
e-mail: jobs@huxley.co.uk

Huxley Associates

The Business

Privately owned Huxley Associates is a very young company. It was established in 1995 by Gary Elden, a consultant working for a large IT-based recruitment group. Fighting against the recession in the early 1990s, he took the opportunity to build networks of contacts and clients and by the time the recession was over, he had fostered strong loyalties between consultant and client – a philosophy that has remained with Huxley Associates today.

Huxley Associates is extremely fast growing and the figures speak for themselves. Turnover in 1996 was £1.7 million; in 1997 it had nearly tripled to £4.9 million. By 1998 this had surged to £13.4 million, and the curve is upward.

Huxley Associates specialises only in IT recruitment. Given the explosion of demand for specialists in all areas of computing and information technology, that's a pretty good business to be in.

Huxley Associates provides its clients with either permanent or contract staff, as required, and separates its operations into the banking & finance and commercial sectors. Contract recruitment is probably the fastest growing, most profitable sector of IT recruitment at the moment, and accounts for 60% of all Huxley placements.

Huxley Associates' range of services includes consultancy, interview and selection, search, advertising and database. Huxley covers most technical areas of systems integration, development, computer programming and support.

Company Culture and Style

Huxley's mission is 'To become the UK's No. 1 IT recruitment consultancy by working as one company, harnessing our power and potential to increase the profitability of us all, creating opportunities and enjoying what we do, and providing our clients and candidates with a service that far exceeds their expectations.'

This is the definitive 'work hard, play hard' culture. The work hard part involves meeting targets that are set quite high. But there's enough incentive to do so – higher remuneration and promotion, as well as other more spontaneous rewards, including weekends and trips away, for individuals, teams or the whole company.

Huxley Associates looks for bright, self-motivated people. Almost mandatory, because this is a high expectation, high pressure environment. 'The rules are working hours of 9 to 6, lunch between 1 and 2. The rest is up to you,' says managing director Gary Elden. 'You can do the minimum amount but very few do, as they want to excel. We provide a desk, and a lot of support, and then it's like running your own business.'

Respect is a prominent word in Huxley Associates' vocabulary. Peer group respect within the company is very important, as is respect for and from clients and in the marketplace generally. 'We're proud of the fact that very few people leave Huxley to join other recruitment consultancies, even though they could walk into them,' says Gary Elden. 'But we rarely take people from other consultancies.'

'It's like a family here,' says Sandy Sood, senior manager. 'Everyone likes working here and it's very supportive.'

Strong client relationships lie at the heart of Huxley's success. The company's established client base is very loyal, and Huxley's client-focused approach requires that its consultants always pull out the stops to deliver results.

In a business which is renowned for its electrifying pace, high earnings potential and pressure deadlines, Huxley Associates wants to be number one – not only in terms of clients, profits and turnover, but in the type of work it does. 'I always believe that you should enjoy what you are doing,' says Gary Elden, 'and that inevitably has the consequence that people produce better quality work.'

This is a very young company. 'I'm the oldest here,' says Gary Elden, 'and from the look on their faces, interviewees didn't expect to see a 31-year old managing director!'

And of course the second half of the 'work hard, play hard' deal is often evident. Particularly when targets are met, there have been trips to Amsterdam, Barcelona, FA Cup Finals, go-karting, and London's top restaurants. 'The social life is unbelievable', according to Huxley's energetic people.

Human Resources

People are vital to Huxley Associates' success. It's all that the business is, effectively, and their calibre, speed, professionalism and hunger have contributed to making Huxley Associates one of the leading IT recruitment consultancies in the UK.

And in a successful, growing company, people are joining all the time.

Personnel – personal would be more appropriate – management is presently handled by line and senior managers. Meeting the expectations of people, so that the needs of the business are met first and then individuals' second, is the most challenging task and the biggest frustration. But with so many sectors of the market for IT professionals still not reached by Huxley, it intends to meet people's expectations for at least the next ten years.

Some 95% of new joiners enter at trainee recruitment consultant level. Generally they are graduates or graduate calibre, but this is just how it turns out and is not by design or decree. They most likely will have two years' sales experience in business or industry-related areas, where they will have demonstrated achievement, or client-handling expertise.

Career Opportunity and Development

Huxley provides extensive training, both internally and externally, in sales, business, industry and technical areas. Huxley people must understand IT, business and sales. And people.

When individuals meet the required criteria, Huxley will start preparing them and getting them involved. Typically, it will be a year before they get to meet clients, and after that, progression is to consultant.

No-one joins as a manager, only as a recruitment consultant. The step from consultant to manager should take two years for talented people with drive and ambition, and one or two exceptional individuals have achieved it more quickly. The only variable is the ability to deliver results – nothing else matters.

Rob Tillett, for example, after less than three years with Huxley, was handed the task of opening, building and developing the new Manchester office with a team of 15 people. Sandy Sood came from a medical recruitment background and within a year at Huxley was running the biggest team in the company.

'Essentially we encourage "intrapreneurs",' says Gary Elden. 'The way we are set up, people can effectively run their own business within a business.'

Everyone has both role and responsibility and Huxley Associates supports its staff fully. Its advertising spend in the computing and IT press is very high measured on a 'per-employee' basis, giving consultants every opportunity to earn higher rewards.

Remuneration

Huxley Associates actively encourages its people to earn money because this is also good for the firm, and for really high achievers there are few boundaries. Earnings are a combination of basic salary and a commission structure, which can allow almost limitless opportunity. Employees qualify for company cars at varying grades.

The IT recruitment business is one of the best-paid industries at present. But this is not a place for bandwagon jumpers. There is a lot of pressure – on deadlines, on performance, and on meeting clients' needs – and Huxley people work incredibly hard. And you must be good. There are no short-cuts.

The Future

Huxley Associates wants to continue creating enough opportunities for its people. That means expansion, initially in the UK, where potentially Huxley might open up to ten offices. Beyond that, perhaps Europe. Managing director Gary Elden says this is a market he wants to hit, and intends to do so in the next few years. Huxley Associates can also maximise the number of business sectors it provides IT recruitment services in, without ever compromising its determination to be the best and always serve its loyal client base with dedication.

Huxley Associates' future growth will depend on good people coming through the system – senior consultants and team leaders pushing the managers hard. In a dynamic, hungry company there seems little chance of this not happening, and Huxley Associates looks set to go from strength to strength.

Hyder plc

Hyder provides high quality infrastructure services, financing, designing, developing, managing and advising on infrastructure both nationally and internationally. It also runs a successful integrated multi-utility business in the UK.

Scorecard:

Remuneration and benefits ★★★★
Progressive attitude ★★★★
Opportunity for promotion ★★★★
Training, development and education ★★★★★
Working atmosphere and environment ★★★★

Biggest plus:
A company where people are highly valued

Biggest minus:
Operates in highly competitive markets worldwide

Hyder plc
PO Box 295
Alexandra Gate
Rover Way
Cardiff CF2 2UE
Tel: 01222 500600
Fax: 01222 585600
website: www.hyder.co.uk

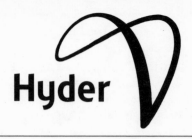

Hyder plc

The Business

Hyder's business is infrastructure: water and waste water, electricity and gas, roads and railways, ports and airports. Indeed, it is the UK's first truly integrated utility company, providing water, waste water treatment, electricity and gas services to customers. Its water business alone serves over three million customers in Wales and parts of England.

Successful though these operations are, however, they are just a part of Hyder's business activities. Formed following the privatisation of Welsh Water, the company made a strategic decision to move from being solely a player in the Welsh water industry to being a provider of infrastructure services. To this end, it acquired an international engineering consulting firm with an excellent performance record. It also acquired Swalec in the mid 1990s in a process known as a 'mergeover' rather than a takeover: recognition that Hyder's aim was not to override Swalec's culture but to take the best from both companies.

Today, the 9,500 Hyder employees work in a range of business areas. Hyder's industrial business provides water and wastewater infrastructure services to private sector organisations, enabling them to outsource non-core activities to reduce costs and meet stringent environmental standards. Its consulting arm designs, builds, finances and operates water and other utility infrastructure projects in 35 countries. Its investment business is involved in key projects such as constructing and maintaining an extension of the Docklands Light Railway in London, and assisting the China Water Company. And it operates an infrastructure management service, conducting mechanical and electrical maintenance services for clients such as the Ministry of Defence.

Company Culture and Style

The company's culture has changed dramatically since privatisation. From an organisation often described as bureaucratic, conservative and autocratic, Hyder today is responsive, concerned and aware. The employees are encouraged to think of themselves as owning the company, and excessive status and hierarchy are certainly things of the past. The company name itself underlines the change: Hyder is derived from the Greek word for water, but is also the Welsh word for confidence. This is very much what the modern company is about. The company is confident about itself; but it is also keen to foster self-confidence in its employees, both in the way they treat their fellow staff members and in the approach they take to customers.

Noel Hufton, director, group development, has a series of key company characteristics which sum up the culture. These include a view of the structure as providing a framework, not a cage; as being enabling, not prescriptive; and moving from procedures to processes. Instead of status as a result of seniority, managers seek to earn the respect of their staff. To sum up, the atmosphere has changed from one of suspicion to one of trust, with people being treated as equals.

Hyder people feel confident with change. Around 56% of employees still work in utility operations in Wales, but others are deployed in the new commercial business areas – with several thousand people working outside the UK. This has led to a big change in how and where Hyder employees work, but the atmosphere of mutual trust and harmony in its industrial relations has allowed this shift to be relatively painless.

The company has a strong community ethic. Its businesses themselves are directly concerned with improving the quality of people's lives. But that's just the start. Hyder has also set up a project on benefit and debt counselling, has strong links with schools and runs education centres, supports the Lifelong Learning Centre at University College, Swansea and has endowed a chair of Organisational Learning in Glamorgan. It also runs programmes called 'Confidence in the Community' and 'Confidence in Youth'. The latter is an annual international programme which takes up to 40 people to age 27 on a team-building trip.

Human Resources

An indication of the importance of HR at Hyder is that the personnel director has sat on the equivalent of the executive board of the company since 1985. Throughout this time, the company has conducted substantial training for its senior management, beginning with the theme 'Awareness and choice equal change'. Overall, the company considers good HR practices as significant as its financial strength. Noel Hufton: 'People are our greatest asset. Lots of companies say that, but it must be *meant*. We really do mean what we say.'

Support for that view comes from the company's attitude surveys, held every 18 months. These show strong satisfaction with the company's approach to HR, the way it encourages an association of equals, and its ability to communicate at all levels.

Career Opportunity and Development

For the last ten years, Hyder has used a 'Capability Map', designed in conjunction with a company of business psychologists as a way of avoiding strategic risk in organisations. This model explores the strategic demands on a business and contrasts these with the supply of capability. The gap is the HR agenda. As a result, developmental training at Hyder is done on a similar supply and demand basis, making it strongly strategically focused. This approach assesses people against a series of mindsets, measuring thinking style, personality, behavioural type and so on.

The result is a profile combining those measures. Individuals are then well placed to put together a personal development plan, aided by their managers, and other directors are tasked with making those plans happen, often by doing 'people trades'.

Hyder sees its workforce as being made up of three populations. The first comprises senior people already in place, and training for them focuses on what they need. Then there are people in their late 20s or early 30s with strong potential. These are identified, then invited to join a fast-track development programme called 'Managing Beyond 2000'. The third group, aged 18–25, forms the basis of its youth programmes. Talented individuals from this group usually end up in the second one.

The company offers lots of opportunities for overseas working. It is also going to some lengths to overcome its more parochial past. For instance, a recent senior managers' conference was held in Geneva, a deliberate move to reinforce the fact that the company is no longer centred on Welsh or even UK business. An increasing number of jobs are beyond the UK and even beyond Europe. Its work on the Kowloon West Railway in Hong Kong, for example, drew together a team made up of British, Thai, Australian and other nationalities, with even Kazakhstan represented as well as local Chinese. In today's Hyder, personal development increasingly doubles up with career development.

Careers at Hyder are very much what you make of them. Individuals are empowered to develop as far as they want to. Central to this is its 'Learning Journey': a whole range of ways to grow in one or more of the company's ten mindsets. This module-based growth can include courses, mentors, distance learning and online, and many of them include some sort of accreditation through the University of Glamorgan, the University of Hong Kong or elsewhere. For instance, the top level of the strategic mindset is an in-house MBA. The key point, though, as the company says, is that learning builds confidence – and your future is up to you.

Remuneration

Hyder conducts a benchmarking survey of remuneration and constructs a formula based on the RPI in conjunction with the University of Cardiff Business School. This results in the company being a very good payer overall, with upper decile pay for its manual workers and at least upper quartile for higher levels. There may also be tax-free profit-related bonus pay.

Benefits include various good pension schemes, life cover, a car scheme (which unlike some employers goes a long way down the organisation, and also offers some flexibility for senior managers), and a range of other non-cash rewards commensurate with a top employer.

The Future

Hyder sees the future as very much about growing its non-regulated businesses. These already contribute 21% of its profits, and they are likely to become even more important in the years ahead. The consultancy industry is hugely competitive worldwide, but Hyder retains an advantage in this area due to its impressive skill base and experience around the globe.

The company intends to grow, in order to maximise the surging demand for infrastructure worldwide; to initiate new infrastructure projects; and to continue to invest in infrastructure, but in a relatively less passive way by bringing its experience in managing long-life assets to the world of project finance.

Hyder has developed strong positioning in the 'green energy' market and in bespoke water cycle management and effluent treatment processes for blue-chip clients.

The managed services market is proving to be an important growth area for Hyder Services and IT business with activity concentrated on the NHS, local government and utility sectors.

The company's highly effective transition from a bureaucratic company to a privatised powerhouse with wide and global ambitions would suggest that it will continue to be successful in the future.

IBM

IBM Corporation is a global information technology company serving more than a billion customers in 163 countries with information technology products, services and solutions. It is the largest computer company in the world – revenues worldwide in 1998 exceeded $80 billion. IBM's operations in the UK, including services, sales, distribution, manufacturing and development, are organised into a number of business units serving customers with a tailored portfolio of products and services.

Scorecard:

Remuneration and benefits	★★★★
Progressive attitude	★★★★★
Opportunity for promotion	★★★★
Training, development and education	★★★★
Working atmosphere and environment	★★★★

Biggest plus:
Effectively a new company, but still the biggest and one of the best

Biggest minus:
Not exactly 'on your own', but a lot of self-reliance required

IBM United Kingdom Limited
PO Box 41
North Harbour
Portsmouth
Hampshire PO6 3AU
Tel: 01705 561000
Fax: 01705 388914
website: www.ibm.com/ukjobs

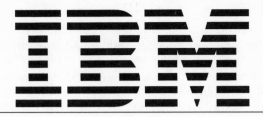

IBM

The Business

In the rapidly changing world of information technology, few organisations have changed as quickly – or as radically – as IBM. 'The New Blue', as the company announced itself in 1997, is still the world's largest IT services, consulting, software and hardware company. It has always set out to define standards rather than follow them, which has meant exploring new ideas, pursuing unconventional approaches, and challenging conventional thinking.

IBM definitely 'blipped' in the 1980s, which led eventually to major restructuring in 1993. Now it has refocused away from hardware and PCs (although IBM did invent the PC back in 1981), to a new emphasis first on solutions and then on services. Much of its business is now driven through IBM Global Services, which works from a single point of contact and is aligned by industry to sell IBM's range of services and solutions to clients.

The company is now organised into four main areas: Global Services, including business and IT consultancy (forming around half of the company); Sales & Distribution; Manufacturing; and Development. IBM Global Services in its own right is the biggest IT services company in the world.

In the jargon-rich world of IT, 'e-business' is a buzz phrase which IBM has claimed as its own (with some attention-grabbing TV advertisements). 'e-business' refers to the value which can be derived from networked computing and the proliferation of networked transactions of every kind. IBM now completes thousands of e-business assignments each year and e-business has become a powerful unifying message for IBM itself.

Company Culture and Style

In recent years, IBM people have worked hard to reinvent not just the mechanics of their work, but the soul of their company

'Teamwork across business units and geographies is the only way we can leverage the breadth of IBM's global skills, services and solutions. In this way, we put the best teams in front of the customer every time and ensure our profitable growth,' according to Mike Lawrie, general manager, Europe, Middle East & Africa.

IBM has perhaps one of the most diverse workforces in the world – a workforce driven by a passionate commitment to teamwork, communication and continuous learning. The types of people who work at IBM are described as resourceful, innovative, enthusiastic, proactive and decisive.

Individuals enjoy high levels of responsibility, a chance to make a real contribution to a modern business and leading-edge technical issues. The work is challenging, and can be inspiring, as groundbreaking solutions are explored in search of answers to questions yet to be asked. At IBM, people have the freedom to define their own role and career path in an environment where excellence is judged on talent, results and commitment.

Perhaps IBM was once too inward-facing. It is now outward-looking, focused on its share price, with principles of operation which go down the organisation. Not that there's too far to go down – IBM today is a much flatter structure, with only four levels between a group director and any employee.

Graduate joiners are sometimes asked whom they compare IBM to. The answers are that it used to be 'box' manufacturers but today is more likely to be firms like Andersen Consulting.

There is fun at work, and the social scene helps with networking. A lot is expected of people and with a lot of movement on sites with customers, people are trusted to be 'mature' at work.

Human Resources

As you would expect with a company of this size, the human resources function is extremely important and the HR director sits on the UK board. 'Our overall mission is to provide policies for a happy, motivated workforce, so that they feel valued,' says Ann Grinstead, HR director. 'It's also about providing guidance, because the key relationship is still with the line manager.'

For example, on remuneration IBM's global philosophy is to look at local rates in pay markets, but each manager then has some scope within the guidelines to pay good contributors well.

And again, HR will help provide individuals with a framework for their careers and a broad back-up skills profile. It is then down to the individual to progress this with their manager, planning their progress to get where they want to be.

IBM's UK workforce of about 23,000 people is a mix of some 19,000 full time employees, supported by contractors, consultants, students and subcontractors. They are found in various locations throughout the UK, including most of the main commercial centres.

Recruitment is a *very* big activity. In the UK, IBM takes on no fewer than 400 graduates each year straight from university, and around 1,800 experienced hires.

Career Opportunity and Development

'A career in IBM is not so much climbing a ladder, but more like gaining a reputation for making things happen. It's a track record of achievements, where we all understand our goals and are committed to achieving them,' says Ann Grinstead.

Because of the growth in services and outsourcing, IBM requires a broad range of IT skills, including applications development, systems integration, network services, product support and programming. In fact, this is one of the most diverse and dynamic career environments imaginable. Graduates from various disciplines will find many challenging roles in IT services, software development, sales, marketing, consultancy, finance, manufacturing and customer support – just about anything in fact.

But people are not expected to be employed into a job and then stay there. Each individual has the responsibility for mapping his or her direction and maintaining a currency of skills. Of course, there is always a balance between the needs of the business and the aspirations of the individual.

Training at IBM is very high quality and whatever a person's degree subject, they will need to acquire strong technical skills. IBM Global Services, for example, has set up the Foundation Group with the specific objective of equipping graduates with the skills required to build rewarding careers. Graduates will spend two years in foundation, but training and development is a process which applies to everyone throughout their career and is ably supported by IBM.

IBM maintains a wide open internal job market over the Internet and Lotus Notes. 'We want the best person for the job at all times,' says Louise Hawkins, UK recruitment manager. 'It's a totally free market, and no ''blocking'' is allowed.'

There was previously a reluctance at IBM to do anything other than 'grow your own'. But any growing business also recruits from outside and IBM is no exception. There is now more of a mix, especially at senior level where people with ability to grow the business have been brought in.

International opportunities will vary with each job, but with so many global clients, many people keep their passport in their desk drawer. Short-term or customer assignments are commonplace, and there are longer-term postings.

Each person's work allegiance is to an individual business, for example IBM Global Services, and the country you work in is only for administration. 'It could be that your first or second line manager is in a different country, and so national boundaries are almost irrelevant,' says Ann Grinstead. You can certainly enjoy a global career with IBM as part of a European or global team. Video conferencing and telecommunications all facilitate international teamworking as a way of life.

Remuneration

In the broadest sense, IBM favours performance-related pay, modified for individual contribution and market rates. The variable element of pay is based on the business performance of the whole of IBM, supporting the concept of 'Team IBM' in its widest definition, and individual contribution. Sales jobs carry incentive arrangements and there are various share option schemes.

Benefits packages include company pension, health cover, company bonus schemes, sickness and accident cover, travel accident cover and various awards and recognition schemes.

The Future

IBM is very conscious of the trends towards work/life balance. 'We didn't realise how far forward we were until we compared IBM with others,' commented Ann Grinstead. IBM is well along the track towards this balance, and more flexible working practices such as homeworking are likely to increase. Getting employees to feel more committed to IBM makes life easier for all and the company is trying to shift its culture to one of empowerment and ownership, concerned only that the job gets done.

Retention of people with key skills will remain central. IBM is aware of the shortages in the market for many IT skill sets, and with the company needing to recruit large numbers, it's task is obviously more difficult.

IBM has reinvented itself in recent times, and it certainly still finds itself at the heart of a high growth market. It will want to continue to change its image, aware that not everyone always thinks of IBM as a services and solutions company rather than a manufacturer of 'boxes'. But the business is in great shape, with services, software and hardware revenue all growing. IBM's comeback – in the marketplace and inside IBM – is firmly on track.

ICI Group

The ICI Group is one of the world's largest speciality products, coatings and materials companies with an impressive record in innovation. ICI operates its main businesses on an international basis, with leading positions in paints, industrial adhesives, speciality starches, fragrances and flavours, catalysts, acrylics and other speciality chemicals. The ICI Group has some 60,000 employees worldwide (15,000 in the UK), over 10,000 products, and more than 200 manufacturing sites and offices in over 30 countries. In 1997, it reported trading profits of £418 million on turnover of £10.7 billion.

Scorecard:
Remuneration and benefits	★★★
Progressive attitude	★★★★
Opportunity for promotion	★★★★
Training, development and education	★★★★
Working atmosphere and environment	★★★★

Biggest plus:
A proud but revitalised company with a clear vision of its future

Biggest minus:
Further to go, a lot of hard work lies ahead

ICI Group Headquarters
Imperial Chemicals House
9 Millbank
London SW1P 3JF
Tel. 0171 834 4444
Fax 0171 834 2042
website: www.ici.com
e-mail: ici@ici.com

ICI Group

The Business

Once the bellwether of British industry, ICI has recently undergone a major reshaping of its operations. In 1997 it acquired Unilever's speciality chemicals business, bringing National Starch (starch, adhesives, speciality resins, electronic materials), Quest (fragrances and food flavours), Unichema (oleochemicals) and Crosfield (silica and alumini derivatives) into its fold. On its 'reverse shopping list', ICI sold its polyester fibre, feedstock and titanium dioxide businesses and its shareholding in ICI Australia.

'ICI's willingness to change has been a strength of the company since its foundation,' says Sir Ronald Hampel, chairman. 'We now have accepted the reality of the decline of cyclical commodity chemicals in the face of global competition. We are therefore bound on a path to transform ICI into a speciality products company where our traditional science, innovation and manufacturing skills can be directed at real differentiated value to our customers.'

The requirement now is more on innovation and creativity in satisfying niche requirements, as opposed to the 'pile it high, sell it cheap' style sometimes associated with commodity products.

The modern ICI is still a leading international organisation, with global businesses multi-cultural in make-up, but now with a stronger North American swing. American job titles have appeared on business cards.

Company Culture and Style

Chief executive Charles Miller Smith's personal style has already made its mark in accelerating culture change and in liberating the talents of ICI staff. In particular, he has forged the 'ICI Vision', in the broadest terms to be the industry leader in creating value for customers and shareholders.

It begins with market-driven innovation in products and services. Each business is responsible for implementing the technology strategy for its own market, with the centre facilitating the sharing of ideas and expertise between businesses. The second value is to win in quality growth markets worldwide – ones where ICI holds strong positions.

The third value is ICI's belief that the inspiration and reward of talented people lies at the heart of the company's future success. If the quest is productivity improvements, the drive is to create a company where everyone knows what is expected of them, but also has the freedom to take initiatives and show creativity. Accountability for the result is matched with appropriate reward for achievement.

ICI also seeks an exemplary performance in safety and health, and responsible care for the environment. Finally, ICI is committed to the relentless pursuit of operational excellence, a drive for 'best in class', excelling in everything it does.

Miller Smith's vision and values have cascaded down the organisation rapidly. Its successful 'Q&A' live satellite hook-up of ICI sites around the world has 'gone down a storm' with its new companies. As ever, it is how vision and values are interpreted by people, and what they do with them, that matters.

The multinational make-up of ICI's top team is causing the culture to change, a process revitalised quite deliberately by adding senior people neither from ICI or Unilever. People have been brought in at all levels, particularly those who are interested in change, movement and creating 'a new way'. 'It can appear very exciting on one hand, bewildering on the other,' suggests Geoff Tudhope, VP, organisation development.

Human Resources

With such a mix of ancestry, the company has deliberately avoided saying 'now you've joined ICI, do it the way we do it'. Instead it has thrown all the balls into the air and taken an uncluttered look at best practices. 'The thing which prevent businesses from getting results is complexity,' suggests Joe McCollum, SVP, human resources.

The result is 'The ICI Way in HR', a process driven by business strategy and geared towards a results culture. It aims to deliver higher performance by combining best practices in business performance reviews, leadership and capability building, performance management, and rewards.

Whereas business performance is the short-term focus, the leadership and capability building 'cluster' is the most important and absolutely essential to the long-term future of the company; led by the chief executive, it is an integral part of the corporate calendar.

ICI leaders need to know how to make money, to span across cultures and issues, be knowledgeable and skilled, flexible, personally motivated, and able to inspire others. Control merchants could not work in the new environment which is ICI today.

HR's overall remit is to support the business strategy of the company. Geoff Tudhope suggests that meeting ICI's requirements to create the most value is about getting 'the right people, the right place, the right time, the right motivation'. HR occupies a lot of airtime at senior management meetings.

Employee survey issues are picked up quickly. The cascade process involves newsletters, noticeboards, corporate briefings, e-mail and Intranet communication. 'The Way Forward' global satellite link-up has become an annual event, but ICI stresses that there is no substitute for the face-to-face meeting of a work group with the leader playing a critical part in the process.

Career Opportunity and Development

The requirement to move across territories, functions and product lines for those with higher potential remains a way of life at ICI. The company is determined to utilise the best people right across the organisation and career development groups are geared to work across country, business and functional boundaries. Experience might be gained through secondments, short-term assignments and projects.

Careers often involve bigger jumps than before, for longer durations, which requires clear, long-term development plans for the individuals involved. But ICI also emphasises the increasing responsibility that individuals have to develop themselves.

Recognising that people cannot do this without the opportunity, the company's responsibility is to provide challenges to stretch individuals, help them improve their capabilities, and deliver results. 'People have to earn the right to get their next challenge by performing well in their current challenge,' says Geoff Tudhope.

Individuals must work through which skills and experiences they need to maximise their potential. ICI has introduced a sophisticated and well-received PC-based self-assessment toolkit for this purpose.

ICI recruits around 50 high-calibre graduates in the UK and many more overseas, in order to sustain a middle/senior management group in future years. ICI's graduate retention rate is good, reflecting good career opportunities, well-managed succession, international exposure, and excellent personal skills and competencies development.

Remuneration

ICI looks at compensation and benefits as a whole, benchmarking against the market of major blue-chip companies. The company continues to move more towards performance-related pay, and the variable element of pay is increasing, based on both individual and team performance.

The company provides the typical benefits package, including a SAYE share scheme and, as a supportive employer, a top quartile company pension scheme. ICI is seeking to share the gains of the company in the form of share options. These are presently available to the top 500 managers, but the company is looking to spread eligibility.

The Future

ICI's greatest business challenge remains to balance, constantly, growth and productivity. The former is now about reading markets, innovation, the harnessing of science, while raising productivity centres on getting more out of what it has got, leveraging best practices and becoming even more effective.

Then there's the hard work involved to ensure ICI stays on its chosen course, managing the many stresses and strains which could blow it off. Further disposals of commodity businesses are likely, as is a greater emphasis on speciality products.

ICI has a good opportunity to blend a 'new' company and 'old' ancestry to improve performance. In times of change, culture becomes a big issue, and ICI will strive to create a climate where people want to learn from one another, and feel free to offer. Mechanisms including workshops and gatherings are already in place. In searching for the new way, external hiring of talent in a 'flagship' approach features increasingly.

'Fresher eyes' will not join ICI unless they are comfortable with change. Many who have joined have brought some novel attitudes and refreshing perspectives on building careers, such as a greater concern with the nature of the challenge instead of job status; actively seeking virtual teamworking and multi-cultural working; and 'flip-flopping' between being a team member and a team leader.

That emphasises interpersonal abilities and a sensitivity to other people's agendas. It requires an ability to handle ambiguity – ICI is not a control centre now – and a willingness to combine with others towards a common purpose, with the confidence to work stand alone. Whilst many people excel in this environment, some are finding the transition less comfortable.

ICI a company in change. It is becoming more multi-cultural, North American rather than European, marketing-focused as opposed to plants and engineering, and results-oriented. Yet ICI has not lost sight of the people dimension and that its employees work hard to help each other. It remains an attractive, but different, company.

John Laing

John Laing is a major player in the construction and housing markets in the UK, with a growing number of operations overseas. The company now employs over 8,000 people worldwide and has managed to ride out the recessions of the 1990s.

Scorecard:

Remuneration and benefits	★★★★
Progressive attitude	★★★
Opportunity for promotion	★★★★
Training, development and education	★★★★
Working atmosphere and environment	★★★★

Biggest plus:
People choose the company because the construction industry excites them and it's an opportunity to leave their mark on the landscape

Biggest minus:
A certain amount of insecurity and people have to be prepared to be mobile

John Laing Limited
Page Street
Mill Hill
London NW7 2ER
Tel: 0181 959 3636
Fax: 0181 906 5297
website: www.Laing.co.uk

John Laing

The Business

John Laing is responsible for some of the UK's most significant modern construction projects, including the Second Severn Crossing and Greenwich Millennium Dome. Laing also utilises the latest technology and has just launched its redesigned website complete with five 360-degree interactive views of the Dome, which is currently under construction.

Recent major transport projects include widening the M40 between Junctions 1A and 3 and building part of the Heathrow Express link. Major clients include Asda, Ford, Whitbread, Grosvenor Estates and Marks & Spencer. Company profits for the first half of 1998 increased by 48% to £18.4 million with a turnover exceeding £1.4 billion. Few other companies offer such a complete range of services within a single organisation, ranging from civil engineering, infrastructure operations, building and management services to technology and capital investment in infrastructure.

The company has an outstanding record within the industry – it has twice been named Building Contractor of the Year during the nineties and Laing projects have secured the Supreme Award at the Annual British Construction Industry Awards four times in the past ten years. Despite its high-profile construction projects the company's roots originated in house building.

The first Laing home was built by James Laing in 1848 and still stands to this day, one of three detached houses built in a village near Carlisle. The business became a limited company in 1920 before relocating to Mill Hill, in north-west London, in 1926. Chairman Sir Martin Laing welcomes the opportunity to work on the government's Private Finance Initiative projects. 'The group is well positioned to respond to new opportunities for the transfer of services from the public sector to the private.'

There are currently four core elements to the business: Laing Limited, Laing Homes, Property Development and Project Infrastructure. The main part of the business, the construction operation, was restructured at the start of 1998 and is called Laing Limited.

'We've reorganised the whole construction operation,' says Andy Geldard, Laing's press officer. 'Laing Limited now provides clients with a seamless "one stop shop" to Laing's entire construction capability.' Laing Limited operates out of three regional centres based in London, Manchester and Birmingham; other locations with Laing offices include Newcastle, Bristol and Glasgow.

Company Culture and Style

John Laing is a solid, traditional organisation, which has retained its connection with the Laing family. The current chairman, Sir Martin Laing, is the grandson of Sir John Laing, who was responsible for building the Laing group into an international organisation.

Despite it's recent restructuring programme the foundations of the company are based on quality, reliability and craftsmanship. 'We restructured the company to improve efficiency. We found that a lot of companies were coming to us for the first time and didn't know about Laing,' says Andy Geldard. 'They found the internal structure confusing, as the different parts of the construction side were almost separate entities which were sometimes competing against each other. This has all changed with the arrival of Laing Limited.'

Long service and loyalty to the company are of paramount importance and promotion tends to be from within, particularly for the overseas positions. Environmental issues are also of prime importance to the company, and it aims to use recyclable materials, a degree of protection against harmful emissions and gives a high priority to creating energy efficient homes. Laing's environmental consultancy services are also in demand externally, currently being used by major banks on loan security assessment of potentially contaminated land and property. It has also carried out a recent assessment on a water recycling system which collects, stores, chemically treats and re-uses 'grey' water with a potential fresh water saving of 30%.

Human Resources

Communication is seen as the key to success, with staff at all levels being offered training and personal development schemes and the potential to be promoted within the company. The company is committed to a regular programme of improving communications through team briefings, group publications and appraising and counselling individual staff members.

The company recruits at four levels – craft trainees, day release trainees, sponsored undergraduates and graduates. Craft trainees between 16 and 17 years old with four GCSEs and over are offered apprenticeships leading to NVQ qualifications at levels 2 and 3. Day-release programme candidates need four GCSEs plus two A-levels to qualify for the three-year training programme. Sponsored undergraduates can apply before university or following a training placement with the company. Graduates in civil or mechanical engineering or quantity surveyors are eligible for the company's Graduate Development Scheme.

The company's internal magazine *Team Spirit* and its close ties with its retired employees are examples of the company's informative and approachable image.

Career Opportunity and Development

There are a number of avenues into the company and a choice of entry schemes. John Laing takes on between 60 and 70 trainees each year in the UK. Once candidates have completed their training they can apply to work overseas with many of the overseas positions advertised internally.

'The philosophy of the company has always been to promote from within,' says Peter Elliott, senior personnel manager. Proof of this is the fact that a significant proportion of promotion is internal. A measure of a company's attitude is how it treats its employees – most people stay with us, or if they leave they often come back,' says Peter Elliott.

There's a great emphasis on developing skills and actively encouraging employees to move locations as part of their career progression. Laing makes no secret of the fact that many jobs can be unpredictable, but equally this can prove an attraction. Peter Whitmore joined the company as a sponsored graduate in construction management. He's now in his first site management position, 'Following a spell as a quantity surveyor at a Halfords store in Southend, I worked on an office refurbishment at Harlow before being posted to the Laing plant yard at Borehamwood. This is not exactly a dull life!'

Remuneration

The average pay rise within the company has been around 2% over 1998. With an increasing number of its employees working overseas on designated projects, the company frequently offers tailor-made packages to suit individuals and rewards loyalty and hard work accordingly.

The principal company terms and conditions are a 37.5 hour working week for office-based staff and 40 hours a week for those on site. Annual leave is set at 25 days and is available for all staff employees for whom the company provides a non-contributory pension scheme. There is also a voluntary private medical scheme open to all management staff.

The company has an appraisal scheme with the aim of employees having one review each year. A performance plan is set with targets and training needs identified. This has recently formed part of a new system called 'Career Profile'.

The Future

Long-term predictions for the construction industry depend on the performance of the economy but Peter Elliott remains confident of the company's continued success. 'We can't divorce ourselves from the economic fortunes of the construction industry – if it goes into recession again we can't prevent the impact of that, but by going for bigger long-term jobs we can iron out the blips. We've got a pretty full order book at the moment and any minor blip during 1999 shouldn't impact upon us too much.'

Overseas projects include a new hospital in Hong Kong and a biological sciences complex at the University of Hong Kong. The British consulate in Hong Kong was also built by Laing, as was the Hong Kong Convention Centre.

Projects extend across South-east Asia. In the Philippines Laing is building the largest private construction project in the country – a joint venture with a local company which will provide a luxury apartment complex in Manila.

Laing pushes its employees hard but is equally supportive when helping them plan their future career within the company. Karen Manning is training to be a quantity surveyor and joined the company on a sponsorship programme: 'The company pays for me to attend the University of Greenwich on a day-release basis. As more and more females opt for management careers in this industry, I would recommend it to anyone who wants to do something which is varied, interesting and challenging.'

John Lewis Partnership

The John Lewis Partnership is a UK retailer which embraces the 25-strong department store chain, many of which operate under the John Lewis name, and Waitrose supermarkets, of which there were 117 at the end of 1998. The group also owns a farming estate in Hampshire and makes some of its own textiles, furniture and bedding in four factories. There are 45,000 staff, producing sales of more than £3 billion. The organisation is a private business which for 50 years has had a unique democratic structure in which all staff are 'partners' in policy-making and profit-sharing

Scorecard:

Remuneration and benefits	★★★
Progressive attitude	★★★★
Opportunity for promotion	★★★★
Training, development and education	★★★★
Working atmosphere and environment	★★★

Biggest plus:
Unique 'partnership' structure, giving everybody a say in the business and a share in profits

Biggest minus:
The partnership's strong traditions and formal constitution result in greater caution and formality than in most conventional companies

John Lewis Partnership
171 Victoria Street
London SW1E 5NN
Tel: 0171 828 1000
Fax: 0171 592 6301
website: johnlewis.co.uk

JOHN LEWIS PARTNERSHIP

John Lewis Partnership

The Business

John Lewis was a fabric buyer who set up his own shop in London in 1864. He subsequently bought the Peter Jones department store in Sloane Square, which became the basis of the current chain. He handed over control to his son, Spedan, who developed the unusual democratic principles which became fully enshrined in a Trust settlement in 1950. Additional department stores were acquired in the 1930s, as was the Waitrose grocery business, but the main expansion of both stores and supermarkets has been since the 1960s. Department stores now operate from Aberdeen to Southampton, while Waitrose is concentrated in the south.

Waitrose occupies an upmarket niche in the supermarket industry, and has prospered against the toughest competition by concentrating on quality foods. The department stores have stuck to their full-assortment philosophy while others have retreated to a fashion and houseware core, operating profitably on their 'never knowingly undersold' price promise and outstanding service levels by attracting high levels of customer traffic.

Company Culture and Style

Like all good retailers, John Lewis focuses on the shop floor and the customer. Most managers at all levels, except for specialist functions such as IT, have worked in the stores early in their careers. This shop-keeping culture is therefore deeply ingrained, key aspects being an emphasis on instinct and observation rather than analysis, an openness and responsiveness to customers and a habit of teamwork which is essential to make the shops operate effectively.

The partnership structure adds a unique dimension, although the associated principles of empowerment, consultation and inclusion are currently fashionable throughout the business world.

'Managers are accountable downwards as well as upwards,' explained Sally Carruthers, head of management development for the department stores. 'That means people have to manage in a different way – not by consensus or committee but by listening and making sure people understand.'

That can lead to stultification, especially given the strong sense of history in the group and the rule-book which ensures that the democratic principles are applied. A sense of this was seen in the BBC documentary on the stores a few years ago – so well-observed that it made insiders cringe and laugh at the same time, Sally Carruthers said.

But that documentary was a sign that things were changing, especially since the promotion of former civil servant Sir Stuart Hampson to chairman in 1993 (one of the occasional appointments of outsiders in their 30s). Sir Stuart has carried the message of partnership to the business world through his involvement in the Royal Society of Arts, but has also brought a whiff of fresh air into the stuffier corners of John Lewis, discouraging insularity and smugness and encouraging openness.

In the words of Sir Stuart: 'Employee ownership has the potential to appeal to the spiritual fulfilment of the employee as well as providing a route for building successful business for tomorrow.'

Sally Carruthers conceded, however, that the group still has a certain traditional feel to it, and that managers are likely to be less pressured than working for other major retailers. And she cites those as important advantages of working there, because they protect the invaluable reputation for customer service. 'Our reputation is built on the customers' belief that they can trust us and they feel they are being looked after. And I would hope that our managers are not under the same profit pressure as others because there has got to be enjoyment at work and the thing that matters most is our people. The company doesn't exist without people. If you start from that, making a profit is something you choose to do, not something that is driven by others.'

That doesn't mean the partnership is uninterested in profit, as the results show. Profits in 1997/8 increased by 15% to £250 million.

Human Resources

Retailing is about as much a people business as you can get, so John Lewis pays plenty of attention to its people. And the paternalistic tradition of Spedan Lewis means that extends from professional recruitment and training methods to a plethora of subsidised clubs and societies (including two country clubs and two holiday centres). A 'long leave' of up to six months is also available to partners who have completed 25 years' service.

It would be an exaggeration to suggest that human resources is the most important function at John Lewis – as a retailer, buying and selling are the key functions. But the group invests substantial sums in recruiting the best personnel, understanding and providing for their training needs, and planning to put the right people in the right jobs at the right time.

The group has a fairly flat management structure but its steady expansion means there is a continual demand for new managers, so there are continued opportunities for people to move around and up the business. In 1999 two new department stores opened, in Glasgow and at the new Bluewater Park regional shopping centre on the south side of the Thames estuary by the M25. Each has a management team of nearly 50, and most of them will come from within the business.

Many of these managers will be women. John Lewis does not entirely escape the traditional pattern of having far fewer women in senior management than lower down the hierarchy, but about a third of store bosses are female, compared with 70% of all management positions.

Career Opportunity and Development

The group recruits separately for the department stores and the food shops, and in two streams for the stores. Waitrose takes in 30–40 graduates a year, while the John Lewis chain recruits 25–30 graduates centrally and a further 100 or so locally. The idea of the separate streams is that the high flyers join in the shops. They follow a traditional multi-department training course, and are expected to become manager of one of the store departments (such as sports or china and glassware) within 18 months.

Those recruited locally are not expected to achieve such a position for three years, but in practice the development is fluid, with some from local recruitment beating some of the central recruits.

Once they have become department managers, the group is their oyster. John Lewis does not believe in fixed career paths, but does still stick to close monitoring of achievement and potential rather than the trendy notion of self-managed careers. But managers are expected to move across disciplines and from the stores into central functions such as HR.

Remuneration

John Lewis operates a unique bonus scheme, under which every partner receives the same proportion of pay as an annual bonus. The proportion is agreed each year following preparation of the annual accounts, and everybody from the lowliest sales assistant to the chairman receives the same proportion of their pay – the average over the past five years has been 16% or two months' pay.

Unlike most companies, John Lewis does not regard this bonus as part of the pay packet, but sees it as more like the dividend paid by public companies to their shareholders. It therefore comes on top of competitive pay rates. It depends on profitability so is not guaranteed, but even in the hard times of the early 1990s the lowest it fell to was 8%.

The group believes in paying what is necessary to recruit the right people, so that varies from location to location and from job to job. There are pay bands, but they are pretty wide, and, in keeping with the norm in the retail sector, not over-generous. Management trainees are likely to start on £17,000–20,000.

Everybody in the group has an annual review, covering personal development and business objectives. Pay is related to performance – there are no automatic increases, and no departmental or store bonuses.

The Future

Retail competition seems to get tougher by the year, as huge new shopping centres compete for the customers already being served by existing shops, and as new competitors arrive in the UK from abroad. Established stores also face a new threat from the growth of home shopping, possibly through the Internet.

John Lewis appreciates that it cannot continue to prosper merely by doing what it has always done, in the same old way. But at the same time the traditions of service and quality, and the democratic, caring heritage, must be preserved, while sticking to its price promise despite the assault of discount stores.

Sally Carruthers said the group also faces a much broader challenge: it needs to develop managers who are more rounded than in the past, who can come up with insights into the way the world is changing and what shoppers' needs are going to be, not just what they are today. 'The greatest challenge is to develop people who are not just damn good retailers, but who can make that leap and understand what people want out of their lives and how that affects us,' she said.

Johnson Matthey

Johnson Matthey is a world leader in advanced materials technology, applying the latest technologies to add value to precious metals and other specialised materials. The group's principal activities are the manufacture of catalysts and pollution control systems, and pharmaceutical compounds; the refining, fabrication and marketing of precious metals; the manufacture of decorative and specialised materials for the ceramics industry; and the manufacture of electronic materials and plastic laminate packages for semiconductors. With British origins, Johnson Matthey is extremely multinational. Of 12,000 employees worldwide, around 2,500 are in the UK. Johnson Matthey has operations in 37 countries, and sells its products around the world. In 1997/98 it reported record operating profits of £139 million on turnover of £3,267 million.

Scorecard:

Remuneration and benefits	★★★★
Progressive attitude	★★★★
Opportunity for promotion	★★★
Training, development and education	★★★★★
Working atmosphere and environment	★★★

Biggest plus:
A friendly company – multinational, but with room for that personal touch

Biggest minus:
Some traditional values still remain

Johnson Matthey plc
2–4 Cockspur Street
London SW1Y 5BQ
Tel: 0171 269 8400
Fax: 0171 269 8477

Johnson Matthey

Johnson Matthey

The Business

Johnson Matthey's business strategy has deliberately shifted away from a dependence on its traditional precious metals businesses towards a wider range of advanced materials products. While Johnson Matthey's precious metals and catalytic systems businesses are well established and still have growth potential, the company is expecting further growth to come from its ceramics and electronic materials businesses. New chief executive Chris Clark is bent on delivering profitable growth for shareholders, and demands a 20% return on assets in all businesses.

Johnson Matthey (JM) is a multinational business, but is able to retain that all-important personal touch. The company is very communicative – to both external and internal audiences – and the directors of the company go to great lengths to know people in the organisation. Employees say, 'it is easy to get noticed'. The charismatic Clark himself is highly visible to staff and, having been with JM for a long time, is familiar with many of them.

The complement at JM's head office overlooking Trafalgar Square is lean – some 70 people – reflecting a hands-off approach to day-to-day operations. The four divisions reporting to Chris Clark are fairly autonomous and are globally managed, reflecting the business organisation of their customers.

Company Culture and Style

The style of the company has changed. Johnson Matthey's origins in Hatton Garden are of a traditional company with a proud history and a reputation for integrity. These values still remain – for example, JM is a very ethical company – but the Johnson Matthey under Chris Clark is progressive, far less bureaucratic, and a lot slicker and faster in its dealings.

Today, JM is characterised by individual leadership, fast decision-making, getting things done and local responsibility. Being an advanced technology company, there is always a heavy emphasis on innovation, but in the widest possible sense. The type of person who flourishes at JM is bright, sparky, quick-thinking and action-oriented. JM employs people with character, not clones. The company's directors are all strong individual characters, and there is a suspicion that they value the same variety in employees.

A combination of old and new ideas has been the key to building a truly modern business for the future. The vision has been clearly communicated and subscribed to by employees, but many of the values were probably latent in the company anyway – they just needed articulating.

Johnson Matthey's company description is 'Technology Driven, Customer Led'. It was written by one of their recent graduate intake in an exercise devised by the company and thrown open to all employees for their suggestions. More importantly to the company, perhaps, the many responses proved that their employees really identify with these values.

Human Resources

Throughout Johnson Matthey, tremendous emphasis is placed on people. The board takes a *major* interest in graduate recruitment, getting involved personally, and the company's HR professionals put a lot of work into it.

JM believes strongly that far too much talent from UK plc is diverted into the City or the civil service instead of British industry, where they argue it is needed most. The company has therefore established very close and personal links with leading UK universities in its quest to attract the cream of British graduates.

The Management Development & Remuneration Committee (MDRC) sees the non-executive directors meet three times a year to establish remuneration for the company's senior executive directors. There is also a meeting every other month of all executive directors at the Executive Development Committee, which plays an operational role in encouraging and facilitating cross-divisional moves, assessing vacancies across the group and the pool of available talent, and implementing development and training programmes.

To support this corporate strategy, each division has its own management development processes, culminating in annual presentations at Trafalgar Square to all group executive directors. Peter Garfield, group personnel controller, then summarises the group's succession plans for the board.

Because of this strong lead taken by the directors, HR policies are linked closely to business goals. The HR function also runs and leads strategy seminars – for example, setting the programme for the annual group conference – and encourages the sharing of best practices.

Garfield knows that 'teamwork' is all the rage in business speak, but recalls that JM was one of the earliest companies to introduce teamwork (at its Royston chemicals facility), inviting *everyone* to apply for the team leader roles and using psychometric tests in the assessment process. Some shop-floor workers suddenly acquired the new title of 'team leader', while former supervisors found themselves concentrating instead on training and problem solving! Garfield noted that there were some 'difficulties' at the time, but believes that the approach works well. Pay systems reflect this team-based way of working and team briefings lie at the heart of internal communications.

JM's chemical business gained Investors in People recognition in mid 1998.

Career Opportunity and Development

JM regards its people development planning as 'excellent'. It considers senior management succession carefully, creating an impact which flows right down the organisation. Graduates and other 'bright' employees go through an annual business training course. Fast-track middle managers join the management development programme, which is mirrored in the UK and US. Senior managers may find themselves on courses at INSEAD, Wharton and Harvard.

High potential people have personal development interviews at appropriate intervals. Demonstrating the board's commitment to recruitment and development, all high potential graduates recruited since 1992 have been 'interviewed by the directors' in an informal, 'get to know you' bridge-building exercise.

There is maybe more emphasis on bringing in people from outside than before, but JM still retains a strong tradition of developing from within. When Peter Garfield adds that 'even if it involves an expatriate, it's better the devil you know', you believe that he may be serious. All vacancies are advertised internally.

Although JM doesn't expatriate people for the sake of it, an international group with divisions organised globally does provide frequent overseas and cross-divisional opportunities. Essentially, the company asks 'who's the best person for the job?', which underlines the importance of acquiring portable skills.

JM is a very technology/science-driven company. Some 15–25 graduates are recruited annually from UK universities, while the number recruited in the States has risen to around 50. Of course the company needs specialists – chemical engineers, scientists, computer analysts and materials technologists – but it recruits non-specialists as well and really wants people who are practical, flexible and ready for the modern business world.

Remuneration

JM is very competitive on pay and benefits, ranking alongside the best in the FTSE-100 Index. The MDRC receives regular advice from consultants on the pay and incentive arrangements among JM's peer group in each country in which it has operations. JM is proud of its highly rated, upper quartile company pension scheme.

Incentive arrangements are prevalent throughout the business. Annual performance related bonuses for senior executives are assessed centrally, below which individual businesses are encouraged to handle their own incentive arrangements. A share-option scheme (with performance criteria that trigger their exercise only if the company is on an upward path) is open to around 1,000 JM managers.

Everyone can join a 1:1 matched share participation scheme (up to 5% of salary each month can be contributed). Over a 12-year period, this has proved to be a very attractive deal and enjoys a good take-up level. Employees gathering outside the restaurant in head office are not pondering the delights on the day's menu on the wall, but checking on JM's latest share price.

The Future

JM faces the immediate challenge of riding the rapids and meeting the growth expectations of its electronic materials and ceramics businesses, while still expanding its other activities. Maintaining world-leading positions is often harder than getting there, and JM is competing, increasingly, on a global stage. But JM's four operating divisions make it easy to describe the company as being 'sensibly diversified'.

This creates a real need for people who can deal with these pressures and be better than the competition. Of course, everyone wants them, and JM recognises that recruitment, training and development are fundamental to having the right people for the right jobs.

Obviously, JM cannot guarantee jobs for life, but it can give people enhanced skills and greater employability. It backs this with a real commitment to open communications, teamworking and personal development, empowering employees, but leaving them in no doubt that they must take control of their own careers. It seems to be working.

Kimberly-Clark

Kimberly-Clark is a leading global manufacturer of personal care, consumer tissue and away-from-home products. Its global brands include Kleenex, Huggies, Pull-Ups, Kotex and Depend. Outside the USA, other well-known brands include Andrex, Scottex and Camelia. The company also produces professional healthcare products and premium business, correspondence and technical paper. It has manufacturing operations in 38 countries and sells its products in more than 150 countries. Kimberly-Clark has 57,000 employees in its worldwide consolidated operations, 3,000 of whom work in the UK and 8,000 in Europe.

Scorecard:

Remuneration and benefits	★★★★
Progressive attitude	★★★★
Opportunity for promotion	★★★★★
Training, development and education	★★★★
Working atmosphere and environment	★★★★★

Biggest plus:
A meritocracy staffed by genuinely helpful and friendly people

Biggest minus:
Not for you if you want formal structures

Kimberly-Clark
1 Tower View
Kings Hill
West Malling
Kent ME19 4HA
Tel: 01732 594503
Fax: 01732 594510
website: www.kimberly-clark.com

Kimberly-Clark

The Business

Kimberly-Clark was founded in 1872 in Neenah, Wisconsin as a producer of newsprint. Kotex feminine pads were first made in 1920, and Kleenex facial tissue in 1924. The company became the Kimberly-Clark Corporation in 1928. In 1995 the company merged with Scott Paper, another innovative corporation whose firsts include the invention of rolled bathroom tissue in the 1890s and household towels in 1907. The merger made Kimberly-Clark the world's leading tissue manufacturer and the second largest household and personal care products company in the USA.

The company began exporting its consumer products to markets outside the USA in the 1930s. It started manufacturing operations in the United Kingdom, Mexico and Germany in the 1950s and launched 17 international operations in the 1960s. Today, more than 40% of revenues come from outside the USA.

The scale of the company's operations is impressive: worldwide sales in 1997 were $12.5 billion, with earnings of $1.35 billion. In tissue alone, Kimberly-Clark produces 1,800,000 tonnes every year – which if placed end to end would stretch 19 times the distance from the earth to the moon!

Company Culture and Style

Shirt-sleeve dress and first-name terms are found throughout the organisation, and this includes the most senior people. It is also a largely status-less organisation. A detail, but a telling one, is that the chief executive eats in the same dining room as all other members of staff – and is not above sharing a table with the newest recruit.

Kimberly-Clark is a highly ethical company, committed to the highest standards of honesty, integrity and fairness. Dealing with retailers can be a cut-throat business: but not for Kimberly-Clark, which is deservedly respected by retailers for its relationships with them. As a result, it looks for these qualities of integrity when recruiting.

The culture is also strikingly diverse. The company's Reigate site in the UK is the HQ for its European operations, and it is not uncommon to hear a wide range of accents in its corridors and meeting rooms. Indeed, a recent training course included no less than 14 nationalities among the trainees!

Another refreshing difference about the company is its attitude to work. Kimberly-Clark people work hard when they need to, but they also enjoy themselves. This is not a driven culture. People respond to the demands of work on the basis of individual empowerment; working for an international company, they might find themselves being asked to go to, say, France or Italy the following day for a meeting or to China or Mexico for a longer visit.

Equal opportunity is the rule, not the exception. Senior women at the company include the general manager for Spain, the president of the away-from-home sector and the head of public relations. Overall, 50% of the UK management team are female, as are 60% of the UK graduate intake. The only requirement for promotion to the highest levels is ability.

Human Resources

Kimberly-Clark recognises that its people are its future and accords an appropriate level of importance to HR. Tim Berkley, European human resource adviser: 'One of the key HR functions at Kimberly-Clark is facilitating learning and career development. For instance, all graduate recruits get a mentor: typically a senior person but not the graduate's team leader. Of course, mentor programmes are increasingly common in industry today, but here mentors take a real and active interest, guiding people through their first two years.'

The mentors are chosen by the career development team because they do the job well. There are also unofficial mentors in the team itself. And beyond that, people are helpful and approachable to a remarkable degree. Rick Woodward, European management development manager: 'At this company, you really can walk into the chief executive's office and talk to him. Similarly, people throughout the organisation are happy to help you wherever they can.'

There is a European Values and Satisfaction Survey every six months which also takes in employee views on matters such as career development and pay. Part of the HR function at the company is about keeping an ear to the ground and staying in touch with staff opinions through these and other means, changing the way things are done if necessary.

Career Opportunity and Development

Able people progress rapidly at Kimberly-Clark, typically gaining varied experience early on. That progression is almost certain to include work experience abroad. Such international mobility is unusual for a consumer goods company. Mick Holbrook, UK training and development manager: 'We're quite likely to start new UK recruits with a period of work in Belgium, Holland or one of our other European sites. Job mobility is a requirement, so anyone joining us needs to be prepared for that. People have international careers here, so language skills are important – or at least the ability to learn new languages.'

Assessment procedures are intensive. The most important attributes for those interested in progressing are flexibility, a creative mind and a willingness to embrace change. Between 20 and 30 graduates are taken on each year and develop their careers through the company's professional development programme, a modular plan of between 15 and 18 months which prepares them well for the future. Rick Woodward: 'We're a matrix organisation. People get things done by consulting others and through reasoned argument. Team skills and time management are vital.' Tim Berkley concurs: 'Kimberly-Clark is built on its teams, so sophisticated teamworking skills are needed. We look for open, communicative people.'

People are expected to develop rapidly. The management team constantly reviews staff and helps them plan their next move. Individuals sit down with their team leaders at least annually and look at their careers five years ahead. This plan includes documentation for training and development, experience, ambitions, obstacles. Considering where they want to be in five years' time and planning to make that possible certainly concentrates the mind. Above all, people own their plans and are responsible for their career development. The route that development takes is substantially down to the individual.

Remuneration

Kimberly-Clark is a median to upper quartile remunerator and has a graded structure based on the evaluation process. This system is pan-European, although pay levels vary according to market conditions in each country. Base pay is calculated on the basis of individual performance with the level of increase based on a review of results against objectives.

Mick Holbrook: 'We are always in the upper quartile for graduate recruitment – and last year we were in the upper decile. We're looking for the cream and recognise we need to pay accordingly.' Graduate pay in 1998 was in the range £19,000–21,000, bearing out that view. However, as Tim Berkley says, salary is not the key factor. 'We want to sell the overall package, not the salary. People should want to work here for reasons other than just the pay levels.'

In the UK, an excellent and very flexible company car scheme operates at appropriate levels, four to five years into working for the company. Employees can add more to their base price – or lease a car for less and receive the remainder as additional salary. There is also a very good 60ths final salary contributory pension scheme with AVC provision.

The Future

The main challenges facing Kimberly-Clark as a business are all about change. As a result, flexibility is a key attribute for its personnel. Tim Berkley: 'The market can change very rapidly. We need to anticipate those changes if possible, but in any case react to them in the most appropriate way. For example, in 1998 a competitor launched a new product. We had to decide whether to follow this trend or introduce a product differentiation based on it. In six months, Kimberly-Clark launched its own upgraded product which is now the preferred choice of the consumer over that of the competitor.'

Dealing with change calls for new ways of thinking. Rick Woodward: 'One of the big surprises when you first come to work here is realising just how innovative we are. It's easy to think that there's little or no opportunity for innovation in our markets; nothing could be further from the truth! For instance, lotion-impregnated tissue, now a popular product, didn't even exist four years' ago. And there are many such examples.'

The other challenge is that the brand names of the company are still better known than the company itself, although this is changing. Tim Berkley: 'We need to get across the message that Kimberly-Clark is a great employer offering rewarding careers. I'm confident that this will be more widely appreciated in the months and years ahead.'

KPMG

KPMG is an international professional services firm. Although formally one of the 'big five' international accountancy and management consultancy firms, it describes itself as 'a global knowledge-based organisation whose aim is to exploit its knowledge for the benefit of its clients, its people and society at large'. Consequently, its people are involved in everything from audits and insolvencies to advising on strategy and implementing information technology projects. Created through the mergers of various British and continental European firms, KPMG presents itself as different from its largely US-oriented counterparts in the Big Five. In 1998, the UK firm employed some 10,000 people and they work increasingly closely with many thousands more spread around the world. Total UK fees were £867 million, with a 'distributable profit' of £179 million.

Scorecard:

Remuneration and benefits	★★★★
Progressive attitude	★★★★
Opportunity for promotion	★★★★
Training, development and education	★★★★★
Working atmosphere and environment	★★★★

Biggest plus:
Plenty of opportunity for advancement

Biggest minus:
Heavy client demands can put strain on life outside work

KPMG
8 Salisbury Square
London EC4Y 8BB
Tel: 0171 311 1000
Fax: 0171 311 3311

KPMG

The Business

As with other firms of its type, KPMG has in recent years shifted its focus away from accountancy towards being general business advisers. Management consultancy has become increasingly important and in many parts of the world the firm has a sizeable legal practice. It now describes itself as a 'knowledge business' that aims to serve clients by harnessing individual and combined knowledge to add value to their businesses, and has set about reorganising itself with the intention of achieving this through the creation of knowledge centres devoted to individual industries or sectors.

In late 1997, the firm responded to the announcement that rivals Price Waterhouse and Coopers & Lybrand (now known as Price Waterhouse Coopers) were planning to merge by holding discussions with Ernst & Young. But the talks were abandoned – largely, says the firm's management, because they made it more aware of its strengths. KPMG now says it is focused on creating a more powerful global presence, partly through a more assertive advertising campaign as well as through the initiative – of which it is particularly proud – in leading the way on financial disclosure by partnerships.

The firm has gone through a major restructuring designed to improve operational efficiency and to service clients. This included the development of nine 'designated lines of business'. The idea is that in each of these lines of business audit and accounting, tax advisory and consulting specialists work together to help clients by offering the skills and the industry knowledge needed. The lines of business are responsible for their own business targets and are seen as distinct businesses united by a common industry focus or specialism. KPMG management believes that the structure supported by geographic strength across the UK 'places emphasis on the teamworking, industry and specialist skills that meet client needs'.

Company Culture and Style

Currently headed in the UK by Mike Rake, while former UK senior partner Colin Sharman is international chairman, KPMG prides itself on being what one executive calls 'a very catholic church'. It embraces diversity, both in terms of the specialisms that people offer and the sorts of people employed.

As befits a partnership – albeit a large one, of more than 600 partners in the UK alone – the leadership style is very consensual. The camaraderie that is markedly different from the atmosphere in typical corporations is felt to be especially attractive to the bright young graduates that the firm sets out to recruit each year.

In common with other professional firms, work at KPMG is relationship-driven. Employees typically have to steer through a 'cobweb of relationships', which managers admit can be very stimulating but 'hugely frustrating' to some people. Moreover, unlike the typical corporation, KPMG is characterised as being a place for the 'intellectually curious' where people are allowed the freedom to build areas of expertise for themselves and, in the words of one executive, 'hopefully make money for the firm'.

Finally the emphasis on teamworking is likened to 'ensemble playing' with individuals bringing their expertise to a project. 'It's much like a theatre company with the lead partner as the director and everybody has a part to play,' says an executive, stressing that the valuing of individuality does not extend to allowing 'lone heroes'.

Human Resources

Since the quality of people is KPMG's only real asset, the firm puts great emphasis on this area and is constantly looking at new ways of developing employees.

Graduate recruitment is clearly an important activity. But in keeping with the move toward developing knowledge centres devoted to industries or sectors, it is increasingly also hiring experienced people, particularly for the consulting business.

The human resources team does, however, acknowledge that this specialism makes KPMG people attractive to rival firms and other organisations, and in an effort to deal with this issue has developed a series of career workshops. The idea is to help employees – particularly those who have just qualified as accountants – think about their long-term careers, even to the extent that they might lie outside the firm at some point.

Career Opportunity and Development

As a professional firm, KPMG obviously puts a lot of effort into development, particularly at the early stages. But it is increasingly building on this by using the increasing flexibility of accountancy qualifications – for example in tax, by sending young recruits to an internal business school where they get their tuition in a big chunk rather than spread out over months.

The firm is also blurring the boundaries between disciplines, particularly between audit and consulting, on the grounds that this should make the training appear more interesting and help the firm compete with the likes of Unilever and Procter & Gamble for the finest graduates. Nowadays, some graduates do not train for an accounting qualification at all, but go through a sort of corporate traineeship.

This shift away from a total emphasis on technical excellence is also seen in the selection of partners, where the firm is increasingly seeking a balance between technical expertise and 'social skills' on the basis that selling is an increasingly important part of the partner's job.

Because of the wide range of work carried out, opportunities are immense. There is also a clear career path through the various stages of qualification and managerial positions before consideration for partnership. A small group of partners spend the majority of their time running the organisation very much like a corporate executive team.

Remuneration

As a top-flight international professional services firm, KPMG is highly competitive on pay and benefits. Though it believes that the compensation package is less important in attracting graduates than the people who do the recruiting; it feels that its flexible benefits system, under which employees can choose from a range of 'perks' according to their need, demonstrates that it treats even young recruits as adults.

In common with other firms of its type, employees receive substantial pay rises as they move up the firm, until they make partner, where a share of the profit is a significant part of the remuneration. However, all staff share in the profitability of the organisation through bonuses and such schemes as profit-related pay.

The Future

At the end of 1998, Mike Rake said that the strategy set out in the wake of the cessation of the talks with Ernst & Young was 'managing domestic growth while playing an important role in the harmonisation and growth of KPMG worldwide'. And he remarked that so far there had been great success.

Though that episode and its aftermath have made the firm more confident, it is anxious not to be seen as complacent. In particular, it sees the need to become even more flexible and versatile and to maximise its intellectual capital and get what it has to offer to market quicker than it has. 'We remain strongly focused on providing excellent service to our clients and on developing new technologies and methodologies to enable us to stay at the forefront of our profession,' says Rake.

Internally, it is keen to break down barriers between partners and the rest of the staff. The major restructuring of the firm also led to the six former UK business regions being replaced by a national structure with three areas to streamline the management structure and enhance efficiency. Managers have pledged to continue to evaluate the firm's operations to ensure that the 'market-facing approach is always at the leading edge of client service'.

But with its open policy and increasingly focused approach apparently paying dividends, KPMG seems well placed to face the challenges of the new millennium.

LEK Consulting

LEK Consulting is an international strategy consulting firm, with extensive experience advising in all areas of corporate strategy. The firm now employs over 370 professionals worldwide, with offices in eight countries and eleven cities in London, continental Europe, North America and Australasia. In the last three years, LEK has worked for over 35% of the UK's largest companies, many public sector organisations, as well as major financial advisors and a number of smaller corporations. LEK Consulting is Britain's only global corporate strategy consulting firm, and 150 professionals work in its headquarters in London's West End.

Scorecard:

Remuneration and benefits	★★★★★
Progressive attitude	★★★★
Opportunity for promotion	★★★★★
Training, development and education	★★★
Working atmosphere and environment	★★★★★

Biggest plus:
A successful, progressive firm with a friendly, supportive culture

Biggest minus:
Hours can be long and unpredictable

LEK Consulting
The Adelphi Building
1–11 John Adam Street
London WC2N 6BW
Tel: 0171 930 1244
Fax: 0171 839 3790
website: www.lek.com

LEK Consulting

The Business

Founded in London in 1983, LEK has grown to employ approximately 190 professional staff in Europe, 130 in the United States and 50 in Australasia. The firm currently has offices in Auckland, Bangkok, Boston, Chicago, London, Los Angeles, Melbourne, Milan, Munich, Paris and Sydney. It is proud to be the only global strategy consultancy firm originated and headquartered in the UK. And LEK is truly a global partnership, not a network of country affiliates as many management consultancies are. LEK is also successful – growing revenue at around 20% each year.

LEK Consulting is dedicated to assisting its clients increase their profitability and shareholder value. It provides an array of 'traditional' strategic consulting services and has extensive experience advising on mergers and acquisitions and on new business development; importantly, it can provide clients with a seamless global perspective.

In the recent MORI 'Captains of Industry' survey, LEK ranked exceptionally highly in its industry for favourability among chairmen and CEOs who were familiar with the firm.

'We aim to motivate teams of the most capable and dedicated staff to solve the highest value, most critical strategic problems of the world's leading organisations. In doing so we will exceed our clients' expectations and stay ahead of our competitors, thus creating a growing and lasting independent force in the field of strategy consulting,' says Iain Evans, chairman and founder of the firm.

Company Culture and Style

While LEK employees represent different nationalities and backgrounds, the firm has a strong culture, which is maintained worldwide. This results in a common set of values, which are shared by all: honesty, hard work, integrity, competence, teamwork and good humour.

Client work, which focuses on strategy and problem-solving, is project based (as opposed to longer duration change or process management assignments that many consultancies take on). 'We spend less time in our clients' offices and more in our own, which has twin benefits of spending more time in each other's company, and that you generally return home to family and friends at the end of the day, rather than to a hotel room,' says Martin Pilkington, recruitment partner.

Above all, people at LEK make the firm an informal fun, enjoyable place to work. Staff at all levels consistently take the initiative to be open and helpful. This spirit of camaraderie makes for a very collegiate and supportive office environment.

The culture of the firm is reinforced through frequent interaction between staff at all levels, whether at company meetings, professional development seminars, or in the course of day-to-day work. A non-hierarchical approach results in high-quality mixing between associates, consultants and senior professionals at LEK, as well as with clients. Indeed, from associate to senior partner, everyone is asked to sustain the firm's culture and values.

LEK's business style is a happy marriage of the hard-nosed professionalism associated with US management consultancies, and the softer British approach which has trust as its strong suit. It's successful because LEK's clients genuinely seem to like their strategy advisors, and client retention levels are high.

The complexion is very much international. Around half of the graduate intake of the London office is made up of foreign nationals. Approximately one third of all LEK projects worldwide and half of London cases involve LEK offices in more than one country, meaning that LEK consultants frequently work with international case teams.

Human Resources

There's no single template for an ideal LEK candidate, but the firm looks for a combination of many skills. Creativity, leadership, motivation and an eagerness to learn; analytical and problem-solving skills; commercial acumen backed by common sense; strong communication skills; a high level of energy and the ability to handle multiple tasks. And uncompromising ethics.

Staff are drawn from a wide range of disciplines and the degree subject is largely irrelevant. You can count on numeracy being valued, but not as much as analytical ability.

'Graduates joining the firm are allocated a mentor at the beginning of their career with the firm, but the network works best informally,' says Martin Pilkington. There is a formal performance review process, but 'minder' may be more appropriate than 'mentor' as managers that associates work with on projects frequently look out for you.

Career Opportunity and Development

LEK manages its European offices as an integrated network. That provides opportunities to work in another country, and means that employees are exposed to a wide range of cultures and international case work – particularly across Europe, but also involving LEK's US and Asia-Pacific practices.

The firm has four levels of professionals: partners, managers, consultants and associates. At consultant level, LEK offers opportunities for both MBAs and people with significant industry experience. Approximately three-quarters of LEK's consultant hires have an MBA, with the balance coming from industry and commerce.

Associates are university graduates seeking an entry to the business world. Typically, associates stay with the firm for three to four years before moving on to business school or positions in industry. LEK provides a generous business school sponsorship package to associates who have the ability to return to the firm as consultants.

In the first three years, LEK offers all graduates the chance to take a six-month posting overseas (more often than not in another English-speaking office). The most exceptional associates have the opportunity to remain with the firm and be promoted to consultant and beyond. Recent evidence is that of the most recent elevations to partner level, five out of eight originally joined LEK as graduates.

Experience is gained fast. After the first three months, associates normally work on two cases at a time, so in a year an individual may work on as many as 15–18 different projects, each typically of 6–8 weeks in duration. Since these projects will typically be in different industries and solving different types of problems, the learning curve is very steep.

LEK provides a variety of training opportunities to ensure that all employees develop a broad set of quantitative and qualitative business skills. Associates receive a foundation in the most important analytical and technical skills in an intensive two-week course upon joining. However, LEK believes that one of the most important training opportunities for a recent university graduate is on-the-job experience.

LEK holds professional development sessions throughout the year, covering a broad range of topics including new techniques for analysing business problems, overviews of recently completed cases, and management techniques. To improve the opportunity for on-the-job learning and provide easy access to all levels of personnel within the firm, LEK's offices are open plan.

Upward mobility is intrinsic. LEK's young and entrepreneurial culture fosters an environment where professionals are promoted commensurate with their capabilities and contribution, rather than their length of service with the firm. It is quite possible to become a partner at LEK within ten years of graduating, including one year at business school.

What do current LEK associates say about the firm? 'One of the main reasons I chose LEK over other consulting firms was the chance to work in another office and my wish was fulfilled with an eight-month transfer to our Boston office during my third year with LEK' (Alyson Cowie, graduated from University of Durham). 'Working at LEK not only means that you are responsible for your own work, but you are also expected to help and learn from the people around you' (Per Dahl, graduated from Stockholm School of Economics). 'Working as an associate means constantly developing a set of "hard" analytical skills while learning how to make the best use of "softer" skills such as creativity, communication and relationship skills' (Alexander Exarchos, graduated from Solvay University, Brussels).

And the seniors? 'High levels of responsibility at a relatively early stage in your consulting career are the hallmark of the way in which LEK is prepared to offer new consultants the opportunity to accelerate their development through challenging assignments' (Gordon Hull, Manager, London office).

Remuneration

Pay, as one has come to expect with management consulting, is very good. Starting salaries are competitive with the other top strategy consulting forms and are among the highest around.

Individual performance is reflected in individual salary. Profit share is based on the performance of the firm globally, which encourages a sharing of mutual objectives.

The Future

LEK has a lot of existing clients in fast growth industries such as transport, financial services, leisure, new media and biotech. That puts an onus on needing to change quickly and learn continuously in order to provide superior consulting services – these are not industries which rely upon a bank of 30 years' experience and knowledge.

But the firm is not really restricted – only by the number of top calibre people it can recruit. LEK has tremendous scope to raise its current low profile and when it does, there will be a lot to go for.

When Martin Pilkington says that he is 'genuinely proud of the firm and its people', it could be anyone at LEK talking.

Levi Strauss (UK) Ltd.

Levi Strauss & Co. markets branded jeanswear and other casual clothing in more than 60 countries. It operates 53 production facilities and 32 customer service centres in 49 countries, and has around 37,600 employees worldwide. Levi Strauss (UK) is an affiliate of this privately owned US firm, with 1,675 employees: 175 at the head office, administration and distribution centre in Northampton, and 1,500 at three manufacturing sites in Scotland. There are 32 Original Levi's stores in the UK mostly franchised, the exceptions being the flagship stores in Regent Street, London and in Birmingham.

Scorecard:

Remuneration and benefits	★★★
Progressive attitude	★★★★
Opportunity for promotion	★★★
Training, development and education	★★★
Working atmosphere and environment	★★★★★

Biggest plus:
A family company with real values in people and business

Biggest minus:
Being a subsidiary of a US firm sometimes restricts opportunities

Levi Strauss (UK) Ltd
Swan Valley
Northampton
NN4 9BA
Tel: 01604 581501
Fax: 01604 599815

Levi Strauss (UK) Ltd.

The Business

Levi Strauss & Co. is one of the world's largest private companies with worldwide headquarters in San Francisco. Ownership returned to the descendants of the original Levi Strauss in 1985 in one of the biggest leveraged buyouts in the US at the time. Being privately owned helps Levi Strauss to do things in its own style.

Chairman and chief executive Bob Haas is the great-great-grandnephew of Levi Strauss and this link to the founder and his values still pervades through the organisation. It has helped make Levi's a values-driven business.

Levi Strauss is a classic brand marketing organisation, with a unique and highly favourable brand name. Levi Strauss invented jeans in 1853, and claims product values and strengths with some justification. Levi's® is synonymous with blue denim jeans, and its legendary 501 jeans are portrayed in memorable advertising campaigns, but other branded products such as Dockers® and SLATES play their part in the portfolio.

Company Culture and Style

When Levi Strauss claims that it is a values-driven business, these are not idle words – they do underpin everything that the company does, and are integrated into the way in which the company does business.

'The mission of Levi Strauss & Co. is to sustain responsible commercial success as a global marketing company of branded apparel' is the opening gambit in the company's mission statement. Not far behind are people. 'The thing that gives us our strength is our people . . . our challenge is to put people at the centre of our business' are the words of chief executive Bob Haas.

Commercial success always comes first. But Levi Strauss believes strongly that *how* you do business is important. Values such as teamwork, diversity, recognition, ethical management practices, communications and empowerment are held in such high regard that the performance management system actually rewards people for success and achievement against these values, and not just against financial results.

These values are held quite genuinely, and employees themselves prove to be the greatest ambassadors of what the company stands for. Non-believers would probably leave.

Levi Strauss moved to state-of-the-art new offices and an automated warehouse in Northampton early in 1999, involving its staff – 'the people who wear the building' – throughout the planning process. It has allowed the company to concentrate on new ways of working, mentally and physically, and layout has been carefully planned to improve integration and work-flow interaction.

The open plan environment has only two offices, one for the managing director and one for the HR director. Facilities include a 'wellness suite' evolved from the gym, and includes classes and advice on health, dealing with stress and good nutrition. The menu in the staff restaurant backs this up.

The environment at Levi Strauss is one of openness, sometimes bordering on vocal. People are more than willing to state their views and challenge situations and ideas. And this is encouraged. The management style is very relaxed and positive, and managers are highly visible, accessible and open – from the general manager down, your views will be heard.

The informal air at the company means that if you expect to find people wearing suits, you will probably be disappointed. Is it fun? Levi Strauss is one of the very few companies which actually puts it in its aspirations statement, inviting staff 'to have fun in our endeavours'.

Human Resources

HR exists to deliver service at three levels: to individuals, to teams, and to the organisation. Cross-functional teams are very important at Levi Strauss and performance assessment attempts to measure their efforts and achievements. Knowing that the company is operating in a very tough market environment, HR is seeking to improve the performance of individuals and teams to make sure that commercial goals are met.

With market dynamics prompting change, HR places a major emphasis on guiding employees through this ongoing process and ensuring that the organisation has the skills and expertise available to manage itself through change. The new office move means that Levi Strauss can capitalise on the chance for 'a fresh start'.

That includes recruitment, which now necessarily includes more external hiring. Levi Strauss is looking for people with potential as well as ability to do the job. It stresses the importance of motivated people of the *right* calibre as being more applicable than high calibre. And it is important that individuals fit into the unique Levi Strauss culture.

Diversity in the workplace has always figured prominently on the company's agenda, employing people from different groups and backgrounds, and creating an environment where all ideas and perspectives are valued and respected. Recognising that 'empowerment' is an overused word, Levi Strauss really does it, and is quite clear about what it means, clarifying to employees the context and boundaries.

Career Opportunity and Development

Levi Strauss doesn't engage in new graduate recruitment. Like many lean US organisations, Levi Strauss is 'hung up on headcount', recruiting only when it has a vacancy. The company recruits internally where possible, but recognises that a balance with external expertise and experience needs to be struck. All jobs are advertised on 'Eureka', Levi's worldwide Intranet.

While the UK affiliate is relatively small in the context of the Levi Strauss worldwide empire, the change within the organisation is creating more international opportunity. UK staff are often in demand by other Levi affiliates across Europe on a permanent, project or task force basis, and more opportunities in the US are emerging. This has given Levi Strauss UK the chance to develop its people with potential.

'Levi Strauss has always been committed to training and development, but there is now a clearer people development strategy built into its organisational structure,' suggests Gillian Rutherford, HR director. This is segmented into what it means for Levi Strauss, and covers personal development, career development and succession planning. 'While we continue to expect people to take individual ownership of their development plan, this framework gives important context to career planing discussions with individuals,' says Gillian.

The performance improvement drive and proliferation of cross-functional teams have helped people acquire new skills. As the organisation becomes flatter, and promotion opportunities less hierarchical, Levi Strauss is succeeding in changing people's mindsets by encouraging them to move horizontally to acquire broader skills and experience.

Remuneration

Remuneration policy is geared to attracting, retaining and rewarding people and is market competitive. Pay comprises base pay, an annual bonus (all employees are eligible) and a long-term component, measured by contribution to the long-term success of the business. Pay increases are based entirely on performance. A package of benefits is offered, but being a private company, there are no employee share schemes.

Levi's staff show tremendous loyalty to the company and this has not gone unnoticed. The much publicised Global Success Sharing Plan is a one-off recognition payment outside pay policy where all employees (it's too late – the eligibility cut-off date has passed!) will receive one year's salary (on top of salary and bonus) in 2002 to mark the new millennium.

The Future

Levi' Strauss's major challenge is to remain competitive in a tough market. It has a world-class brand backed by quality production, and Levi's® remains synonymous with 501 and with blue denim. But market trends (particularly in the UK) away from denim pose a major challenge, even though Levi's® is the clear market leader. Expect new brands to be developed and acquired and watch the new generations of attention-grabbing advertisements that don't immediately reveal the products behind them.

While it is very good at marketing, the business probably needs to be more externally focused. It will look to define what exceptional customer service means to Levi Strauss and to its customers and provide a better, revamped service for the twenty-first century. That might mean a fresh outlook, a more flexible approach to employee recruitment and retention, and a better understanding of the needs of its high potential staff.

Communication plays an important part. Levi Strauss is open and honest about what is happening in the company, even if it doesn't always have all the answers. It wants to be even better, and have realistic, personal conversations. While it is difficult to keep a balance in that area, keeping staff informed of all developments and how change is to be achieved is a top priority.

Some change is inevitable, and the company is working hard to continually motivate employees, maintain their unquestioned loyalty, and prepare and equip them to face the future. The values inherent in the business should hold it in good stead through challenging times.

The Maersk Company Limited

The Maersk Company is a large shipowner and a significant transportation operator. It employs more than 2,500 people ashore and at sea, and owns over 30 vessels, ranging from tankers, gas carriers and container ships to some of the world's most powerful offshore vessels.

Scorecard:

Remuneration and benefits	★★★★
Progressive attitude	★★★★★
Opportunity for promotion	★★★★★
Training, development and education	★★★★★
Working atmosphere and environment	★★★★

Biggest plus:
Ability is the only requirement for promotion, which can come early

Biggest minus:
Not for people who dislike the idea of working overseas

The Maersk Company Limited
1 Canada Square
Canary Wharf
London E14 5DP
Tel: 0171 712 5000
Fax: 0171 712 5010
website: www.maersk.co.uk

MAERSK

The Maersk Company Limited

The Business

The Maersk Company is part of a global group. Its parent organisation, the A. P. Moller Group, was founded in 1904 in Copenhagen. It employs over 35,000 people and is engaged in shipping, the exploration for and the production of oil and gas, shipbuilding, aviation, industry, supermarkets and IT services.

The group has long since recognised the importance of the UK to its operations, and in 1951 founded the Maersk Company as a ship-broker in the City of London. The company has grown steadily since then and now has three main business areas. The first area is a container business which moves containers to and from the UK. Within that area is Mercantile (GB), a relatively new but fast-growing supply chain management logistics company, providing value-added services to customers.

The second area is shipowning: the Maersk Company is among the three largest British-owned, British-flagged owners. Its fleet now exceeds 30 vessels, and the majority of its crew is British. Activities of this business range from anchor-handlers and tug supply vessels for the offshore oil industry to gas carriers and container vessels.

The final business area is concerned with the oil-related market. This comprises two entities: one is Maersk Contractors, which provides equipment and expertise to the oil exploration and production industry. This includes drilling rigs and FPSOs (Floating Production Storage and Offloading units) – effectively, mobile oil installations. The other part is Maersk's maintenance division, known as Salamis, which provides services such as surface and other maintenance for offshore and onshore installations: including gritting, rust-scraping, painting, fire-proofing and related activities.

Company Culture and Style

The ethics of the company, and the parent group, provide a strong, personally communicated culture. These ethics remain largely unchanged from its foundation, a continuity underpinned by the fact that the parent company has had only two chairmen since 1904. That culture is very much about the company's name and reputation, and of being able to deliver on its promises. 'No effort too great, no detail too small' – a strapline of the company – sums up this aspect of the culture.

Additionally, Maersk is a company where careful planning and attention to detail is key. A watchword of A. P. Moller himself was, 'No loss should hit us which can be avoided with constant care.' This remains true of Maersk today.

A distinctive feature of Maersk is that it seeks to offer people long-term careers. Thomas Andersen, Maersk's managing director: 'My view is that there should be no reason for our people to want to look for another job. Our duty, I believe, is to offer the right career opportunities and a climate which is interesting, challenging and rewarding.' The career path at Maersk typically includes both local and overseas jobs; and job circulation is relatively fast, allowing people to progress their careers through a range of different responsibilities.

The company has a strongly international environment. People of many nationalities work together at Maersk. Anyone joining the company is expected to be prepared to move overseas to work, and even locally based people are likely to be asked to fly to, say, Singapore for a few days as work requires. It is also a fairly young organisation with an average employee age of around 34. This is partly due to the fact that Maersk is growing rapidly and therefore taking on young people to fuel that growth; but it has always had a name as a dynamic, fast-moving company.

Human Resources

HR is paramount at Maersk: indeed, Thomas Andersen calls it 'the single most important element of the organisation'. One element of this area is to seek to develop the company by bringing out the best in its people, both individually and by fostering a strong sense of teamwork. Many different types of people work at Maersk, from seafarers and offshore workers to onshore administrators and managers. One task of HR at the company is to integrate their efforts successfully.

The company's policy is not to bring people in to fill vacancies but to recruit wherever possible from within. It is aided here by its strong education, development and training programmes. Maersk also devotes considerable resources to ensuring that it selects the right people to join it. Its rigorous procedures are designed to ensure that nobody it hires will fail to realise their potential, or fall by the wayside.

Career Opportunity and Development

The company has a system of education and career development designed to bring out the best in its recruits. Young people with management potential are invited to join a two-year programme which includes office experience during the day and study during the evening using correspondence courses designed by Maersk. The company has links with its three shipping colleges: in Copenhagen, the USA and Singapore. The majority of the training takes place on modular courses over eight weeks at an internationally run business school in Copenhagen. Topics studied include both general and specific skills, from economics to IT and languages (all candidates on the course must take two languages other than their mother tongue), and also industry and business training.

The course provides an excellent insight into the Maersk culture. On completion of the course, the typical route is to receive an overseas posting. There is no shortage of training once the course is over: Maersk has excellent internal training facilities as well as links with outside organisations including the London School of Business and the Harvard Business School. Individual staff members can apply for further training at any time to further their career, and they then discuss with their managers the appropriate route forward.

Another example of training is the 'Maersk Challenge' where staff of different backgrounds have the opportunity to become part of a crew of a tall ship. This is an outstanding opportunity to build trust in oneself, develop character and foster teamwork.

Open-door communication characterises the company, and this is fostered by its desire to develop a cross-departmental approach. For instance, officers on ships with top management potential are regularly identified and offered onshore opportunities. A similar exercise takes place across all functions. Maersk is a broad-based company with a wide range of openings; and, through its parent, offers even more possibilities – from aviation to supermarket management.

Ability is far more important than seniority at Maersk. It would not be unusual to find that your boss was ten years younger than yourself! This can be either refreshing or disconcerting depending on the individual's background, of course. Nevertheless, it remains true that the opportunities for career development are vast, as the company and its parent operate in over 80 countries worldwide.

Remuneration

The company aims to pay market rates for its posts. In particular, it seeks to avoid any of its people being underpaid by industry standards. This is made easier because in a sense Maersk *is* the industry; smaller companies may need to hire only one good member of staff a year, but Maersk has a substantial and growing annual intake. Pay should also be seen in the context of the unusually rapid career development prospects. The company certainly offers its people more opportunity, at younger ages, than many other organisations.

Maersk provides all the benefits one would expect of an excellent employer. These include a good pension plan, lunch facilities, medical schemes, a car where appropriate, and holiday cottages.

The Future

As an organisation, Maersk remains committed to the UK and has grown strongly, especially recently. The aim now is to build on this to create even more growth for the future. The company believes that the UK market is the right place to allow this, due to both existing core activities and to a planned further diversification of those activities in the next century.

The challenges for the company are summed up by Thomas Andersen: 'The world is becoming more international, and only those who can benchmark themselves as the best internationally will survive. We have to be the best not only locally but globally, which will call for even more efforts in integrating and aligning cultural understanding. We must also source human resources from wherever they are best, and ensure we continue to provide the best education and training for those people.'

The challenge is therefore to manage international cultural differences and maintain an environment which continues to give true career satisfaction, coupled with an entrepreneurial attitude to business. Work, Maersk believes, should be interesting, stimulating and fun if those challenges are to be met. The company looks in good shape to meet those challenges and to continue to grow in the years to come.

Marks & Spencer

Marks & Spencer is a UK-based retailer that trades throughout the world. Renowned for its innovation in both the products it sells and how it sources and sells them, it is also Europe's most profitable retailer and has repeatedly figured strongly in UK and international quality of management surveys. Marks & Spencer's reputation for value and honesty extends beyond the organisation and has helped it make a success of its launch into financial services. In 1998, the company's turnover grew by just over 5%, to £8.24 billion, while profits rose 6%, to £1.17 billion. The number of employees increased in the period from 68,200 to 71,300.

Scorecard:

Remuneration and benefits	★★★★
Progressive attitude	★★★
Opportunity for promotion	★★★★
Training, development and education	★★★★★
Working atmosphere and environment	★★★★

Biggest plus:
Commitment to developing workforce

Biggest minus:
Perception that it is less exciting than other retailers

Marks & Spencer
Michael House
Baker Street
London W1A 1DN
Tel: 0171 935 4422
Fax: 0171 487 2679
website: www.marks-and-spencer.co.uk

MARKS & SPENCER

Marks & Spencer

The Business

From humble origins on a market stall in Leeds, Marks & Spencer has built itself into one of the most admired companies in the world, winning in 1997 the British Quality of Management Award for the fourth year in succession. Dubbed 'Marks and Sparks' by the British public, the company with its St Michael brand set the standards for others to follow in terms of value-for-money and quality, backed up by a famous no-quibble returns policy. However, the company has also been highly innovative, pioneering the development of close relationships with suppliers and working with them to develop new products and services. For example, the company claims to have introduced the grapefruit to Britain through its work in creating a 'cold chain' that enabled the produce to be kept chilled all the way from the field to the store.

Although still seen as predominantly a UK high street store selling food and clothing, it has branched out into home furnishings, operating large edge-of-town stores and providing financial services as well as expanding overseas. In the United States, for example, it owns the renowned Brooks Brothers stores group and the Kings Super Markets chain. There are also extensive operations in continental Europe and the Far East. In 1998, overseas activities in 30 countries generated profits of nearly £68 million on sales of £1.27 billion.

In the UK, the company claims to sell one in four of the country's men's suits, 40% of the nation's lingerie and a third of prepared sandwiches.

Company Culture and Style

Marks & Spencer puts great store by its twin focus on the customer and its people. Paul Smith, the executive responsible for recruitment and training, says that this is reflected in the type of training carried out. 'It's very much attitudinal-type training, not just how to operate the till.'

In recent years, the company has taken steps to move away from its old, somewhat paternalist image – though it still puts great emphasis on ensuring that its employment policies are fair and that people are treated fairly. And the family atmosphere is still prevalent, with the company becoming many employees' life to such an extent that they socialise with and even marry colleagues.

The change has become apparent in people being required to take a greater role in their own development and to become more used to change than perhaps would have been the case in the more settled 'old-style' Marks & Spencer. Company executives see the announcement at the end of 1998 that Peter Salsbury would take over as chief executive from Sir Richard Greenbury as a catalyst in this change process.

However, even before a period of difficult trading was followed by the decision to split the roles of chairman and chief executive of the company, the style was changing. Parts of the Baker Street headquarters building remain dominated by traditional corridors, but in other areas such concepts as 'hot desking', flexible working and home-working are becoming more prevalent. Moreover, the company's positive outlook is demonstrated by its early support for the euro and its decision to equip its stores to handle the new currency – as well as many others – regardless of the political uncertainty about Britain's participation in economic and monetary union.

Human Resources

The company has long been recognised for its commitment to looking after its staff. But in keeping with the overall effort to modernise, it has recently been working to reposition itself in the recruitment market. Paul Smith explains that the aim is to attract a variety of people and a range of skills. As a result, the company has reviewed its list of desired skills in managers. The criteria are now focus on the customer and the business issue; ability to manage change; ability to develop people; personal impact; enterprise and innovation. However, the importance given to each can shift according to needs.

Contrary to the experience of many large companies, but in common with other retailers, Marks and Spencer has more of a problem hiring men than women. And in addition to tackling this issue, the company has been working with the Eureka children's museum in Halifax – on the grounds that research indicates that attitudes towards retailers are formed as early as the age of six – with a view to promoting itself as an exciting place in which to work. The working with education initiative is designed to enable stores around Britain to work practically with schoolchildren and students in examining retail as a business and a possible career.

At the same time, the company is giving managers greater responsibilities earlier than was previously the case. Paul Smith says this is a necessary result of the enhanced training being carried out throughout the organisation. 'As the capability of people is freed up, you need to give them opportunities,' he says, pointing to the danger of demotivating them.

Sir Richard Greenbury, the chairman, says: 'We encourage all members of the company to develop as individuals to enable them, whatever their position, to contribute to the success of the business.'

More than 12,000 of the 71,300 staff have gained national vocational qualifications and more sales assistants are being encouraged to develop specialist training in such areas as jewellery, home furnishings and bra fitting.

But training is not handed out across the board. Increasingly, employees are expected to take responsibility for their own careers through means of 'personal development reviews'. The idea is that they seek out what types of development they feel they need to create the sort of careers they want. It is, in the words of one executive, 'a learning environment which gives individuals as much opportunity as they want to take'.

Career Opportunity and Development

There are many opportunities for promotion within Marks & Spencer, not least because it is committed to expansion in Britain and overseas through more and larger stores.

Overseas postings are not as common as might be thought because of the company's success in developing local management, but there are chances to gain experience working in such operations.

Much more common is movement within divisions and functions of the company. The idea is that people are more adaptable and useful to the company if they have experience of different parts of the operation.

Remuneration

Marks & Spencer, in the words of a senior executive, 'takes pay and benefits very seriously'. Such longstanding benefits as subsidised lunches and hairdressing are legendary, but the company keeps its package under constant review in order to ensure that it stays in line with the needs of the company and employees.

In common with other employers of its size, employees of a certain level and above are eligible for company cars. But the policy is highly flexible, so that an employee can take the whole or part of a car leasing allowance as a cash alternative, or even top up the allowance out of their own funds. In addition, like other international companies, Marks & Spencer is recognising that employees are particularly interested in certain benefits at different stages of their career, and the package is constantly being adapted to reflect that. One of the more recently introduced options is the opportunity for certain employees to obtain further learning at the company's expense.

However, the company is wedded to its past in feeling that it has a sort of moral obligation to encourage employees to save for their retirement by providing non-contributory pensions – at a cost that goes unacknowledged by much of the staff. It also continues to offer a generous discount package on goods sold in the stores.

The Future

At the end of the 1990s, Marks & Spencer is seen by many to be at a crossroads. A sharp fall in profits and what one commentator called 'an undignified scramble' to take over the chief executive post being relinquished by chairman Sir Richard Greenbury have left the company looking less impregnable than it used to. However, executives insist that the strategic review put in place before those events has given them and the workforce in general great confidence about tackling the challenges ahead.

First and foremost, the company realises that – with such a strong position in its domestic market – it is going to have to develop rapidly overseas if it is to continue to grow. That aim brings its own challenges, particularly 'adapting the offer to suit local needs' and organising its famed supply and distribution chain to suit new requirements.

But executives aim to trade on what they see as the 'strength in depth' of Marks & Spencer's people. Decision-making will be devolved and there will be much greater autonomy for individual managers in general.

Admitting that the company has got some things wrong, executives quote their football-loving chairman as saying that that does not suddenly make the company useless. 'It's like Manchester United coming second after years of winning.'

Mars

Mars, Incorporated, is a worldwide leader in its main markets with global sales of $13 billion. Mars has factories and offices in over 60 countries and employs 30,000 people. This privately owned US giant is famous for its confectionery brands such as Mars, Snickers and M&Ms. Mars brands are market leaders in petfood through Whiskas and Pedigree Chum; and the company also produces a range of leading main meal foods, including Uncle Ben's and Dolmio. Its drinks group Four Square is at the forefront of drinks vending systems. Mars Electronics International (MEI) and Information Services International complete Mars's portfolio of businesses.

Scorecard:

Remuneration and benefits	★★★★
Progressive attitude	★★★★★
Opportunity for promotion	★★★★
Training, development and education	★★★★★
Working atmosphere and environment	★★★★★

Biggest plus:
A strong, unique culture that you might love

Biggest minus:
A strong, unique culture that you might hate

Mars UK
3D Dundee Road
Slough
Berkshire SL1 4LG
Tel: 01753 693000
Fax: 01753 533172

Mars

The Business

Mars is characterised by superb brands and a unique corporate philosophy. In terms of brands, Mars is a global business and its markets are huge. In the UK alone, £4 billion is spent on confectionery each year – 70% on chocolate, of which Mars holds a 30% share. The canning factory at Melton Mowbray produces up to 400,000 tonnes of petfood each year. Every day, over 100 million people worldwide use MEI coin, note and card payment systems.

Turning to culture, 40 years ago Mars adopted a 'no status' policy, a truly radical approach for the 1950s and still by no means common today. There is a flat corporate structure. All employees are known as associates. Managers are paid more but enjoy no perks: no separate dining room, no special car-parking facilities. Managers sit with the other associates in an open, integrated layout organised logically by work functions. Furthermore, all staff have to clock on each day. In short, every employee is treated in the same way: with respect. This is embodied in the company's 'Five Principles' of quality, responsibility, mutuality, efficiency and freedom. The result of this policy is that people at all levels are committed to the company and feel part of it.

Mars's open, informal working environment makes for easy communication and a fast-moving, responsive organisation where decisions are made quickly. Above all it is a meritocracy; rewards are high and reflect individual levels of responsibility. It is also a harmonious place. In 66 years of operating in the UK, Mars has never lost a second due to a dispute with its associates. The lack of bureaucracy, the flat structure and above all the trust engendered by an open, communicative company must take much of the credit for that.

Company Culture and Style

The ethos at Mars is apparent the moment you walk through the door. The Five Principles demand that Mars's associates think and act differently towards other associates, brands and the business. The principles are demanding, and while Mars accepts that they may not always be achieved on every single occasion, they run deeply through the organisation and underpin everything the company does.

These principles lead on to a set of shared values which Mars believes should be kept firmly in sight at all times. Shared values may be between two individuals, a team, or a business unit. It requires a different emphasis, looking at what people want from their jobs and the interdependency of working. The current buzzword 'stakeholder' may cause a wry smile at Mars, since this approach has been in practice there for forty years!

So what shape does the Mars culture take? A human resources manager talks of 'healthy dissatisfaction', which he outlines as follows: 'We're very hard on ourselves. Mars tends to attract people who are their own biggest critics, who set themselves almost unachievable targets.'

Individuals have real freedom to make a difference: individuality is encouraged, as is the ability to think for yourself and challenge the status quo. Not surprisingly, Mars believes that there is real strength in diversity and that to continue to succeed, it must harness all diversities – of culture, style and geography. Mars wants a workforce which reflects these diversities, since it believes that it must have the right mix of people to properly understand the opinions of the communities in which it operates and the consumers of its brands.

Mars has a senior manager responsible for driving towards diversity and bringing about a multi-cultural business at all levels, uninfluenced by factors of race, gender or religion. The company has taken a number of steps to adopt recruitment processes which maximise diversity, for example advertising in the ethnic press.

The company is keen to ensure that all candidates for employment have an excellent understanding of the company, the opportunities for advancement, and the job itself – recognising the importance of such a decision for the individual. If any candidates feel that the company has not offered them enough information, Mars will invite them back to spend a day in the workplace.

Human Resources

Human resource management at Mars is principally the responsibility of line managers working with a technical function known as Personnel and Organisation. This is very much linked to the 'associate' concept.

Mars recruits around 40 graduates a year who can follow a range of career paths, including those leading to technical management as well as more general management.

The Personnel Liaison Group, chaired by UK personnel director

Mike Smith, ensures that all UK-based businesses of the company operate consistently. 'Because the culture is so strong, you have to work hard to live up to it. Having a "no status" principle can be hard to achieve unless you spend time and effort maintaining it.'

Effective internal communications include job involvement sessions, team briefings, and company newsletters and magazines. Line managers are used as conduits for two-way communication. Mars has an array of electronic communications, including bulletin boards, e-mail, and access to minutes of meetings from anywhere in the organisation. Having said that, face-to-face communication always comes first at Mars.

Career Opportunity and Development

There are outstanding career opportunities to be had at Mars. The vaunted Mars Management Training Programme will stand people in good stead for the rest of their careers. Its design gives trainees a variety of experiences and challenges across functional and national boundaries, equipping them with the commercial, market and cultural perspectives needed to become a successful manager.

Once through the management training programme, the typical job cycle is two to three years. The 'job size' is large and its scope can change considerably over that period. Jobs are not rigidly defined; on the contrary, they can be whatever the individuals want them to be, within reason. As Mike Smith says, 'Boredom is a word seldom heard at Mars.'

International opportunities are plentiful – associates are part of Mars, Inc. – and almost all jobs are advertised internally. Mars is expanding heavily into Eastern Europe, Asia/Pacific and South America. While the company wants local management in these regions, many Western European Mars associates are seconded to these emerging markets, enjoying fascinating opportunities as a result.

Remuneration

Mars believes that a prerequisite for success in its environment is an employment formula which is made up of high-calibre people, low numbers and high pay. All three elements of the formula are essential for success. Having fewer people means that the company can reward them with high pay. To attract, retain and motivate high-calibre people, Mars pays at the ninetieth percentile of top-paying UK companies. All associates have parts of their pay linked into the overall performance of the business.

The company offers an excellent range of benefits. These include a non-contributory pension scheme, private health insurance for every associate, life cover, maternity benefits and much more.

The Future

A key challenge for Mars is to take its enormously successful and formerly unique way of doing business and move it forward. Mike Smith: 'We need to look at our "no status" approach and make sure it becomes even more relevant for future generations. Our differences are always in danger of being eroded unless we work hard to retain our leading edge.'

In the same way, the company needs to become even more innovative in terms of its products. Mars is no stranger to innovation: it invented the confectionery ice-cream market, was first out with filled chocolate bars, launched prepared petfood, and was at the forefront of electronic coin mechanisms. It needs to maintain this cutting edge into the twenty-first century with new product launches geared to lifestyle changes.

Finally, it needs to continue to attract and retain the top people. Given the past success of the company coupled with its genuinely enthusiastic and able people, Mars looks set fair for all three goals.

MCI WorldCom

MCI WorldCom is the world's first fully integrated, global communications services company with operations in over 65 countries including the Americas, Europe and Asia Pacific regions. It came about following the merger in 1998 of two world leaders in communications – MCI and WorldCom. MCI WorldCom provides global customers with a full set of data, Internet, local, long-distance and international communications services over its fully integrated 'local-to-global-to-local' network. MCI WorldCom's international business outside the Americas is headquartered in London, as is the UK operating company. Worldwide, MCI WorldCom had revenues in excess of $30 billion in 1997 and 75,000 employees; 1,100 employees were based in London at the end of 1998.

Scorecard:

Remuneration and benefits	★★★★
Progressive attitude	★★★★★
Opportunity for promotion	★★★★★
Training, development and education	★★★★
Working atmosphere and environment	★★★★

Biggest plus:
Rapid growth business, lots of opportunity and
early responsibility

Biggest minus:
Not for the work shy or those who don't totally embrace real
customer service

MCI WorldCom Ltd.
14 Gray's Inn Road
London WC1X 8HN
Tel: 0171 675 5000
Fax: 0171 675 5711
website: mciworldcom.com

MCI WorldCom

The Business

MCI WorldCom is positioned at the very forefront of the fast-growing global business of telecommunications. According to Bernard J. Ebbers, president and chief executive officer, 'MCI WorldCom is uniquely qualified to lead the industry in growth and to build on the tremendous value we have created for our shareholders. We have the right network – built for the explosive demand for high-speed data and Internet services – the right talent, and the right strategy at the right time. Simply put, MCI WorldCom is out in front and sets the standard by which all other communications companies will be measured.'

The merger of MCI and WorldCom in 1998 was a happy marriage and combined some core strengths. MCI was a leading player in the Americas; WorldCom had an extensive Pan-European network and an expanding presence in Asia. MCI WorldCom is the second largest long-distance carrier in the US and the second largest carrier of international voice traffic in the world.

With UUNET, whose UK operation is based in Cambridge, MCI WorldCom is one of the world's leading providers of Internet services. The worldwide demand for data and Internet services is phenomenal, growing at something like 70% each year.

Around half of the people in London are dedicated to the UK operation, the remainder to MCI WorldCom International, which has responsibility for all operations outside the Americas.

Company Culture and Style

First and foremost, the culture at MCI WorldCom is one of growth which rests fundamentally on a dedication to customers in the form of innovation, excellent service and competitive prices.

In that sense, the merger of MCI and WorldCom's businesses required no corresponding merger of cultures. 'We just changed the name,' suggests Michael Butler, managing director of MCI WorldCom Limited. MCI (which grew rapidly in the 1970s/80s) has a very strong marketing culture – it invented the 'Friends & Family' concept for example – and the younger WorldCom has fully taken this on board.

This is a company where entrepreneurial spirit, fast-moving and alive are genuine descriptions, and ones heard from the employees themselves. People feel that they can really make a difference and control their own careers. 'We aspire to be the largest small company in the world,' says John Sidgmore, vice chairman.

As MCI WorldCom grows, it would be easy to allow bureaucracy to creep in. It resists. 'Around three-quarters of our people in the UK have direct contact with customers and are more in tune with their needs,' says Michael Butler. 'Few telecommunications companies can quote these kinds of numbers.'

And it's no surprise that the company is very results-oriented. People are paid on what they do for the company, the revenue they earn and what they do for customers (or measured against performance objectives if not in a sales/customer role). It is not a 'hire and fire' organisation; people are supported and encouraged, but they are expected to perform. It's also an ethical company and in selecting its managers, a strong moral code is applied about dealing with people.

There is a strong UK culture but there is no tribalism and everyone feels very much part of a global company. It's a very 'together' company – surveys reveal a high proportion of staff who can articulate the company's strategy, and there are many international forums and collaboration.

Human Resources

HR is very much an integral part of the business. There are very many commercially aware people working in the HR department – by deliberate design.

When you mention the word recruitment to the HR team, you can see in their faces what a task this is. Having grown quickly to 1,100 full-time employees in the UK, the target for 1999 is to reach 2,700 people. Finding enough office space is a perpetual challenge.

'We try something new each year,' says Alison Peggs, UK HR director, referring to the need to find energetic, ambitious, high-calibre people to keep the company ahead of this rapidly evolving market. Quality and quantity are every bit as important. In 1998 one recruitment consultancy was hired to manage the entire screening process, outsourcing in turn to around 60 others, allowing MCI WorldCom to retain essential control but let go of the reins at certain points.

There is a lot of direct interest of course – from people at communications companies and further afield – and a referral scheme pays employees if their recommendation joins and stays. The company feels justified in head-hunting talent, but also monitors companies which are shedding people and even works closely with them in outplacement. 'We're constantly thinking of new ways, who else, where else?' says Alison.

Individuals are put through a rigorous selection process, with HR always involved. In looking for people with the right attitudes and behaviour towards others, MCI WorldCom believes that if its senior people get it right, they in turn will find and choose others with similar qualities.

Career Opportunity and Development

MCI WorldCom's graduate programme took in a number of general management trainees and engineers in 1998 and a larger programme is expected in 1999. Obviously, other graduates are recruited directly into positions. 'We are mindful to manage development carefully so we don't overdo things,' adds Alison Peggs. 'We want to maintain the quality of our graduate programme.'

Engineers form the backbone of the organisation, designing, developing, delivering and supporting the networks and systems that allow MCI WorldCom to provide high-quality services to customers. Information systems is another major occupation.

General management covers management, sales, marketing, customer service and other general business skills, and there is the chance to move into more specialist areas like international business development, network trading and property management.

MCI WorldCom is particularly interested in people looking for a career in sales and account management. There are many other commercial and customer-facing roles and of course the professional areas including finance, accounting and legal.

Individuals on the graduate programme discuss where they would like to be in 9–12 months' time and then start a year of business projects in different areas. People often end up in a completely different area to what they expected! But most will during the programme be given a huge amount of responsibility and gain insights into real business issues. The company also offers one month abroad during the programme.

And that sets the tone. This is a young company where responsibility comes early and in whatever quantity you can handle. The average age of the UK workforce is only 33, but experience is always highly valued.

Across all functions, MCI WorldCom provides training in areas such as project management, presentation and communication skills, and formalised training running its own courses in sales and customer service. The company supports the majority of people doing external qualifications including MBAs and professional courses.

There is always a balance to be struck between self-development and training, and people often develop because the job grows and they grow with it.

Not surprisingly, there are international opportunities for transfers, secondments (UK communications engineers are very highly rated abroad) and international co-operation is the norm. 'Because of the global angle I visit the US three or four times a year and talk to American colleagues every day,' says Fergus Haddow, senior manager in engineering, who joined as a graduate in 1993.

Remuneration

MCI WorldCom pays salaries around the median level and benchmarks regularly in a competitive market to avoid 'salary drift'. Bonuses are performance related and have averaged around 18% of salary recently.

The MCI WorldCom stock plan is very attractive. After a qualifying period, all employees are given shares at a strike price and vested over three years. MCI WorldCom's stock price has outperformed the telecommunications sector by a considerable margin, and the value of an individual's shares vested each year can be worth a five-figure dollar sum.

The Future

MCI WorldCom has now reached a sufficient critical mass, with a range of sophisticated global services, that expectations are high and the challenge is for the business to keep growing, offer a consistent level of service, meet regulatory requirements and allow people to still make a difference. 'We know that we must have the process parameters to maintain our edge,' says Michael Butler.

Telecommunications is riding an explosion at the moment, and as MCI WorldCom's fibre optic networks expand, so it will provide new challenges for people throughout the UK and in Europe.

With the sheer numbers of people joining MCI WorldCom, there is the question of how to 'sheep dip' them in the culture which has helped the company get to where it is today. 'Not necessarily everyone who walks through the doors is customer focused as we define it,' says Michael Butler, 'but they will be after working here.'

Meanwhile there will be a lot more attention to organisational planning, recognising that the business has grown so quickly, to avoid lack of clarity on tasks and responsibilities. If it gets these things right, MCI WorldCom will remain a front runner, offering tremendous opportunities in a very dynamic business.

McKinsey & Company

McKinsey & Company is, arguably, the leading management consulting firm in the world. Founded in 1926, McKinsey has enjoyed continued growth since that time and is now a truly international firm serving many of the world's most prominent organisations. McKinsey has worldwide revenues of around $18 billion, over 550 partners and some 4,000 consultants working in 76 offices in 38 countries. The London office is one of McKinsey's largest, employing around 275 consultants and 210 support staff, representing 30 nationalities.

Scorecard:

Remuneration and benefits	★★★★★
Progressive attitude	★★★★
Opportunity for promotion	★★★★★
Training, development and education	★★★★★
Working atmosphere and environment	★★★★

Biggest plus:
The blue-chip consulting firm with blue-chip clients worldwide

Biggest minus:
A very demanding, intellectual and hard-working environment

McKinsey & Company
1 Jermyn Street
London SW1Y 4UH
Tel: 0171 839 8040
Fax: 0171 873 9777
website: www.mckinsey.co.uk

McKinsey & Company

McKinsey & Company

The Business

In the words of *Business Week*, 'McKinsey is by far the most influential consulting firm in the world.' The firm focuses on business issues of most importance to senior management, advising on strategy and organisation, and how to improve operations such as sales or manufacturing.

McKinsey's pre-eminence stems from the reputation it has earned for objectivity and independence, and for bringing the highest intellectual and analytical skills to bear on the major challenges confronting the world's leading businesses and institutions. For this, McKinsey – or 'The Firm' as its members have long since called it – relies on the professionalism and dedication of its consultants worldwide.

Other firms may have the same brainpower, but they lack the same reputation. Rajat Gupta, McKinsey's managing director, says: 'All I know is that every consulting firm anybody talks to always says they're second to McKinsey.'

McKinsey's (confidential) client list is impressive, virtually a 'Who's Who' of the world's major organisations including multinational companies, national governments and charities, as well as fast-growing smaller firms. McKinsey's work cuts across all business sectors – from investment banking to retailing, from television to oil companies – and the firm is proud that many of its clients are leaders in their sectors.

Company Culture and Style

McKinsey consultants really do think that they are the best. They certainly inspire awe in many people, reflecting the premium placed within the McKinsey culture on very bright people.

McKinsey's stated mission is 'To help our clients make distinctive, lasting and substantial improvements in their performance, and to build a great firm that is able to attract, develop, excite and retain exceptional people.'

McKinsey operates a 'one-firm principle'. While each office is strongly rooted in its national culture, all consultants share a common working approach and the same high standards of client service. Consulting teams are often pulled together from all over the world.

What makes McKinsey special? It only accepts assignments where it believes that it can make a positive, lasting impact. McKinsey works *with* its clients, not *for* them, so that it can make solutions stick. The firm only works on issues that are really important to senior management. It considers the problem from all angles, but always puts together an integrated view of the way forward from a top management perspective.

Outsiders have never regarded McKinsey as an open organisation, and the company certainly shuns publicity. This all adds to its mystique. It tends to deal with things internally. McKinsey accommodates a broad diversity of opinions, fostering rigorous debate to get the right answer. Yet it tries to achieve things collectively and the McKinsey culture probably functions so well because it hires the same people over and over.

Teamworking is absolutely fundamental. A team's success hinges on the ability of its members to work together in gathering information and performing the analysis that will prove or disprove their hypotheses. The McKinsey environment is therefore a mutually supportive one, with clients the primary focus. Ian Davis, head of the London office, says 'Although now managing partner, I still see myself primarily as a consultant and strive to spend about half my time working with clients.'

Human Resources

Human resources is an absolutely critical function in McKinsey. Necessarily, a major priority is placed on hiring exceptional individuals. The recruitment process can be a gruelling one, but this makes sure that the candidate is right for the firm, and vice versa. McKinsey typically recruits around 20 people in the UK each year – graduates and postgraduates – to become business analysts.

Strategy consulting is all about solving problems and influencing people. McKinsey therefore seeks individuals with outstanding intellectual ability and interpersonal skills. The qualities it looks for in candidates are problem-solving ability, personal impact, leadership and drive.

McKinsey believes that developing its people is just as crucial as serving its clients, although of course this is a virtuous circle. The firm invests heavily in each consultant's personal learning, through both formal training and on-the-job coaching.

Career Opportunity and Development

McKinsey is a special place to work, both for those interested in consulting long term and for people who want a major boost to their CV for the rest of their working life.

Operating as one global firm, the firm's range of training programmes takes place all over the world, mixing participants from various offices.

A three-week Induction Programme aims at providing business consultants with the skills needed to get started. The Analyst Training Programme is a firm-wide programme to further develop consulting skills such as problem structuring and solving, analytical techniques, accounting and interviewing. Communication training and language training courses are also encouraged.

Consultants at McKinsey are responsible for managing their own careers. There are development leaders to support individuals, however, who monitor their development based on appraisals received after each study, provide formal feedback twice a year, and advise on career issues.

After two years, business analysts may opt to take an MBA at business school, or pursue a career in industry. Most choose to attend business school and McKinsey offers financial help to people who have performed well in the firm and secured a place. And those who decide that management consultancy is not for them will still find that their time with McKinsey has opened doors to positions they would probably not otherwise have achieved.

This remains a demanding environment. If at any stage in the career path a consultant ceases to progress, he or she is asked to leave McKinsey. This 'up or out' policy applies throughout the firm, from associates to senior partners, and ensures that McKinsey continues to motivate exceptional people and provide superior client service.

Of course, many people return to McKinsey after business school and enjoy long and rewarding careers with the firm. Their career paths then tend to be more clearly defined and, as consultants, they will gradually undertake larger and more complex sections of work. Training continues as careers progress.

Working for a large management consultancy like McKinsey offers advantages. Consultants are likely to encounter a greater range of industries, clients and issues. Due to the multinational client list, many projects will have an international component. The firm's level of accumulated knowledge is deep, and there is a readily available network of experts to contact worldwide.

Opportunities for career progression are not confined to the firm. McKinsey's reputation, and the work carried out by its consultants, make people very attractive propositions to other employers. McKinsey alumni are found all over the business world, many at the head of very large companies and corporations. Alumni of the London office include Sir John Banham, chairman of Kingfisher; Howard Davies, deputy governor of the Bank of England; Nick Kirkbride, managing director of Virgin Cola; and William Hague, leader of the Conservative Party.

As another McKinsey graduate, Archie Norman, chairman of Asda, puts it: 'When you leave McKinsey, you see immediately how translatable many of your skills are. The accelerated learning curve, and the fact that you have been working for clients who look to McKinsey for advice on their most important corporate decisions, means that you've acquired an excellent foundation to move into a major role in industry.'

Remuneration

Management consulting is renowned as a well-paid industry; McKinsey certainly pays attractively and is at least competitive with other leading management consultancies. To get some indication of long-term possibility, a junior director in the US can earn around $800,000 a year, and a junior partner around half a million.

The Future

In troubled global markets, several financial and manufacturing firms are said to have curtailed their use of management consultants. But McKinsey, along with other leading firms, says it expects to continue to hire people and to continue to grow revenues.

In a world seemingly overpopulated with consultants, the main question remains whether McKinsey can endure as one of the ultimate worldwide brand names. Or are the others catching up?

Other consultancies may claim that McKinsey's consultants are no brighter than their own, probably with some justification. But McKinsey has the reputation, aura and credibility that appears to be unquestionable and unstoppable. No chief executive ever lost his job by hiring McKinsey. The Firm just goes from strength to strength.

As a 'top management' strategy consultancy, McKinsey was slower to venture too far into areas such as implementation and information technology-based consultancy, which it had left to others. With the increasing importance of technology in just about every industry and business, this shift will have to accelerate.

And there is the question whether management consultancy can and should be sold as 'products' rather then services. McKinsey has always eschewed 'flavour of the month' consulting ideas, preferring instead to market intelligent thinking to strategic issues. But it may have to consider shifting this stance and try to sell the next 'big idea'.

These may only be distractions. McKinsey's core consulting service rests on deep relationships with senior managers in business, who return to the firm time and time again. McKinsey remains the consulting firm others would like to emulate.

Nationwide Building Society

Nationwide is the world's largest building society and remains committed to mutuality. Nationwide offers its eight million customers a broad range of retail financial services including mortgages, savings, current accounts, life assurance, investment products, personal loans and household insurance. In 1997/98, Nationwide reported operating profits of £413 million and, in October 1998, assets passed the £50 billion mark. With headquarters in Swindon and a second major administrative centre in Northampton, Nationwide has 681 branches and 10,727 employees in the UK, including approximately 2,000 at the group's head office.

Scorecard:

Remuneration and benefits	★★★★
Progressive attitude	★★★★
Opportunity for promotion	★★★★
Training, development and education	★★★★★
Working atmosphere and environment	★★★★★

Biggest plus:
A genuine, happy culture with the right balance between interests of customers and staff

Biggest minus:
No room for complacency in a tough market

Nationwide Building Society
Nationwide House
Pipers Way
Swindon SN38 1NW
Tel: 01793 513513
Fax: 01793 455045
website: www.nationwide.co.uk

Nationwide Building Society

The Business

Nationwide celebrated its 150-year anniversary at the end of 1998, and is the product of over a hundred mergers of smaller building societies.

In deciding to remain a mutual building society, Nationwide has underlined its commitment to putting its customers first. Nationwide's chief executive Brian Davis is a true champion of mutuality, but stresses, 'I am not a crusader for mutuality as a substitute for running a good business operation. Nobody owes us a living and they will certainly not provide it if we simply insist that they come to us because we are mutual. We have to deliver the best value and that means running an efficient and effective organisation.'

Nevertheless, by putting customer, not shareholder, satisfaction as its long-term goal, Nationwide is able to operate on narrower margins and reduced planned profit in order to give customers long-term benefits. And it 'walks the talk', returning over £300 million to members in 1998/99 in the form of improved rates and better services.

Nationwide is indeed aptly named. Its business remains primarily branch-based, and its coverage is throughout the UK. A better sponsor for the Nationwide Football League (as well as the local club, Swindon Town) could not be imagined. It is also growing its sales force, which is fully occupied just serving the existing customer base, and Nationwide Direct.

Company Culture and Style

Nationwide's customer proposition says: 'Nationwide puts customers first by providing a full range of top value, quality financial services that are widely available and delivered with speed, courtesy and reliability backed by underlying policies of fairness, honesty, employee importance and corporate responsibility.'

There is a genuine commitment by all staff to focus on the customer, and this is integral to Nationwide's culture. Everyone in Nationwide knows what they are doing and why, and more importantly, agree with it. Words like 'trust' and 'teamwork' find a happy home here – just as well, because balancing the business proposition of mutuality is actually quite tough. But being a part of a customer-focused organisation seems to be motivating. 'There was cheering heard over the tannoy when the results of our annual general meeting were announced,' says Dennis Brockwell, divisional director, personnel and development.

In building its 'good business to work for' culture, Nationwide invests heavily in training and development, linking business planning with personal development. Investors in People accreditation is highly valued as exactly the type of framework and independent recognition the society wants. Nationwide believes that people need to feel fairly rewarded for what they do, and 'fairness' is one of the most frequently used words in the society.

A similar priority is put on honest, open communication. Nationwide canvasses employee opinions confidentially through its ever-improving Employee Attitude Survey, *Viewpoint*. Acting quickly upon observations, Nationwide really does want to be 'the place where you want to work'.

Nationwide also plays an active part in the community. In addition to its core community affairs programme, the Nationwide Macmillan Campaign has been very important to the society, helping to build team values. With Nationwide's support, its employees have organised events that have raised over £1.25 million for this cancer charity. Nationwide Building Society has also established the Nationwide Foundation which is the vehicle used for charitable donations.

Human Resources

The human resources function, known as Personnel and Development (P&D) at Nationwide, has become very closely integrated with the business. 'To support the aims of the organisation we have to understand the drivers in the business environment,' suggests Keith Astill, head of retail personnel and development, 'and that means working with the business, not in a bunker. That way we discover what our customers want and translate this back to our employees.'

In an industry undergoing rapid change, P&D shoulders the key task of building a more flexible organisation. This has meant removing organisational blockages, bureaucracies and obstacles to help people absorb change. Flexible working is rapidly climbing the agenda. Nationwide already has some people working different hours, for example in the call centres, but the branches traditionally opened from 9 to 5. Now, driven by changing customer needs such as late night and weekend shopping, Nationwide knows that its branches have to stay open longer.

Fortunately, employees suggested that 9 to 5 didn't suit them either. Nationwide's style is not to dictate, but to consult staff and to ensure that rewards match any new ways of working. Now the society is finding that people in other parts of the business want to join in! Even some who had left the society want to return and there is a rich seam of people attracted to the proposition of flexible working.

P&D is committed to instilling the right competencies at the crucial customer–staff interface. Particularly in the branches, many managers have progressed quickly by P&D blending in vital management skills of leadership and people management with excellent technical, product or process skills.

Career Opportunity and Development

There is a wide range of jobs at Nationwide. While there are always opportunities for people with a specialisation, technical expertise or profession, Nationwide would like to see career development become more wide-ranging and give people experience across the business.

You can move quite quickly at Nationwide. There are directors in their late 30s and Nationwide tries hard to promote from within.

The Retail Management Trainee Scheme has now become a corporate scheme, which trainees and graduates join annually. The Corporate Management Trainee Scheme includes a two-year training period, followed by a job placement. Participants should filter through to the 'High Potential Scheme' designed for individuals who can progress quickly and, with appropriate training and development, should expect to reach senior manager level. This route is not exclusive, and many on the scheme are non-graduates.

Everyone in the business has a performance agreement ('what should I contribute this year?') and their own development plan. This makes for a better relationship and understanding between manager and employee as to what a person can achieve and how.

Nationwide takes equal opportunity very seriously indeed – not a gratuitous gesture, but good business sense. 'If we have a widespread customer base, it surely makes sense to have a diversified workforce and gain access to as wide a base of talent as possible,' suggests Dennis Brockwell.

More than half of Nationwide's managers are women and it seeks a fair representation among its employees of the diverse make-up of the UK population. Nationwide is an active member of Opportunity 2000 and the Employers Forum on Disability, and a founder member of the Employers Forum on Age. The society employs some 900 people over the age of 50. Nationwide has also jointly won the Newcomer category in the Parents at Work 'Employer of the Year Award'.

Remuneration

Nationwide staff receive fair reward and are paid rates competitive with its peer group. An employee's performance is reflected in his or her individual salary.

The corporate bonus scheme is calculated on a common basis of overall efficiency, profitability and customer satisfaction (in 1997/98 it paid 9.2%). The flexible benefits package 'Choices' enjoys a high take-up, as does Nationwide's excellent group pension scheme, which is ranked in the top three out of 200 in the recent Union Pension Services Limited Survey.

The Future

Nationwide wants to be number one in terms of business efficiency and customer service and looks to technology – but only in the right amount – to deepen the customer relationship. Homeworking, an e-mail response unit for customers, e-mail and an Intranet for better internal communications and effective working are all playing a part.

Improving access is something which Nationwide is keen on in the widest sense. In the marketplace, the scope for electronic commerce, Internet, telephone and customer information services is driven by what customers want. But the branch will remain vitally important to Nationwide. Believing that the personal and advisory function is crucial, the branches feature more advisors and bigger interview areas for customers.

Nationwide is a great innovator though. Interactive methods include the 'Virtual Branch' accessed by customers from multimedia kiosks to learn about Nationwide products, a touch-screen video conferencing facility that takes you live to a person at Nationwide, and a pioneering automated teller machine that recognises an individual's unique iris rather than a PIN number.

The financial services business is expected to consolidate further, though there is also a view that smaller, regional building societies will continue to thrive on local customer loyalty. But Nationwide is hardly small. And with the public being encouraged to make their own pension provision and long-term care, there is a lot to go for.

Nationwide is growing into its role as the UK's leading mutual building society and believes that it is right for its members that it remains a mutual organisation. The real challenge is to demonstrate that there are real customer benefits from what it is doing and to continue to deliver them. It must always convince customers that it has more to offer than the banks. Nationwide's spirit, and its commitment that 'it pays to decide Nationwide', gives it every chance of success.

NDS

NDS is a world-leading provider of digital broadcasting solutions to prestigious clients including BSkyB, BBC, Reuters, NBC and Deutsche Telecom. NDS designs, manufactures and integrates digital broadcasting systems, digital compression, multiplexing and modulation equipment, as well as conditional access and subscriber management systems. Part of the News Corporation and with headquarters in Heathrow, this British company operates a global network with major customer sales and support offices in the US, Hong Kong and Australia. Of some 1,400 employees worldwide, 750 are in the UK. More than 50% of its staff are involved in research and development activities in the UK and Israel. Turnover in 1997/98 reached around £200 million.

Scorecard:

Remuneration and benefits	★★★★★
Progressive attitude	★★★★
Opportunity for promotion	★★★★★
Training, development and education	★★★★
Working atmosphere and environment	★★★

Biggest plus:
Fast growth company in the right industry

Biggest minus:
Growing too fast to develop organised career structures

NDS
Strategic Park
Comines Way
Hedge End
Southampton SO30 4DA
Tel: 01703 484393
Fax: 01703 484399
e-mail: jobs@ndsuk.com
website: www.ndsworld.com

WORLD LEADER · WORLD VISION

NDS

The Business

NDS is a real British success story in the exciting and specialist high-tech world of digital broadcasting technology. Holding Queens Awards for Export and Technology, NDS is a technology leader, creating new and innovative ways to optimise bandwidth, improve picture quality, enhance and protect broadcaster revenues and provide solutions to deliver entertainment and information to televisions and personal computers.

NDS technology, products and broadcast 'know how' have been used to provide coverage of major world events including the handover of Hong Kong, the Pope's visit to Cuba, Princess Diana's funeral as well as the Nagano 1998 Winter Olympics, Wimbledon '97, the US Open Golf Championship and the 1998 World Cup in France.

Some 80% of the business is overseas, but in the UK, NDS systems and equipment have been key to the successful launch of SkyDigital and the Digital Terrestrial Services being set up by Channels 3 and 4.

NDS in its current form dates from March 1997, but its antecedents can be traced back many years. The broadcast engineering division, for example, has its roots in the research division of the Independent Broadcasting Authority, pioneers in the development and exploitation of digital compression technology. NDS is the leading supplier of the MPEG-2/DVB compression, multiplexing and modulation products for cable, satellite and terrestrial applications. A constituent business, News Datacom, revolutionised the satellite Pay TV industry and became the world's leading designer of smart card-based VideoCrypt™, NewsCrypt™ and VideoGuard™ conditional access systems.

Company Culture and Style

There are effectively several cultures within the NDS organisation springing from the main locations and functions in Southampton (focused primarily on broadcast engineering), Heathrow (business applications and IT system products) and Jerusalem (conditional access and set-top box technology). NDS has evolved a federal culture without a strongly centralised command and control environment.

This deliberately makes decision-making chains as short as possible. Anything seen as interfering with the speed of designing and delivering technical solutions takes second place. According to Mike Windram, senior VP, broadcast engineering, 'You won't get down-marked for making a bad decision, but you will for not making a decision at all.' NDS knows that with cutting edge technology you won't always get it right first time – and a blame culture just would not succeed.

Cultural differences between different sites can lead to a certain amount of creative tension, but the company's core philosophy is common to them all, namely, to find the best way of meeting customers' needs and exceeding expectations.

Technically more innovative than the competition, NDS also gets its product to market faster. 'You don't get a second chance to come first with customers,' points out Abe Peled, chief executive officer.

NDS recognises that you have to give creativity space. Its engineers value highly that once the company has set the scene, they are allowed to 'get on with it'. And if there is a self-appointed élite, as there is in most companies, then at NDS it is the design and development engineers.

The structure at NDS is very flat. Management is very open and 'will talk to anyone'. Job titles are American rather than British – you'll be aiming for vice president rather than general manager – reflecting the importance of the US market.

Human Resources

While NDS recognises that it is 'not perfect', it does offer people leading-edge work, considerable training and development opportunities, and good remuneration packages.

A staff survey – the first under the auspices of NDS – is currently underway. It has some quite specific objectives. The company thinks that there are too many 'blue sky' surveys with no useable information, and wants instead tangible things to work on so that it can match perceptions and establish HR priorities. The degree of structure to the salary system, working relationships and communications are on the agenda.

This is an intellectually stimulating environment, and the company looks for good degrees in (typically) computer sciences, electronics or communications engineering. NDS also wants people with the vision, inspiration and conceptual abilities to push the boundaries of digital broadcasting technology. Interpersonal skills are extremely important, given the need to liaise in a multidisciplinary culture.

NDS is rather preoccupied with growth, and recruiting for growth, leaving less time to develop formalised career structures. But because of the company's compact size and the way it works, if you have talent it will get exposed fairly quickly. And if an individual requests an opportunity, they are likely to be given the work experience and training appropriate to the needs. It is almost a self-selection process, where the more assertive individuals with a clear idea of where they want to get to, are likely to get there first.

Career Opportunity and Development

The relative lack of defined structures or a prescriptive framework calls for a degree of self-reliance. 'If an individual needs well-defined boxes to feel comfortable within, then this is not the environment for them,' says Phillip Hodson, resourcing manager. This is a domain of achieved rather than ascribed authority. People are recognised for the expertise they deliver and the contribution they make to the business whatever their position.

About 75% of the NDS population is qualified in engineering or related disciplines, and half the staff are involved in research and development. Engineers are likely to be involved in either product design or core systems integration, adapting, building and installing specific systems for clients. NDS has a good track record of its design engineers developing into project engineers. Marketing and sales specialists are also in demand and, of course, the company requires the other professional support functions.

NDS takes between 6–12 new graduates a year on a direct entry basis, and they are given the opportunity to 'get stuck in' and contribute from a fairly early stage, with the back-up of training and support.

Outsiders do try and pinch people from NDS, 'luckily without too much success', claims Phillip Hodson. Conversely, NDS does manage to pull in many more people from other broadcasting and digital communication companies.

Technical training is handled in-house using specialists dedicated exclusively to this task. TV technology, MPEG technology, database design all represent examples of underpinning technology which go into product design. There is also development in the 'softer' areas of competencies and personal skills.

NDS was a 1998 finalist in the Knowledge Culture category of the Information Strategy Training award scheme organised under the auspices of *The Economist*. This recognised the innovative training programme the company had developed for its own specific needs, not only looking at training issues which affected the company, but also taking the skills developed in training to apply to solutions for particular problems.

Remuneration

Remuneration is very competitive and flexible, based on two key elements: market value and personal contribution. There are no grade boundaries, which facilitates flexible reward strategies. HR's role is therefore not to police a structure but to help managers make the right salary decisions for their people, whether this is to recruit or to retain. Pay consists of salary and an annual bonus, supplemented by the usual package of benefits.

Offering competitive market rates is a key driver, particularly for disciplines in short supply such as software developers and digital communication specialists, and those which are equally employable in the City and industry. HR has responsibility for benchmarking salaries externally and keeping an eye on internal relativities.

The Future

NDS has set itself ambitious targets, such as trebling turnover over the next four years. Much will depend on the direction technology takes. With the convergence of technologies, for example between TVs and personal computers, NDS is putting greater focus on alternative delivery systems using new media and interactive technologies as opposed to TV systems.

There is a limit to how far the process of its key technologies – compression and conditional access – can go. When these become mature technologies, the issue will become what applications they can be used for.

For NDS, the main danger will be losing the edge. There doesn't appear to be any immediate chance of it becoming a middle-aged company just yet, but the point is taken on board.

Then there is the considerable challenge of finding the people. A lot will be needed. In the key disciplines of electronic and communications engineering, it appears that not enough of the right quality are being produced. A critical judgement of the British universities perhaps, but NDS believes that too many graduates just don't have quite the edge to 'think beyond what they've been taught' for the demanding work of design. Sponsoring PhD students is one option that it has commenced, but so too has the recruitment of graduates from Europe. The opportunities for NDS are clear enough, and finding enough of the right people may prove to be its toughest test.

Nestlé

Nestlé is the largest food manufacturing company in the world. The Nestlé Group employs 225,000 people in 77 countries, and sells over 15,000 products in almost every country in the world. Nestlé sells 250 different products in the UK, including many household names such as Nescafé, Kit Kat, Crosse & Blackwell and Quality Street. It has 28 UK factories and employs around 14,000 people.

Scorecard:

Remuneration and benefits	★★★★
Progressive attitude	★★★★
Opportunity for promotion	★★★★★
Training, development and education	★★★★★
Working atmosphere and environment	★★★★

Biggest plus:
A lively, focused business with a strong sense of direction

Biggest minus:
Not a company for people who can't cope with rapid change!

Nestlé UK Limited
St George's House
Croydon
Surrey CR9 1NR
Tel: 0181 686 3333
Fax: 0181 686 6072
website: www.nestle.com

Nestlé

The Business

The origins of Nestlé go back to 1866. The present company was formed following the acquisition of Rowntree Macintosh in 1988. Today, Nestlé UK comprises three main divisions: Nestlé Beverage Division, Nestlé Rowntree Division and Nestlé Food Division. Nestlé UK also incorporates Nestlé Ice Cream, a business development unit which grows new product ideas and handles various corporate functions.

Essentially a branded food manufacturer, Nestlé markets a remarkable array of well-known names. Confectionery may be the first thing that springs to mind when the company is mentioned – no surprise with such brands as Kit Kat, Rolo, Aero and Yorkie under its belt. But that's just the beginning. It holds the number one brand in no fewer than 28 UK market sectors, with Nescafé Buitoni, Branston, Sun-Pat and Crosse & Blackwell. Nestlé has two further businesses in the UK Friskies Petcare and Perrier Vittel, and a joint venture, Cereal Partners, which sells cereals under the Nestlé brand.

Nestlé is as international as any company in the world. Despite its wide coverage, each country is highly autonomous. It employs local people who know their own consumers' tastes and preferences and takes a long-term view of its markets in order to establish a solid, growth-oriented business.

Company Culture and Style

Nestlé is highly professional in the way it treats and develops its people – as its low staff turnover confirms. Striving for excellence may be a cliché, but it accurately describes the Nestlé approach. Consumers expect its products to be of the highest standard, every time. Such high standards demand equally high quality staff.

So what are the qualities needed to succeed in the world's largest food manufacturer? Graham Prentice, director of HR development and remuneration: 'The people who do well here are highly effective and professional in everything they do. They are open-minded and willing to drive change. They are able to demonstrate that they can add value; they're focused, driven, and have a sense of energy and passion about what they're trying to do. Our people genuinely get excited about our products and how to develop them, which of course helps to make work fun – as it should be.'

Nestlé UK recently overhauled its graduate development programme, the result of considerable time spent talking to its own graduate employees, researching what makes graduate recruitment successful, and also discussing with undergraduates what they wanted. The company takes on 25 graduates each year, offering them challenging work, extensive learning, exciting career development and early responsibility. The development programme typically lasts for 18 months to two years and, unlike some companies, follows an individually tailored flexible path.

Niall O'Brien joined the programme with an MSc in food science. 'Working on the development of new products is one of the most exciting areas for me. I have learned that the abilities to organise, prioritise, work alone and work within a team are all crucial.' Hayley Glasby graduated with a degree in PPE. 'Since joining, I've had three very different placements. There is no routine to this job – the only given is that I know I will arrive and leave, and be challenged, stimulated and entertained in the bits in between!' History graduate Elizabeth Roscoe: 'Working for the largest food manufacturer in the world means it's important to make your achievements stand out, and that's where it's down to you to use your determination and initiative to steer your career.'

Nestlé has set out what it wants from its managers and leaders. These qualities and characteristics include courage, composure and the capacity to handle business demands; the ability to learn, communicate and motivate others; the willingness to accept and manage change; and the possession of credibility – in other words, practising what they preach. Its style favours flat organisations with few levels of management and broad spans of control including project teams and task forces. Informality, friendliness and first-name terms characterise the culture.

Human Resources

Most appointments at Nestlé UK are made from within, apart from a relatively small number of senior level posts. This means that the development of its people has a particularly high emphasis at the company, and, in turn, the organisational capability of its HR division is vital.

The HR team has identified five areas where it can make a difference: resourcing, development, performance, reward and recognition, and costs. Graham Prentice: 'We've done lots of work on people performance issues. A major development within that has been the development of our performance management system: this is all about measuring, tracking, and, above all, improving an individual's performance in line with business goals.' All managers over the next few years will undertake development in the people performance area.

As Graham Prentice says, 'People want security, development and challenging work. The HR team is here to help our line managers provide these by developing their skills and capabilities.' For senior managers the company encourages action-based learning. It has a programme run in conjunction with the Swiss business school IMD: managers take time out to work on a real business consultancy project. More junior levels also spend lots of time learning how to manage people, teams, money and projects – foundation skills for future managers, in effect.

Career Opportunity and Development

There are career management groups right across the business which meet twice a year. These groups are each made up of six to ten senior managers, who discuss people's career development. The majority of vacancies are openly advertised (including being posted on the company's Intranet).

Being such an international company, there are plenty of chances to work abroad for those who want them. This would often be as two- to three-year assignments, and would be part of the individual's overall career development as assessed by the performance management process. Managers going overseas have to have a solid record of good performance. Nestlé as an international company is divided into three zones so most Nestlé UK staff who work abroad go to Europe, but there are opportunities to live and work further afield. Anyone about to work abroad can have language training beforehand – including the employee's partner and children.

There is no pressure to work overseas, however, and most people are happy to develop their careers in the UK, where there is more than enough to challenge them in any case! With a large number of factories operating in the UK, some choose to develop their career by moving around. The company provides full relocation support.

Career development is a shared responsibility at Nestlé, and there is a strong development culture to assist with study which is relevant to the current or a future post. This sharing may include time off for home study, payment of study fees, and so on. One-to-one reviews help to identify each individual's needs and focus on them. There is a huge commitment to training in the company. Nestlé runs the bulk of its courses at its own residential training centre in Berkshire and at its York facility. It will also run outside courses, for instance senior management development courses structured in conjunction with Warwick University and with IMD in Switzerland.

Remuneration

Nestlé's pay scales are around the median/upper quartile level. Graham Prentice: 'Our rates must be competitive to attract the best people, and we don't have a problem recruiting top managers into the business, so I'd say we had that right. We're also flexible; if the market rate for a function changes, we will pay accordingly.'

The company is moving towards a reward and recognition system with strong links between pay and development. Bonuses vary according to seniority but, in principle, when people deliver they receive appropriate recognition and reward for their work.

All staff receive health insurance cover, and there are private medical insurance arrangements for certain groups of people. There is a highly rated final salary pension scheme, and an attractive and flexible company car scheme for middle and senior managers (and those who need a car as part of their job).

The Future

Nestlé UK is much concerned with growth – and recent years have seen exactly that, especially 1998. This has been led by a strategy of fostering consumer communications, innovation, product availability and low-cost, high-quality operations. A new integrated computer system, SAP, is allowing people to track the performance of manufacturing lines hour by hour rather than on a daily or weekly basis.

More than ever, Nestlé UK is determined to be innovative in all it does. This will continue to generate exciting new products; but, above all, its continued success will be about employing the right people, having good business processes and being close to its consumers.

Nortel Networks

Nortel Networks is a leading supplier of digital networks. Formed from the merger of Nortel and Bay Networks in June 1998, it designs, builds and integrates digital networks for customers in the information, communications, entertainment, education and commerce markets. Nortel Networks had 1998 revenues of US$17.6 billion and has approximately 75,000 employees worldwide.

Scorecard:

Remuneration and benefits	★★★★
Progressive attitude	★★★★★
Opportunity for promotion	★★★★
Training, development and education	★★★★
Working atmosphere and environment	★★★★★

Biggest plus:
Superb leading-edge technology and job mobility opportunities

Biggest minus:
Don't consider joining unless you are passionate about the business

Nortel Networks
Maidenhead Office Park
Westacott Way
Maidenhead
Berkshire SL6 3QH
Tel: 01628 437494
Fax: 01628 437479
website: www.nortelnetworks.com

NØRTEL
NETWORKS™

How the world shares ideas.

Nortel Networks

The Business

Formed from the merger of Nortel and Bay Networks, Nortel Networks was the first company to successfully pioneer GSM technology in a moving car; it invented fibre optics transmission; and it is currently perfecting the method of sending and receiving the Internet through powerlines, at speeds of up to ten times the pace of ISDNs. It employs 75,000 people worldwide, 19,000 of whom work in Europe with 8,500 of those in the UK. Its 1998 global revenues were US$17.6 billion, and it operates in over 150 countries.

Nortel Networks is organised along five business lines: enterprise networks, enterprise data networks, wireless networks, broadband networks and public carrier networks. These work together to meet customer needs, allowing the company to offer genuine network solutions rather than simply sell products.

The company is recognised as a world leader in technology and innovation. Indeed, it has laid the foundation for tomorrow's economies in its work on optical networks, leading to a radical shift in the perception of what telephones and computers should be able to do.

Europe accounts for 22% of the company's global business. It has a presence in 30 countries, and has both independent and joint venture operations (including five major joint ventures in Germany, Austria, France, Turkey and Israel). Of its 19,000 European employees, 25% work in R&D. It also has 23 major distribution partners in Europe.

Company Culture and Style

Nortel Networks is a highly innovative company, one that attracts pioneers capable of finding unexpected solutions. Maurice Duffy, European resourcing director, describes it as a matrix organisation that is also very flexible: 'Individuals get a high degree of independence. It's a fascinating place to work; we deal with the world's largest PTTs, but we also have the excitement of working with new businesses. There's a huge spread, in fact.'

Anyone joining Nortel Networks will quickly have the chance to work with large groups of people with diverse backgrounds. Its leading-edge technology means that change is rapid, as is growth. People thinking of joining the company must be able to work at a fast pace – and generate ideas at an equally rapid rate.

The culture is certainly entrepreneurial. It is about freedom, independence, risk-taking and smart decisions. It focuses significantly on teamwork, and is ultimately driven by the company's customers. Work may be non-traditional: the company encourages teleworking, home-working and other, sometimes more effective, ways of doing business.

The type of person Nortel Networks looks for is bright, untroubled by change, able to take decisions, enjoys a fast pace and a somewhat unstructured environment, and has a strong sense of self-belief. To such people, it offers the chance to work with leading-edge technology for a broad spectrum of clients.

Nortel Networks is certainly not hierarchical or bureaucratic; it has just five levels of job. It is an informal place, uninterested in the trappings of status. The president of the company is known by his first name, for instance. Its speed of response is in part due to its decision to cut out links in the chain, and people are encouraged to communicate across business areas.

In short, Nortel Networks is fun to work for. Maurice Duffy: 'It's a serious business which enjoys itself. Many of our people are creative, innovative, fun to be around. We invest lots of time in external activities, and we also make an impact on society through such things as education assistance. We are involved with the Barton Training Trust which takes underprivileged children on holiday – we provide the people to help run it, as part of our leadership training programme.'

Human Resources

The HR strategy for Nortel Networks is linked to the overall business strategy: and a model produced by the London Business School ensures that this link remains in place. The company has a sophisticated resourcing strategy which is second to none. An internal resourcing group has bases in Maidenhead, Paris, Frankfurt and North America. A learning group focuses on maintaining the intellectual capital of individuals.

The company has consolidated the transactional parts of HR, with a resultant improvement in productivity. This means that one telephone call to its HR information centre can find all relevant details of an individual's employment.

All people are surveyed on an annual basis, followed up by quarterly reviews with targeted groups. More than 89% claim they love the work they do. This is perhaps to be expected, since the work is both meaningful and has an impact on the way the world does its business. This results in a low attrition rate; and many of those who leave opt to return to the company.

Career Opportunity and Development

Not surprisingly, Nortel Networks has a high intellectual base: 60% to 70% of its workforce are graduates. Nortel Networks also sponsors a large number of students going through university, whom it identifies during their final year of school. The company takes on around 500 graduate recruits across Europe each year, 300 in the UK. Successful candidates come through a rigorous and advanced selection process, then create a development plan for themselves for the first 10 months.

The career management process makes use of an appraisal system, Managing for Achievement. This features both annual and quarterly reviews and focuses on development within the business. As to advancement, Nortel Networks advertises all its jobs on the World Wide Web. All employees have access to the website, and can search by skill type, location and managers. Career development workshops are available to help managers develop their people. The Assessment Development Options Guide helps people identify both the skills they have and the skills they need to advance further.

Nortel Networks is very much a learning-based organisation. It offers internal and external training to both employees and customers. Most needs can be met by classroom training, but the company goes beyond that to create sophisticated modular training programmes. Every new recruit has a 2½ day induction course, and these people can later make use of a suite of management development programmes.

There are many opportunities to work overseas, and hundreds of UK employees are currently taking advantage of this opening. For those interested in working abroad who are selected to do so, the company offers lots of help with language and other acclimatisation skills. Its International Services Centre provides a complete support structure for the delegate and his or her family.

The company encourages cross-fertilisation, so the typical employee gets lots of movement. Business people move into the HR area and vice versa. Maurice Duffy: 'The career management process is about helping you move from employment to employability. Individuals want to have as many transportable skills as possible. We aim to constantly challenge and stretch people.'

Remuneration

Nortel Networks pays in the upper quartile, and benchmarks extensively to ensure that it remains on this level. Payment is flexible, structured in bands with a huge range of salaries within each, so managers can reward higher achievers appropriately.

Benefits include medical health cover for employees and their family members, health screening, a contributory pension plan, company cars dependent on level, and bonus, incentive and stock options.

The Future

The future for the company looks remarkably good. The latest growth driver has been European deregulation. Maurice Duffy: 'We have the right technology and the best people. This combination has allowed us to win substantial amounts of business relative to our competitors. We also look at our positioning continually. This focuses on the type of organisation we want to be.'

This means that the face of the company is changing. It is now moving from a technical to a knowledge-based company, built around self-organising teams and flatter structures. Increasingly, the culture will be dynamic and unique, global and diverse, open and candid. It will offer its people multiple roles while being ever more focused on the customer.

The market will undoubtedly see more use of data networks as customers move towards e-commerce, real-time and Internet-time. All this places Nortel Networks in an enviable position of strength.

Oracle

Oracle Corporation is the largest supplier of database software and the second largest supplier of business applications in the world. Oracle also has a booming services division and this integrated services capability, comprising consulting, support services and education, is central to Oracle's full solution strategy. Tremendously successful, Oracle's revenue and employees trebled over 1996–98, when revenue reached $8 billion. Oracle Corporation UK Limited, the largest subsidiary outside the USA, has its headquarters in Reading, with other offices in Bracknell, the City, Manchester and Scotland. Over 45,000 people work for Oracle worldwide, 4,500 in the UK.

Scorecard:
Remuneration and benefits	★★★★
Progressive attitude	★★★★★
Opportunity for promotion	★★★★★
Training, development and education	★★★★
Working atmosphere and environment	★★★★

Biggest plus:
Fast growth, vast opportunity

Biggest minus:
A very demanding environment – be sure you can handle it

Oracle Corporation UK Limited
Oracle Parkway
Thames Valley Park
Reading
Berkshire RG6 1RA
Tel: 0118 924 0000
Fax: 0118 924 3000
website: www.oracle.com

ORACLE®

Oracle

The Business

Oracle is a big organisation – it's annual revenues exceed $8 billion and it has offices in 140 countries – but it's a young company, having been formed in San Francisco in 1977.

For 22 years Oracle has championed the importance and versatility of the database. Oracle's product strategy is to link key information technologies into complete integrated solutions. Oracle's integrated family of portable software includes the Oracle8 co-operative database, the Designer 2000 and Developer 2000 set of life-cycle applications development tools and a strong suite of business applications.

Oracle continues to increase its share of the world market for database software, where Oracle has been number one for some time. Name an industry sector and Oracle is there. In fact, virtually every major company around the globe uses the Oracle database.

While database is Oracle's largest business, application software is the company's fastest growing business. And its service businesses – consulting, education and support – now represent around half of Oracle's annual income.

The company has enjoyed rapid growth over the last decade, doubling revenues each year for many years. It has reached such a size now that such 'repeat business' is not feasible – but Oracle still grew revenue and earnings by 30% in 1998.

These figures strengthen Oracle's position as the world's largest supplier of information software. As chairman and chief executive Larry Ellison puts it: 'At the dawn of the Information Age, that's a pretty good place to be.'

Company Culture and Style

The Internet has really opened the door for Oracle's strategy based on integrated products and services, and could prove to be the single decisive factor in its battle with Microsoft. As Larry Ellison argues: 'My prediction is that the PC will become a peripheral product.'

Oracle's 45,000 dedicated professionals provide clients with innovative products, consulting, education and support services. This is a real 'go get' company, rich in innovative spirit and visionary in its outlook.

Oracle has a real purpose and ambition about it, and its results-driven culture is one that calls for a particular blend of personal and professional skills. It is an extremely demanding environment – self-regulating due to the high standards and expectations of the thousands of bright people who work there. People may work long hours, but they do so in the knowledge that they are achieving real success. Those who are not succeeding tend to move on to other companies. It's as simple as that.

Above all, Oracle is driven by a passion for innovation. It rejects suggestions of being 'market-led'. Larry Ellison regards it as part of Oracle's role to define and lead the market through continuous innovation.

Consequently, the people charged with delivering Oracle's future vision are original thinkers, individuals who look beyond conventional ways of doing things in pursuit of creative solutions. But they do have certain traits in common. They are all self-motivated and in charge of their own careers and lives. They have strong self-belief backed by energy and enthusiasm. They welcome ambitious targets and take full responsibility for meeting them. They thrive on constant challenge and expect their achievements to be acknowledged and rewarded. This is not a place where you can stay in the background.

Oracle does have a certain reputation for being an aggressive company. But as Vance Kearney, vice president for human resources, puts it, 'Oracle has not grown from nothing into an $8 billion company by being shy and retiring. If our sales effort is forceful, we are still delivering outstanding value and outstanding products to our customers.'

Human Resources

With a clear external focus on the ever-changing needs of its customers, Oracle has little desire for formal policies, rules and frameworks. The human resources team seeks instead to support and nourish an environment in which people can succeed.

Vance Kearney suggests there is no place for loners in the company – interaction with and support from your work colleagues is vital. Although you will need to work out some complex problems for yourself, you will be encouraged to share experiences and aspirations with your colleagues. HR instils and encourages teamworking, ensuring that people communicate in teams in pursuit of common business objectives.

It's not all tough – Oracle is a friendly company and the team culture extends into the social environment as well. Oracle wants people to have room to enjoy themselves.

Recruiting high-calibre staff in large numbers, in an under-supplied market, is a huge task. Deciding whether to join Oracle may be a tough decision for individuals, but it is a serious decision for Oracle. There is currently a full-time team of 16 people dedicated to recruitment alone.

Career Opportunity and Development

When it comes to providing great career opportunities, nothing beats a rapidly growing company. Oracle expects to recruit around 1,000 more people in the UK by the year 2000, including at least 100 new graduates.

The Oracle life is not always easy, but it is full and rewarding for people with the same high aspirations that the company has. The only certainty is that the future will be very different – and it's a fairly good bet that Oracle will be leading the way.

Work areas include applications design and development, systems integration, consulting, customer support, training and IT, along with the professional areas of finance, marketing and sales, legal and HR. *All* work is focused around Oracle's customers.

International opportunities abound, and many hundreds of Oracle's UK staff have worked in the US, Asia Pacific and across Europe. Oracle, as a global organisation, requires the same skills wherever its products and services are used. And the continuous growth of its subsidiaries creates even more opportunities for overseas assignments and experience.

Performance standards are set very high. Allan Miller, employee development manager, believes that Oracle needs people who can accept change, embrace ambiguity and respond flexibly to new challenges and opportunities.

Each Oracle professional must have an in-depth understanding of Oracle products and services. Considering the size and scale of its operation, and the speed at which new ideas are hatched and made to work, this is no small task. But it is an important part of grooming its leaders of tomorrow. New arrivals who need familiarising with Oracle technology join an intensive training course, which lasts five to eight weeks and involves practical exercises and working on a recent 'real' project.

Professional education doesn't end once you're good enough to do the job you were brought in for. This is a company with a vast array of opportunities and a thriving culture of personal success. Oracle will also support people who want to gain further qualifications. It runs a full range of business-related programmes in association with the University of Reading, from a Certificate in Management to an MBA.

Allan Miller suggests that people perhaps have two levels of required development. 'Just dealing and coping with Oracle is the first stage. When they are able to move on, real personal development can begin, given the scope that Oracle can offer.'

Remuneration

Oracle is very competitive on pay, at the upper quartile of the computer industry. Oracle recognises the wide range of individual employees' needs and priorities by providing a flexible benefits package, offering choice, flexibility and innovation in the range of benefits they wish to have, to maximise each employee's personal satisfaction.

The Future

Oracle's meteoric rise looks set to continue for a good while yet. In 1998 Oracle launched Oracle8i, the Internet version of Oracle's database, which could prove to be the most important set of enhancements to its database technology yet. The Oracle database is already a key building block of the Internet. Eighty % of the Web's most popular sites, from Amazon.com to Yahoo!, depend on Oracle's ability to handle huge numbers of users and enormous quantities of information: text, images, audio, video – everything. Oracle8i does more than this, as it is designed specifically for corporate Internets and the World Wide Web.

Oracle also delivered Release 11 of its sales and service, manufacturing and supply chain, and finance and human resources applications, and is the only suite of business applications that runs entirely on corporate Internets and the World Wide Web. Meanwhile, Oracle's services activities are proving to be a real driver of the business, having grown by 42% in 1998.

Oracle's continual growth and innovation presents a challenge in recruiting and developing the right people – people who can learn quickly and match the rate of change in the business. The company knows that the ideal Oracle manager is someone who believes in empowering others rather than simply exercising power, who creates opportunities with both clients and staff, and who combines leadership skills with a determination to ensure that work always retains an element of fun.

But perhaps the single most important feature of Oracle is the sheer scale of its ambitions. And having realised the potential of the Internet earlier than many others, Oracle has a very powerful friend.

Pearl Assurance plc

Pearl Assurance has been a wholly owned subsidiary of AMP since 1989. In a market transformed by regulation, Pearl remains one of the strongest life offices in financial terms: it has a triple 'A' rating from Standard and Poors. Pearl is committed to being an employer of choice. It currently employs 8,700 people in the UK. The company's assets now exceed £17 billion and its holding of stocks and shares is worth over £7 billion. It has more than 3.5 million customers.

Scorecard:

Remuneration and benefits	★★★★
Progressive attitude	★★★★★
Opportunity for promotion	★★★★
Training, development and education	★★★★
Working atmosphere and environment	★★★★★

Biggest plus:
A business-focused, adaptable and flexible company which thrives on change

Biggest minus:
Sector-wide uncertainty which creates threats but also opportunities

Pearl Assurance plc
Lynch Wood
Peterborough PE2 6FY
Tel: 01733 470470
Fax: 01733 472300
website: www.pearl.co.uk

Pearl Assurance plc

The Business

Pearl's core business focuses on providing middle and low income families with a range of straightforward financial products and services. The company values home service as fundamental and emphasises the importance of building relationships with its customers. Pearl has also widened its operational scope, including the development of telephone call centres, database marketing, and wider use of technology by its sales force.

The company, for decades a traditional, slow-moving player with a complex product range, was transformed in 1995 when its present managing director Richard Surface was appointed. He introduced radical reforms, including overhauling management, slashing costs and halving the product range. The sales force, now led by Terry Shrimpton who joined from Prudential, was also reorganised. Today's Pearl is clearly a success story. New business of £80 million in 1995 shot up to over £150 million by 1998.

Part of this success is due to the company's rebranding. This reminds customers and the public that they need to take responsibility for their own financial welfare, aided by Pearl and its fully trained (to FPC3 level) financial advisers, because state provision is reducing. Pearl takes pride in the fact that although 278 companies have to date been fined by the PIA for mis-selling, it has never been on that list. Pearl today is based on five core values: trust, forward looking, professionalism, realism and straightforwardness.

Pearl was established in 1864 and was bought by AMP in 1989. In 1998, AMP floated on the Australian Stock Exchange. Now all employees of Pearl are shareholders in AMP, with a correspondingly greater incentive to perform well. Pearl retains operational autonomy within the AMP group.

Company Culture and Style

Central to the new culture is a proven ability to cope with change. Pearl today is a far cry from the old world of cosy, monolithic insurers. Instead, it has a real buzz. Indeed, the independent company Corporate Vision assessed Pearl as having made the biggest cultural change over the last two years of any financial services business. People are constantly exploring new and more effective ways of working. This may include greater informality. Fridays are 'dress down' days – something that would have been unthinkable at Pearl twenty years ago. As Louise Barney, graduate recruitment and development manager puts it: 'Work must be challenging and it must be rewarding, but we also think it should be fun.'

The company has firmly embraced the new market reality. This means a new spirit inside and outside Pearl. For instance, staff are positively encouraged to take control of their own careers, aided by a Development Centre, a prestigious Training Centre, a Brand Discovery Experience (which includes interactive learning, workshops and videos) and other facilities. They also take ownership of any customer problems, irrespective of where those problems arise.

Pearl is a friendly organisation, and a palpable sense of camaraderie is evident at its impressive, award-winning offices in Peterborough. The average length of service is still over eight years, a significant point at such a time of change.

The company comprises both a sales force and its head office administrative operation, but is keen to stress that a single culture exists. Much of its recent success has been due to forging stronger links between the two arms and encouraging people to move between them, with benefits for all concerned. For instance, a Roll of Honour of top salespeople dominates the main building in Peterborough.

Open communication is key to Pearl. Terry Shrimpton and Richard Surface tour the country at the beginning of each year, communicating strategy. The company's 'A-list' of priorities is cascaded through the organisation. The strategy is widely known and accepted throughout Pearl. Key messages are communicated face-to-face throughout the company in a series of meetings. Plasma screens in the Pearl Centre display information including job vacancies. The company's monthly magazine, *Xpress*, also fosters good communications. Additionally, Pearl is noted for its excellent communication with its clients; it won the Plain English Campaign's Crystal Clear award for insurance companies for the second year running in 1998.

Human Resources

HR at Pearl is divided into two functions: effectiveness and efficiency. The former includes operations and development people giving strategic HR advice to line managers. These HR people are trained in consultancy skills, psychometrics and other talents. The latter is concerned with processes such as payroll, database management and so on. This will slim down as technology streamlines some processes, but the split gives far greater clarity to the HR task.

The company videos general managers and the managing director and asks for frank feedback on HR as a function: a rare move, but one which has certainly helped the department to develop. As a result of such initiatives, HR priorities are definitely the business's priority. Jeremy Rance, Head of HR Operations: 'There is a clear linkage between the two, giving us a greater pragmatism. For instance, where we once had HR people working on our sales force located at the Pearl Centre, many such people now work in the branches.'

Career Opportunity and Development

Pearl keeps a close eye on individuals identified as having the greatest ability to shape the future of the business. A structured development process, initiated by the managing director, identifies Pearl's future senior management and plans their development and succession. Succession planning is now cascaded to all levels.

Fast-track mechanisms are in place throughout the organisation, developing those with high potential by placing them in a range of business situations and in contact with different managers. In 1999 the company will take on 29 graduates in its head office and 40 in its sales force – its biggest intake yet. All positions up to management level are advertised internally, and Pearl employees are considered before external candidates.

Training has a huge priority from top management downwards. Senior managers have the opportunity to attend development programmes, and in Pearl itself the Better By Miles (BBM) programme is a key training initiative for the staff. BBM is probably the largest accredited company training scheme in Europe. Each year, the company spends £10 million on training its sales force, and £3–5 million on its head office people. All employees receive at least five days' training a year. The company recruits MBAs, and is also jointly sponsoring an MBA course with Loughborough University.

As part of the AMP group, Pearl can offer its employees secondment opportunities to the parent company in Australia, New Zealand and elsewhere, and also with other group members including Virgin Direct, London Life, Henderson Investors and NPI.

Remuneration

The overall remuneration package offered by Pearl is widely recognised as one of the best in the industry. Salaries are determined by a mix of factors including benchmarking with competitors, inflation, business profitability, and individual and team performance.

Reward philosophy across the group is to offer a package that is upper quartile in the marketplace. The total package comprises base salaries, a non-contributory pension scheme, up to 30 days' holiday, employee options and employee share schemes, flexible company car schemes and a modern, high-tech working environment.

The Future

The rapid pace of change in the financial services industry will surely accelerate. Further mergers and sharper competition seem inevitable. Pearl is addressing this reality by seeking to streamline operations and make them more cost-effective.

The goal of the company is to dominate the advice for life market.

Richard Surface backs his colleagues unreservedly. 'The changes make it exciting to work at Pearl. We are taking the first steps towards the rebirth of one of the UK's most important companies. The result will be that Pearl reclaims its birthright as a major provider of essential retirement and savings needs in this country.'

Peugeot Motor Co.

Peugeot is part of the PSA Peugeot Citroën automotive group, which has principal manufacturing centres across Europe and further sites in Africa, Asia and South America. The Peugeot production operation in the UK is centred at Ryton, Coventry and it also owns a national dealership chain, Robins & Day. The company directly employs over 5,000 people in the UK but estimates that at least twice that number of jobs are directly supported by its activities. The success of the 206 model, launched in late 1998, will increase employment at Ryton by around 1,000 in 1999. In 1997, pre-tax profits stood at £52 million. The company enjoys over 8% of the UK car market and in 1998 recorded the third-largest car sales after Ford and Vauxhall.

Scorecard:

Remuneration and benefits	★★★
Progressive attitude	★★★★★
Opportunity for promotion	★★★
Training, development and education	★★★★
Working atmosphere and environment	★★★

Biggest plus:
State-of-the-art production ensures competitiveness

Biggest minus:
Demand is closely linked to general economic conditions

Peugeot Motor Co. plc
Aldermoor House
PO Box 227
Aldermoor Lane
Coventry CV3 1LT
Tel: 01203 884000
Fax: 01203 884288

PEUGEOT

Peugeot Motor Co.

The Business

Peugeot is part of the PSA Group, which employs 140,000 worldwide and is France's leading motor manufacturer. The group also includes Citroën, but the two marques are commercially separate and compete with each other. UK production of Peugeot cars is centred on the Ryton plant, which was originally built by the Rootes Group before the Second World War. It passed to Chrysler in 1967 before becoming part of Peugeot in 1978. Well over one million Peugeot cars have been built at Ryton.

As well as manufacturing cars at Ryton, Peugeot has a national distribution, dealership and after-sales network, with communications technology ensuring prompt and accurate delivery both of vehicles and spares. As a major consumer of vehicle components, Peugeot's activities support thousands of jobs nationwide.

Company Culture and Style

The history of the UK motor manufacturing industry contains many reference points for the country's industrial relations as a whole. In the 1970s, it was common for factories to lie idle for weeks on end as management and unions battled over negotiations concerning pay and conditions. In the subsequent decades, however, the number of strikes has fallen dramatically. Indeed, it is Peugeot's proud boast that, since a 14-week strike in 1978, it has enjoyed 20 trouble-free years, during which time it has 'not lost a car'.

This happy situation is not the result of either union-breaking or management capitulation but of 'investment in industrial relations'. The management and employee representatives are now eager to engage in constructive dialogue, with all concerned remaining conscious of two key points: the need to maintain an efficient and competitive business in a crowded and competitive market; and the need to recognise the merits and worth of individual employees.

In 1998 there was a crucial test of the strength of the employer-employee relationship. The success of the 206 model was such that the company wanted to introduce extra shifts and weekend working – the first time in a generation that the UK car industry had seen such an increase in activity. Thanks to skilled negotiation and an exhaustive process of communication and consultation, this was achieved smoothly – securing favourable national press comment for Peugeot along the way.

Communications lie at the heart of Peugeot's culture. In addition to a lively and informative staff newsletter (which is read by 95% of target readership), there are regular team briefings, whereby news and views are disseminated to the shop-floor. Supervisors are specifically trained to talk to team members to identify concerns and address issues. To coincide with the launch of the 206, all employees were taken to a series of meetings at the International Conference Centre in Birmingham.

In a recent staff survey, 60% of employees returned a questionnaire covering a variety of issues, such as overall levels of job satisfaction and relationships with management. While the results were generally positive, the management did not shrink from disclosing unfavourable figures, such as the fact that only 42% of respondents believed the management would actually act on the results of the survey. Indeed, Richard Parham, managing director, issued a response saying: 'You have my commitment that survey responses will remain a senior management priority during the year ahead.'

Human Resources

While the dark days of sour industrial relations would seem to be firmly behind the UK motor manufacturing industry in general and Peugeot in particular, those involved in personnel have sufficiently long memories to know how painful those experiences were. For that reason, they remain committed to developing a positive climate where problems can either be averted altogether or swiftly nipped in the bud.

The Peugeot company charter maintains that 'Nothing is more important in a company than the motivation and commitment of its employees.' It seeks continuous improvement so that working lives can be made more satisfying, company performance can be improved and prosperity secured. Feedback is actively encouraged so that the quality of work can be enhanced.

The rich manufacturing heritage of the West Midlands, particularly in the motor industry, means there is a healthy supply of skilled labour. However, Peugeot remains conscious of the need to attract and retain committed and enthusiastic staff for its shop-floor operations as well as talented and progressive individuals for its white-collar functions. Investment in the latest production-line technology and the pursuit of innovative and market-beating product development is helping promote the company as an attractive organisation to work for.

The company has also demonstrated its commitment to its people beyond the workplace. Among a range of initiatives is Britain's first day-care centre designed specifically to look after the elderly dependants of employees. Peugeot pioneered it in conjunction with BEN, the motor industry charity.

Career Opportunity and Development

The total number of people employed in motor manufacturing has fallen in recent years as robotics and computerisation have automated many of the production-line processes. Peugeot still regards people as its most important resource, however, and devotes substantial effort and investment towards training and re-training and development. Indeed, frequent technological advances make such endeavour essential.

Peugeot fosters a learning culture where the acquisition of new skills is regarded as a lifelong activity, not simply a process that is undergone at the beginning of working life. As a company with French parentage, the company also encourages employees to learn the French language so as to improve communications with international colleagues. At any given time, around 500 employees are engaged in language training at all levels.

The company has links with a number of local schools and colleges through the Peugeot Partnership Centre. It is also a member of the local education Business Partnership Initiative.

In order to tap the expertise of its workforce and to reward those showing initiative and inspiration, Peugeot runs a scheme whereby those who come up with useful suggestions can win up to £1,000. An example would be the improvement to a leak-testing process, which saved 600,000 gallons of water every year – enough to fill an Olympic-sized swimming pool.

The company also runs an Assisted Development Programme, which provides grants of up to £250 per annum to be spent on non-vocational training and education, with courses taken outside working hours. Language training and computer skills figure among the most popular options taken up at local colleges. Both the educational establishments and Peugeot have developed courses and facilities to cater for those employees working shifts.

Remuneration

Peugeot's company charter commits the organisation to providing decent pay and conditions. The large number of motor manufacturers in the area and the surviving strength of union representation means that the wage levels paid to production line workers throughout the industry are reasonably standard, although Peugeot looks to be at least in line if not above its peers in this respect. A very competitive defined benefit pension scheme is also provided.

The company runs the Peugeot Employee Car Ownership Scheme, which provides eligible staff with a loan to purchase, on very advantageous terms, a new car (built at Ryton, naturally). It undertakes to buy the vehicle back from the employee after 12 months or the completion of 12,000 miles, which ever comes first, at which point the process begins again. Employees become eligible after five years' service.

The Future

Peugeot considers complacency to be the greatest danger it faces. Intense competition throughout the motor manufacturing industry is spurring its rivals to improve their performance, which means Peugeot itself must be constantly pushing forward if it is to retain its edge. The successful launch of the 206 model is seen as pivotal for the future of the company, although pressure on margins as companies pursue market share means that improvements in productivity and general cost savings will still be required.

In terms of staff, Peugeot has to manage the delicate task of introducing labour-saving technology without risking its impressive labour relations. In recent years this has been done successfully; as staff have left the company, they have not been replaced, which has seen overall headcount reduce to the required level. The high levels of demand for the 206 actually necessitated the recruitment of an extra shift – a recruitment phenomenon not seen in the industry for some years.

As with all large-scale manufacturers, Peugeot's success is closely linked to the state of the economy as a whole. Consumer demand for new cars has continued to grow in recent months, and Peugeot's success with the 206 should mean that it will defend if not increase its market share. Political issues, such as taxes on car use and ownership, are other factors beyond the control of the company, which may shape its future.

Environment concerns also loom large in the thinking of motor manufacturers. Peugeot has confronted these head-on, however, with its development of small and medium-sized fuel efficient vehicles, including an electric car that is already on the road. Its parent company's commitment to researching and developing alternative fuels should also stand it in good stead in the years to come.

PowerGen

PowerGen is a UK leader in power generation and energy supply with global interests stretching from Europe to Asia-Pacific. A publicly listed company, it was privatised by the British government in 1990. With the acquisition and subsequent absorption of East Midlands Electricity (EME) in July 1998, the company refocused its business on being an end-to-end electricity and gas company with 2.3 million customers. The group employs some 8,000 people (including EME) of whom over 680 are based overseas.

Scorecard:

Remuneration and benefits	★★★★★
Progressive attitude	★★★★
Opportunity for promotion	★★★★
Training, development and education	★★★
Working atmosphere and environment	★★★★

Biggest plus:
Strategic vision to be a leading integrated energy business

Biggest minus:
Regulatory constraints on power businesses

PowerGen plc
Westwood Way
Westwood Business Park
Coventry
CV4 8LG
Tel: 01203 424000
Fax: 01203 425432
website: www.pgen.com

PowerGen

The Business

PowerGen is a well-established player in the global electricity market. It has taken advantage of the deregulation of the UK gas market to develop a position as a supplier and distributor of both electricity and gas. It took a significant step forward when it acquired East Midlands Electricity (EME) and is integrating the culture and workforce of the two companies.

PowerGen is actively engaged in the competitive market for power projects overseas. It has operations and projects in Europe, India, the Far East and Australia. The company also has ambitions to expand into the deregulated US market, should the right opportunities come along.

Company Culture and Style

PowerGen has rapidly shaken off the stifling, bureaucratic culture of public ownership and recreated itself as a fiercely competitive, market-oriented group which is willing to improve its skills, its technology base and its reach. The strength of its ambition can be measured by the rapid expansion of its non-regulated international projects – in some of the most promising markets in the world – and the speed with which it has moved beyond a narrow base of power generation to add gas and distribution to its base.

The company has a 'can do' attitude reflecting the ambitions of its top team chairman Ed Wallis, group finance director Peter Hickson and Nick Baldwin, executive director, UK operations. They believe that the liberalisation of the UK energy market has given it the skills to exploit other liberalising markets so that it can create new growth platforms for success. This approach makes PowerGen an exciting place to work, because of the opportunities for younger executives, engineers and technicians to advance through the group and benefit from the opportunity to work overseas.

The company believes there is common purpose among all

employees in the group and its core values are based on the theme: 'Working Together, Working Better'. In working together the company places emphasis on the mutual benefits for the whole workforce; the importance of integrity, honesty and trust; and the need for the workforce, at all times, to show respect and consideration for others. By working better PowerGen engenders a strong focus on safety, innovation and improvement, looking to the future and delivering what it promises.

All of these principles have been tested over the last seven years as PowerGen has transformed itself with staff numbers falling from 10,000 to 3,000 – before doubling again as a result of the EME absorption. Individual employees have taken on greater responsibilities and the workforce as a whole has responded well to the liberalisation of the UK energy market.

PowerGen is seen as a challenging corporation in which to work with real opportunities at it extends its reach both in the UK and internationally. In the past the company relied on technical expertise and strong centralised management. PowerGen is now a much more flexible organisation with diverse requirements, which include commercial and trading skills, project finance, sales and marketing and a high quality management communication.

Human Resources

Within PowerGen the line managers have key responsibility for the people who work with them and for their effective management. Emphasis is placed on effective employee relations, with managers expected to communicate changes to staff directly rather than hear about impending switches from the newspapers, trades unions or on the rumour mill. The goal is to ensure that there are no nasty surprises and that there is a constructive relationship between managers, staff and trade unions. This has assisted the company in shrinking its workforce without disruption.

The current human resources priority for the group is the integration of PowerGen with East Midlands Electricity and the associated cultural change. To help achieve this change the company is focusing on management development and graduate recruitment and development. It also is seeking to build strong retail skills for dealing with domestic and industrial customers.

Career Opportunity and Development

PowerGen operates on a flexible basis, which allows a wide variety of career options including the chance to work abroad on major projects. The senior management has tended to work in a variety of roles in the organisation and the company has encouraged managers to gain experience in different functions and across a variety of disciplines. The transformation in the group's culture has made it a place of opportunity for younger managers and PowerGen has been willing to advance them through the organisation so that they gain greater responsibility at an early age.

As part of the process of building a flexible, knowledgeable and younger management structure the group encourages the development of new skills. This has been pursued through management development programmes at Henley and Ashridge Management Colleges and encouraging executives to attend management development programmes in Europe and the United States.

The company has encouraged individuals to take ownership of their own careers and their development. This has been assisted by the introduction in 1997 of career development centres which seek to provide support and encouragement to 'high potential' people. There also is a Continuing Education programme, which provides financial support and time to those staff members seeking to undertake further studies. A significant number of PowerGen staff have gained MBAs by making use of these facilities.

Flexibility in career development has been demonstrated by moving people into different roles in the business, including the appointment of non-engineers as station managers.

Training is an important part of the group's activities. Through Power Training, the company's training and consultancy business, it provides a wide range of services. These include consultancy on all aspects of training; tailored training programmes; power plant appreciation and operation; power plant maintenance, team development and event management for conferences.

The build-up of the group's international activities, on almost every continent, has made the company an attractive prospect for those seeking to pursue international careers. There is already a wide variety of roles including business development, project management, plant operations and maintenance as well as the central functions of finance and human resources. Normally such assignments are made for 2/3 years, and are seen as stepping-stones to further overseas appointments in a career pattern which may include a return to the UK. The company believes in preparing people carefully for international posts by acquainting them with the infrastructure and culture of the countries concerned.

Remuneration

The company has deliberately set its pay at competitive levels so as to attract and retain the most capable and talented people within the group, setting pay levels in the upper quartile for the energy sector. In addition to good pay levels, PowerGen encourages achievement of high-performance levels through bonus schemes.

The overall package of pay and benefits is regarded as superior. The company's contribution to the pension scheme is twice the 6% paid by employees, making it among the most generous in the UK. Staff have become encouraged to be more involved in the group through share save schemes which makes them genuine stakeholders. In addition there is a range of other staff benefits, including health services and a medical insurance scheme for permanent staff; an Employee Assistance Programme which is available to provide staff with confidential advice on a variety of problems; childcare provision; flexible working arrangements, as well as sports, social clubs and gym facilities.

The Future

PowerGen is a group that has been through enormous changes over the last decade moving from the public sector to the London Stock Exchange. As a quoted firm it has introduced new management disciplines, expanded from power generation into energy distribution and established itself internationally. The group's chairman Ed Wallis is determined to maintain the momentum of growth and change which has propelled the company forward. In the UK PowerGen hopes to build a national supply business. Overseas it plans to take advantage of the new deregulated utilities market in the US and to establish itself as one of the world's top ten power companies.

The expansion of the company into energy distribution at home and overseas will provide increasing opportunities for existing staff. But it will also require the acquisition of new skills and disciplines. The company recognises that it will need to build a strong retail function to improve its interface with the domestic customer. The addition of EME and potential future acquisitions means that the company will need to focus on integrating new management and staff into the 'working together, working better' ethos of PowerGen. It will also require sophisticated financial skills. These are considerable challenges in an increasingly competitive energy marketplace. The history of PowerGen, which has established itself as a strong brand and corporation at home and overseas, suggests that it is capable of meeting them.

Procter & Gamble

In the UK, Procter & Gamble consists of five diverse businesses, covering consumer products, health and beauty care, cosmetics and fragrances, pharmaceuticals, and food service and industrial products. Worldwide net sales exceed $37 billion.

Scorecard:

Remuneration and benefits	★★★★★
Progressive attitude	★★★★★
Opportunity for promotion	★★★★
Training, development and education	★★★★
Working atmosphere and environment	★★★★

Biggest plus:
Lots of opportunity to develop your career as you wish

Biggest minus:
A challenging and demanding company which may not suit everyone

Procter & Gamble UK
The Heights
Brooklands
Weybridge
Surrey KT13
Tel: 01932 896000
Fax: 01932 896666
website: www.pg.com

Procter&Gamble

Procter & Gamble

The Business

Procter & Gamble produces and markets a wide range of products for consumer and industrial use. Its famous brand names include Ariel, Fairy Liquid, Max Factor, Pampers, Vidal Sassoon, Pringles, Pantene, Oil of Ulay and Sunny Delight. The company employs 100,000 people worldwide, has factories in 57 countries and conducts business in over 150 countries.

The Procter & Gamble company was founded in 1837 and has its world HQ in Cincinnati, Ohio. In the UK, Procter & Gamble has seven manufacturing units, three research centres and technical centres at Egham, Newcastle and Staines. It also has three administrative bases in Weybridge, Newcastle-upon-Tyne and Staines.

Company Culture and Style

The company has a strong and distinctive culture. At its heart are a purpose, core values and principles. The purpose is to provide products of superior quality and value that improve the lives of the world's consumers. This is supported by core values of attracting and recruiting the best people, leadership, ownership, integrity, trust and passion for winning. Its principles flow from the purpose and core values and include showing respect for all individuals, a belief that the interests of the company and the individual are inseparable, a clear strategy, external focus and a commitment to innovation.

All the company's values are important and imbue everything it does: but the one concerning people is paramount. Mohan Mohan, general manager and vice-president of health and beauty care, UK and Ireland: 'People are the key to successful operations. The knowledge held in the minds of our employees is irreplaceable and gives us our competitive advantage.'

As a result of this strong belief in its people, Procter & Gamble never hires senior people from outside the company; all promotion comes from within. Chris Armstrong, human resources manager of Procter

& Gamble Pharmaceuticals: 'Everybody who gets to the top has been with the company for most of their working life. The sky really is the limit here. With so many opportunities, you can do virtually whatever you want in your career and certainly never be bored. The only requirement is to act with integrity at all times. We do not tolerate unethical behaviour.'

The culture is an open one, with managers always accessible to staff. Everyone is on first-name terms and the company even allows its people to dress informally. Having said that, the company should not be seen as a benevolent society. It is tough, rigorous and demanding. But those who perform are well rewarded, and are given everything they need in the way of skills, development and opportunity to sustain that performance. Procter & Gamble is also well known for its honesty in dealing with people. Its appraisals, for instance, are specific in identifying what individuals need to make progress.

No one type of person flourishes within Procter & Gamble; indeed, the company relishes diversity in its workforce. However, successful people will almost certainly be bright and assertive and will know what they want to do. In making its 100 or so graduate hires each year, for instance, the company does not seek particular disciplines or even grades of degree: but it does look for management and leadership potential.

Typically, graduates starting their first job expect to stay at a company for just four years. But Procter & Gamble strives to give people such excellent opportunities, motivation and rewards that graduates decide to stay with the company for much longer, or indeed for their entire working life. A career with the company will involve lots of different types of work and be constantly stimulating and interesting.

Human Resources

At the heart of the company's HR policy is its concern for its people. It has a long-term strategy for the future, 'Stretch, innovation and speed', which is designed to equip Procter & Gamble to achieve its challenging corporate goal of doubling its size every ten years.

'Stretch' is about reaching for the almost unreachable and involves changing its internal processes. Whereas in the past the company might have had a target of increasing sales of a given product by 10%, the approach now is to go for whatever is achievable and reward people for facilitating that achievement.

'Innovation' relates to technical excellence: finding new products and improving existing ones. The company prides itself on its superior products, which again result from recruiting and retaining the best people.

'Speed' is concerned with the company's desire to be truly global in its operations. While it once took seven years to introduce a winning product from another country, the process now takes only one year – and Proctor & Gamble is endeavouring to make this even faster.

Career Opportunity and Development

There is great emphasis on developing people. Managers are measured on how well they develop their staff, and their remuneration is linked into their success in this area. Chris Armstrong: 'We have to provide the right environment for learning, growth and development. If we don't, people will not stay with the company. We recognise that we may be dealing with the next general manager of Procter & Gamble every time we make a recruitment decision.'

People have assignments rather than jobs, and they are likely to move assignments quite often. This helps make a career at Procter & Gamble constantly interesting and challenging. There is always a new opening on the horizon for talented, committed individuals.

Increasingly, the company is global in its operations. As a result, those assignments may involve overseas postings. Indeed, anyone joining Procter & Gamble should expect to work abroad at some stage. While the company does not exert pressure on people to do so, it is true to say that anyone regularly passing up overseas assignments would not be likely to emerge as a high-flyer.

Lisa Connolly joined the company as a graduate trainee. She comments: 'I started with P&G in their Italian office based in Rome. A very challenging start, a new language, new culture and my first job, but this was exactly what I wanted.'

There is lots of internal training. On average, an employee can expect around 25 days' training each year. This can be classroom-based, but will also involve substantial on-the-job training. All managers have to coach and develop their people as part of their job description. Training is provided as needed, to equip people to contribute more and work to their full potential. But the best way to learn a skill is to do it; so someone needing finance skills would be likely to be given an assignment working in the finance area, for instance. Procter & Gamble believes an employee can learn more – and earn more – in two years working within the business than by spending a similar time acquiring an MBA.

Each member of staff has his or her development plan. This is reviewed on a regular basis in consultation with the manager. As a result of this, training and other development needs are identified and planned in.

Remuneration

Procter & Gamble pays in line with other leading national companies engaged in similar work. All salaries are determined individually, based on performance. The two principles governing its pay policy are to be competitive and to reward good performance. Although some people leave the company, exit interviews have never yet found that the reason for leaving is inadequate pay. Each individual salary is planned and reviewed at least annually, but an increase can be granted at any time.

Each group function has a pay structure usually based on three pay ranges below director level. Individuals are paid within that band according to their experience and performance.

Procter & Gamble has a competitive range of benefits including a share purchase scheme, a family medical insurance plan, health checks, life assurance cover, a non-contributory pension scheme and generous maternity conditions. Other benefits introduced more recently include childcare breaks and other family-related support. There is also an active sports and social club – and if any sport is not covered, employees are more than welcome to add it in!

The Future

The company is constantly looking to renew itself, since it recognises that its success depends on never standing still. It is an externally-focused organisation which fosters a challenging, competitive environment. This will be as true tomorrow as it is today.

Its priority is to integrate its diverse businesses into a truly global organisation. Its strategy of 'stretch, innovation and speed' is geared towards making this a reality.

Railtrack

Railtrack is the arm of the former British Rail that owns the track, signalling and stations. It employs nearly 11,000 people, all in the UK except for a small Brussels office, with sales of £2.5 billion and £388 million profit in the year to March 1998. It became a public company in 1996.

Scorecard:

Remuneration and benefits	★★★★
Progressive attitude	★★★
Opportunity for promotion	★★★★
Training, development and education	★★★★
Working atmosphere and environment	★★★

Biggest plus:
Opportunity to work for a major national organisation at several locations around the UK at a time of rapid change

Biggest minus:
The perception among some employers that managing a railway is a specialist activity different from mainstream business management

Railtrack Group plc
Railtrack House
Euston Square
London NW1 2EE
Tel: 0171 557 8000
Fax: 0171 557 9000

RAILTRACK

Railtrack

The Business

When British Rail was privatised it was split so that the companies which run the trains became customers of Railtrack, which is responsible for providing the track, signalling and station infrastructure. As with the rest of the privatised utilities, the prices which Railtrack can charge the operating companies are tightly regulated, and are expected to come down as the company becomes more efficient. It is therefore essential for the company to maintain constant pressure to reduce overheads and increase efficiency.

For the time being, Railtrack is a purely British company. But It has already taken a major role in building the Channel Tunnel rail link, and has ambitions to become involved in London Underground if that becomes possible through a relaxation of state ownership.

The company is organised regionally in seven 'zones', with key centres in major cities such as Birmingham, Manchester, Glasgow and York. Its head office is in London.

Company Culture and Style

When it was part of British Rail, Railtrack was effectively under government control. Rules and regulations were essential and tended to dominate commercial influences. The transition to becoming a plc (as recently as 1996) required a different approach to managing the business, and has involved a fundamental change in culture throughout the organisation.

The introduction of thoroughly commercial attitudes was encouraged by a programme called C-Change, the pun intended to emphasise the extent of the reorientation necessary. 'The changes have resulted in a totally different outlook', explained Paul Radley, head of employee relations, who was involved in the head-to-head battles with trade unions in the old days of comprehensive negotiations over pay and conditions throughout the company. 'Now there is an understanding that we all work together in a business environment where the focus is on improving the service to our customers. There is an understanding of the need to improve our performance continually. And with the majority of employees being shareholders, everybody is very aware of the share price.'

What Railtrack now wants from employees is therefore very similar to what every company is looking for – an eagerness to ensure customer needs are met, in this case the companies which actually run the trains. Railtrack is looking for managers who can work with and manage other people, including colleagues in the company, customers and the many contractors who do the work on the ground to maintain and improve the rail network.

Linsey Perry, the graduate management training manager, said some recruits are 'in love with the railway'. But others are looking for the same as they would from any employer: a good grounding in management, early responsibility and the prospect of rapid development.

Linsey Perry, and the resource planning manager, David Worcester, are keen to stress that this is no longer a male-dominated or an engineering-led business. Women did make up only 17% of the total workforce in 1998, but that is up from 13% in 1994, showing that the influence of male strongholds in signal boxes and elsewhere at operational level is reducing. The number of women in management has doubled since 1994. They include four directors and the managers of four of Railtrack's 14 main line stations.

Engineers are crucial to the safety and the improvement of the infrastructure, but there are a lot of general managers as well. 'We may have an engineering base but we are not engineering led,' David Worcester said.

Human Resources

The HR function has changed with the transformation of Railtrack from a service operation whose main job was to negotiate with the unions to a unit which the new director, Debbie Page, regards as a key part of the business. Its importance is indicated by her presence on the executive committee of the most senior managers in the company.

She intends to build a unified HR operation that is aligned to the business. She wants her team to pay as much attention to its internal customers as other parts of the company pay to theirs. 'HR has been in the wings. Now we are moving centre stage,' explained David Worcester. 'We now need to know the business and be "customer facing" the same as everybody else, and not just be custodians of the rule book.'

Career Opportunity and Development

The railway is likely to be an expanding industry as the government attempts to move people and freight from road to rail, with faster, more frequent trains competing effectively with other forms of transport such as airlines. That helps to improve career prospects for new recruits now.

While the company has a strong engineering base, and needs a continuous flow of professionals in the three disciplines of civil, mechanical and telecoms engineering, the business needs even more new general managers.

Of about 40 graduate recruits each year, less than half are specialists in the three key disciplines. The rest come with as wide a range of degrees as in any other major company, and train in the same kind of managerial roles. Generalists go through a 15-month formal programme where they receive exposure to every facet of the business before taking on a line management position. That might be in one of the head office functions such as commercial or operations, or as a field manager responsible for 'real-time' day-to-day operational issues, managing contractors and development projects.

Engineering recruits train for three to four years in their specialist discipline, following a programme which takes them most of the way to the requirements for chartered engineer status.

The success of the graduate training schemes is indicated by the 80% retention rate for those hired since 1994.

Remuneration

Railtrack is keen to pay the right price for the right person. It has moved away from a rigid pay structure for management grades to a more competitive regime, related to performance and market conditions. Operating staff are still in trade unions and covered by collective bargaining.

Linsey Perry said graduate pay is very competitive and sufficiently flexible to pay what is necessary to recruit the right people. 'Graduate pay is extremely good,' she said. 'We try and keep sufficiently ahead to remain attractive.'

Virtually all employees are also shareholders, stemming from both the issue of shares on privatisation and an annual performance share bonus scheme. The annual award is based on company performance, and resulted in a bonus of shares worth £1,000 in the first year – shares which are held in trust for a minimum of three years.

Senior managers are also eligible for an annual cash bonus, which can be up to 20 per cent of salary. Railtrack is looking at ways of extending incentives to other employees below senior management level.

The Future

The railway has a key role in future transport policy, but Railtrack still needs to move further away from its nationalised industry past to take full advantage of the opportunities which will present themselves. The cultural transformation will continue, with the aim of pushing the commercial awareness down through the business and ensuring that every employee puts customer requirements first.

There are also substantial commercial challenges. Railtrack is keen to expand elsewhere but must first ensure that it delivers in its core business. That includes the tremendous technical challenge of upgrading the West Coast main line, a huge project with major engineering obstacles.

While dealing with these issues, Railtrack must also continue to address regulatory demands and customers' needs.

Rolls-Royce

Rolls-Royce is one of the most famous names in engineering, leading the world in gas turbine technology. Rolls-Royce plc serves customers in the civil aerospace, defence and energy sectors of international markets and has facilities in 14 countries. The gas turbine technology of Rolls-Royce generates 95% of the group's sales and has created one of the broadest product ranges of aero engines in the world. Civil represents 50% of Rolls-Royce's business, defence and marine 30% and energy 20%. There are some 53,000 engines in service with 300 airlines, 2,400 corporate and utility operators and more than 100 armed forces, powering both fixed-wing and rotary aircraft. Rolls-Royce employs some 40,000 people worldwide, 30,000 of whom are in the UK.

Scorecard:
Remuneration and benefits ★★★
Progressive attitude ★★★★
Opportunity for promotion ★★★★★
Training, development and education ★★★★★
Working atmosphere and environment ★★★★

Biggest plus:
The world's first name in engineering

Biggest minus:
Still a lot of traditions and structures

Rolls-Royce plc
65 Buckingham Gate
London SW1 6AT
Tel: 0171 222 9020
Fax: 0171 227 9170
website: www.Rolls-Royce.com

Rolls-Royce

The Business

Rolls-Royce is a true class act with a proud 93-year history. Founded by Henry Royce and Charles Rolls in 1906 to sell exclusive motor cars, the company has nearly always made aero engines. Although still the owner of the Rolls-Royce marque, the real pioneering achievements of Rolls-Royce have been in aero engines, where it has repeatedly furthered the cause of aviation.

Generations of quality Rolls-Royce engines have powered flying machines, from the first non-stop transatlantic flight in 1919 by Alcock and Brown in a Vickers Vimy to the Trent family of engines today – the most modern and powerful three-shaft engine, the first to be certificated at 90,000lb of thrust and the only engine family to power every large airliner, existing or planned.

Rolls-Royce today designs and manufactures the engines that power many of the world's most famous civil and military aircraft, including the Airbus range, Eurofighter 2000 and the US Joint Strike Fighter.

Since 1987, before which Rolls-Royce was government-owned though not nationalised, the company has been transformed by following clear, consistent strategies which are now bearing fruit, the reward for considerable investment and patience.

In doing this, Rolls-Royce has focused almost exclusively on its strong foundation in gas turbine technology. 'We are a market leader, and our task is to take this technology to our target market sectors, gain market value and retain competitive advantage,' says John Rose, chief executive.

Company Culture and Style

Rolls-Royce's core values of reliability, integrity and innovation have stayed with the company since it was formed, and quality is synonymous with the name. Great pride is taken in the name, and Rolls-Royce has always made clear provisions to protect its use, emphasising that the Rolls-Royce name belongs to Rolls-Royce plc. Now with the transfer of the use of the name on motor cars from Vickers to BMW there is a satisfactory outcome – BMW is a joint-venture partner with a neater, more symmetrical fit with Rolls-Royce's business.

'When people see Rolls-Royce on your business card, it makes a strong impression. It carries a cachet that many of our competitors seek to emulate,' says Peter Barnes-Wallis, director of corporate communications. 'This reputation has been extremely hard won and you are expected to conduct yourself with absolute integrity and honesty.' No-one is embarrassed to say they work for Rolls-Royce; they take pride in doing so.

Rolls-Royce is constantly evolving to meet the challenges presented by new circumstances. From its early days as a motor car manufacturer until the present day as a major power systems supplier, the structure of the company has changed dramatically.

In 1998 Rolls-Royce introduced a new customer-facing organisation which recognised that both strategy and structure begin with the customers' requirements. Under a comprehensive company-wide programme 'Better Performance Faster', a series of initiatives including outsourcing have been introduced to improve productivity in systems, plant and equipment throughout the group, making it the most efficient supplier in its target market sectors.

As a result, the company has become less monolithic, sweeping away a number of boards and layers. From once being product-driven, Rolls-Royce has now created a number of customer-facing business units. A greater transparency and awareness of individual units and their contribution to the whole has empowered personal accountability and responsibility within the overall business.

Human Resources

Rolls-Royce is driven to provide a working climate that allows for freedom, energy and the ability to get the task done well and quickly. The internal emphasis has moved towards a greater emphasis on trust and teamwork, with decisions taken in the best interests of Rolls-Royce. This all represents significant cultural change, and has necessitated a lot of internal education and communication.

While shareholders, customers and suppliers are three of the four key constituents to financial success, the fourth is employees. Rolls-Royce recognises this and links the future of the company closely to its employees because it is they who will drive the continuing success of the company. Rolls-Royce invests an increasing amount of time and money in the development of its employees to support the company's values of quality and excellence.

Rolls-Royce operates at the cutting edge of advanced power technology, and the gifted scientist will be able to stretch his or her talents to the limit, helped by the practical engineering, teamwork and entrepreneurial skills of all our employees, including general managers and other specialists.

'When it comes to addressing complex issues, nothing beats a combination of technical knowledge and seasoned experienced,' suggests John Rivers, director, human resources. 'An objective, analytical approach is essential, but you also need to know when it's time to trust your instincts.'

The sort of people who run Rolls-Royce have achieved results and demonstrated certain key qualities in their behaviour. Qualities such as self-confidence, achievement, integrity, robustness, leadership, judgement, creativity, persuasiveness and the ability to embrace a culture of continuous learning.

Many people stay with Rolls-Royce for a very long time; the chairman joined in 1955, proving that its is quite possible to go from the bottom to the top. Whilst the company fosters long-term service, it is also prepared to learn from outside as well. 'If you're a world-leading company you must have world-leading people, and that means having the right balance between your own and expertise recruited from outside,' says John Rivers.

Career Opportunity and Development

Rolls-Royce takes on graduates and professionals who it believes have the potential to become leaders or acknowledged experts in their field. Some will want to be managers of people; others will choose to specialise in a particular area.

The company has therefore created parallel career opportunities which allow for the aspirations of both general managers and experts in their field to be recognised.

Rolls-Royce can offer many career paths in either its civil, defence or energy businesses. People work in areas such as aerospace engineering, procurement, manufacturing, commercial, finance, marketing, logistics, repair and refurbishment, product support or HR.

There are many opportunities to work overseas and to move between the businesses. The increasingly global nature of Rolls-Royce's businesses actually requires a commitment to mobility for those aspiring to senior positions.

Rolls-Royce has sites all over the world. The main locations are in the UK, USA, Canada, South America, South Africa and Australasia.

Graduate development is characterised by a culture of professionalism, an emphasis on global and business awareness, career planning, the development of both general managers and specialists, and development related to performance and aptitude.

Career responsibility is shared between the individual and the company and professional development continues throughout one's career.

Remuneration

Salaries are pitched at the median level after benchmarking against a peer group of some 50 industrial companies. Employees are increasingly rewarded on their individual performance, and there is also a well-established, annual all-employee bonus scheme. Directors and senior executives participate in both annual and long-term incentive schemes. All company employees can join a Sharesave scheme and are entitled to a company pension and various other benefits.

The Future

Managing technical risk remains top of Rolls-Royce's agenda. Its product development will continue to build on existing technologies rather than 'step in the dark' research. The Trent series illustrates how technology is fed across the family and other family members often learn from each other, adding up to low risk development.

Rolls-Royce has set itself the financial challenge of producing double-digit earnings growth over five years. Rolls-Royce is fortunate enough in that its order book is worth £12 billion with a high visibility workload, and with financial targets set, target cost reductions fall out of that equation.

Keeping customers satisfied is arguably the number one challenge, and Rolls-Royce is doing a good job. A broader product range and better access to customers represents opportunity, but also provides more scope to get it wrong. Rolls-Royce, with that superlative brand name, could be judged by its weakest product. It must therefore make sure that the quality associated with the name is integrated across the entire product range. Excellent Rolls-Royce performance – of engines, financial results and of its people – looks set to continue for a long time.

Royal Bank of Scotland Group

The Royal Bank of Scotland, founded in 1727, is one of the UK's top 50 companies and, with assets of £80 billion, is Scotland's largest bank. It has 650 branches throughout Great Britain, around half of which are in Scotland, and over 22,000 staff. It operates internationally, with offices in North America, the Far East, the Channel Islands, the Isle of Man, Greece and the Bahamas.

Scorecard:

Remuneration and benefits	★★★★
Progressive attitude	★★★★
Opportunity for promotion	★★★★
Training, development and education	★★★★
Working atmosphere and environment	★★★

Biggest plus:
Consistent ability to be bold and innovative

Biggest minus:
Still comparatively small in a predatory sector

The Royal Bank of Scotland Group
36 St Andrew Square
Edinburgh EH2 2YB
Tel: 0131 556 8555
Fax: 0131 557 4343
website: www.rbos.co.uk

❋ The Royal Bank
❋ of Scotland

Royal Bank of Scotland Group

The Business

The Royal Bank of Scotland aims to be recognised as the best performing financial services group in the UK. Striving towards this aim
it is mindful of its responsibilities to shareholders, customers,
employees and the communities in which it operates. Achieving these
aims while successfully balancing these responsibilities is the Royal
Bank's primary challenge.

The word 'bank' in the company's name, though, is a bit of a mis-
nomer. To be sure, traditional banking is at the heart of the operation,
and with roughly an equal number of branches north and south
of the Border it enjoys unrivalled coverage of England and Scotland.
But it has moved into so many other areas at a breathtaking pace. It
does not dip its toe in the water – it dives in and confidently swims
on.

The main business areas of the Royal Bank of Scotland Group
include the UK bank, serving retail, business, corporate and institutional customers; Direct Line Group, which is the UK's largest private
motor insurer, and Citizens Financial Group, a retail and corporate
bank operating in New England, USA. It is one of Europe's oldest
banking names which, through mergers, has acquired a unique British
banking pedigree.

Its CV is full of words like 'first' and 'pioneered'. It started on this
route in 1728 by pioneering the first overdraft – arguably the most
significant innovation in banking – when an Edinburgh merchant was
allowed to withdraw more money than he had deposited.

It developed the concept of branch banking, produced Europe's
first multicoloured banknote in 1777 to combat fraud, developed the
world's busiest network of cash-dispenser machines, pioneered the use
of video-conferencing and so on.

Given that track record it is no surprise that it is a pioneer of supermarket banking through its joint venture with Tesco, establishing a
significant and innovative new force in UK banking; it has partnered
up with Virgin to introduce a distinctive bank account; and it has

established what has become the UK's largest private motor insurer.

It has also forged a strategic alliance with Banco Santander of Spain and the most important fruit of this alliance has been the creation of IBOS, which links European banks electronically and is being extended to become a global cash management system.

That's only part of the story, but the bottom line is that profits before tax last year reached a record high in the Royal Bank's 270-year history – £1,001 million – making it the first Scottish company to break the £1 billion profit barrier.

Company Culture and Style

The bank is intent on achieving a strong, clear Royal Bank culture which will underpin everything it does and which will help it to deliver the best that it can for its customers, for the communities it serves and for its shareholders.

The bank wants its shared set of values to become an integral part of the way its employees live and work and to that end it is building a 'values' element into the expectations placed on its employees as they do their jobs – basically this will become a performance measure for staff throughout the bank.

The bank is introducing a more balanced way of setting both individual and business targets. Performance will be assessed not just on financial targets, although these will remain an important measurement, but also on how staff treat their customers and colleagues and how they develop themselves.

Investment in people has always been recognised as being important for the challenging way ahead and it is part of the bank's culture and one of its key values. The bank has developed a shared set of values, which include being customer-driven, fit for the purpose, interdependent and with individual responsibility.

Most of them speak for themselves, but fit for the purpose? This is linked to one of the motivating forces for the staff – being innovative and creative. This is very much encouraged – the 'to boldly go' philosophy – but the bank recognises that there is no point in going there if it is not delivering a solution or a product that the customer wants; it must be fit for its purpose.

The bank believes it has developed a culture of self-reliance, co-operation and collaboration.

Human Resources

The main priority is simple: to recruit and keep the best, people who will give the utmost value to the organisation, and the bank will do what it can to ensure that it happens. Chief executive George

Mathewson puts it this way: 'We are looking for exceptional people – something in the CV that says "achieved".'

Viscount Younger of Leckie, the group chairman, believes that the group benefits from the flexibility of the organisation. He explained: 'We are not a monolithic organisation. we have a broad range of different businesses and expect our managers to run these in an innovative and entrepreneurial manner so that we can respond quickly to changing circumstances and new opportunities, giving us greater options for the future than many of our competitors.'

According to Neil Roden, director, human resources: 'In the world of financial services you can get the competitive edge here and there with the quality and distinction of your products but the real differential is people. Everything we do is geared to making sure that our people want to work for us. We want to make sure our staff are highly motivated, highly trained, highly developed – providing the key element of differentiation that we need.'

The bank says it was 'extremely pleased' with a recent staff opinion survey which showed that out of 18 UK financial service organisations the bank's scores were significantly better than is typical in financial services in all but one of the 15 categories.

But it emerged that there are some areas where improvement can be made – such as the induction of new employees and job stress and pressure – and these are being addressed. The HR operation is being re-focused – a 'pretty intensive change' was how it was described – to cut down on the administration work and to deliver an even better service to the bank and its customers. Neil Roden stated: 'We want to deliver increased excellence. We are maybe a top employer but we are not going to become complacent.'

Career Opportunity and Development

Given the diversity of the bank's operations career opportunities and openings abound. Within the bank there is retail banking, corporate and institutional banking, and service and operations, which provides a range of services to the bank itself, including information technology. Within the group is Direct Line, the largest insurer of motor vehicles in the UK and the US subsidiary, Citizens Bank, which has 300 branches. The bank has also formed a strategic alliance with Banco Santander, has joint ventures with Tesco and Virgin and over the last two years has developed a close relationship with Scottish Widows.

Remuneration

The bank has what it calls business unit pay. Individual business areas face different pay markets and this is reflected in the salary policy.

All employees have the opportunity for a performance-related variable pay element, with the schemes tailored to the individual needs of the various business units.

An innovative flexible benefits package incorporating radical changes to pay and benefits has been launched to over 18,000 employees. All staff can make their choices under the new scheme, called RBSelect, making the Royal Bank the largest UK company to make such radical changes to its pay and benefits package in the one go.

The Future

The question remains as to whether the Scottish parliament will strengthen the position of the bank, which has already undertaken a number of initiatives to ensure that it continues to make a positive contribution to the governance of Scotland.

At the same time it continues to shrug off the constant takeover talk which is endemic in its sector. The bank continues to display a profit-making innovative and expansionist flair which increases its strength – and its attraction.

Its future will be anything but dull.

Sage Group

The Sage Group provides accounting and payroll software for small to medium-sized businesses in over 100 countries. Its main operating centres are the UK, France, Germany and the US, with global expansion facilitated through organic growth and acquisition. The company has almost 2,500 employees world-wide, including 700 in the UK, and services 1.2 million customers through an extensive, 15,000-strong re-seller network, retailers and a direct sales operation. In the year ending September 1998, the group made pre-tax profits of £47 million on turnover of £191 million.

Scorecard:

Remuneration and benefits	★★★★
Progressive attitude	★★★★★
Opportunity for promotion	★★★★
Training, development and education	★★★
Working atmosphere and environment	★★★★

Biggest plus:
Sage is undoubted market leader with a strengthening international brand

Biggest minus:
Finding the necessary skilled staff to support growth

Sage Group plc
Sage House
Benton Park Road
Newcastle-upon-Tyne NE7 7LZ
Tel: 0191 255 3000
Fax: 0191 255 0308
website: www.sage.com

Sage Group

The Business

The Sage Group, which was founded in 1981, manufactures and sells business solutions, predominantly accounting and payroll software, for use on personal computers. Its market comprises small to medium-sized enterprises (up to 100 employees) and it has over 1.2 million customers worldwide. It has grown steadily, both organically and through a programme of acquisition, which has seen expansion into mainland Europe and America.

Sage's approach is to give newly-acquired businesses a high degree of autonomy. In 1997, however, the decision was taken to confirm Sage as the international brand, where appropriate marrying it to the original company identity (such as Sage Sybel in France and Sage KHK in Germany). The intention is to provide customers with the comfort of dealing with a large, financially stable institution of high international pedigree.

Company Culture and Style

Formed in 1981, Sage is a young company that has experienced rapid growth. One of the founders, Graham Wylie, is still with the company as managing director of Sage Software Limited in the UK. None of the executive board is over 50 and Paul Walker, chief executive, is 41. This age profile helps reaffirm the image of the business as fresh, energetic and dynamic. The directors remain closely-involved with the day-to-day operations, as Paul Walker confirms: 'Only recently has the steady increase in headcount defeated our ability to remain on first-name terms with every member of staff.'

To cope with the rapid growth of the company, Sage has strengthened its management capability with additional appointments. However, staff are still expected to take responsibility for their own development. The company pays a lot of attention to recruiting the right people so that it can empower them and subsequently reap the benefits of their creativity and willingness to work hard. It has therefore developed a remuneration structure which rewards effort and success. This is of particular relevance since a general skills shortage in the technology market means it is crucial to retain key individuals.

While individual development and achievement is encouraged, Sage also endeavours to foster a team culture, where mutual support is to the fore. High demand for existing products and the need to remain at the cutting edge of product development means staff are sometimes required to 'go the extra mile', but the company is fastidious in showing its appreciation. A clear central management objective is to maintain high morale and great effort is expended to this end.

The pace and scale of Sage's growth might suggest that it is a hectic place in which to work. However, Sage promises to make its customers' lives easier by providing peace of mind and this is reflected by a general air of calm, both at its premises and in its corporate literature. Indeed, the advertising strap 'Through Knowledge Comes Control' hints at the Sage philosophy of maintaining a measured and thoughtful approach in a fast-moving and challenging environment.

Sage acknowledges that, within the information technology market generally, change is the only constant. It is therefore geared up for change and aims to be nimble enough to respond to customers' developing requirements. That said, it is determined to provide consistent levels of product excellence and customer service throughout its expanding field of operations.

Human Resources

Sage's human resources function has increased in importance as the company has grown in size and expanded overseas. This fact is eloquently articulated by the fact that the head of HR, Karen Geary, has been appointed a director of the company in the UK.

One of the problems facing companies such as Sage is the technology skills shortage. In terms of HR, this has prompted the company to motivate staff to develop their careers as much as possible, with training available to allow people to move from one discipline to another if appropriate. As the company has grown, management training (as opposed to pure technical training) has itself become increasingly important, with managers having to learn to identify and nurture talented individuals for the long-term benefit of the company.

The skills shortage, according to Sage, is partly due to the fact that schools and universities are failing to equip students with the necessary knowledge and aptitudes. The company therefore works closely with educational establishments in a bid to correct the problem. It has also identified people who have left the IT industry as a rich potential source of recruits. The need to provide products which align with client needs at the same time as recognising and assisting the developing use of computers throughout the commercial environment means Sage is constantly on the look out for the brightest candidates.

Career Opportunity and Development

Sage has created an environment where people are given maximum encouragement, support and opportunity to develop there own careers. In-house training is provided across the company's various departments but staff are expected to be self-starters. A 'spoon-feeding' approach is not offered. For those that have the energy and commitment, there is no limit on the progress that can be made. The continued growth of the company means that opportunities for promotion are plentiful. Given the youth of the senior management, age is certainly no barrier to progress.

Staff at Sage are expected to work hard but it is acknowledged that effort will be rewarded. 'The high profile of the HR facility within the management structure and the close interest of the directors in the nitty-gritty of the business ensures that individual effort and achievement will always be recognised.' says Karen Geary, HR director.

Sage's extensive international operations across Europe and America mean that opportunities exist for transfers to overseas companies. That said, it has been group practice to acquire successful businesses that already have a winning formula and, as far as is practicable, to allow them to continue in existing fashion. What is more, the growth of the UK business is such that there are plenty of opportunities for career development without venturing abroad.

Remuneration

The shortage of qualified, experienced and skilled staff in the IT industry means talented individuals can command high salaries. Sage is fully aware of this and pays competitive rates for its people. Indeed, remuneration levels of its highest-paid research and development staff are on a par with the directors themselves.

In addition to attractive salaries, the company offers a pension, healthcare and a Sharesave scheme. Where appropriate, relocation expenses will be paid to bring the right people to the required site. To aid recruitment activity, payments will be made to staff members who introduce people who are subsequently taken on by the company.

The Future

Sage is in the happy situation of having to cope with profitable growth, both in the UK and throughout its international operations. There is no shortage of demand for its products since its target market represents 99% of all businesses. What is more, legislative change, such as the introduction of rules governing late payment, is making companies more conscious of their accounting requirements.

The problem Sage faces is finding the right people to support ambitious expansion plans. There are an estimated 500,000 vacancies in the IT industry throughout Europe; Sage itself, at any given time, has up to 100 vacancies. Recruiting and retaining top people will therefore remain a priority. This will be achieved not by throwing money at the problem but by fostering an atmosphere where people are encouraged to develop their own potential and are properly rewarded for their effort and dedication.

Sage has realised that it cannot staff-up adequately simply by cherry-picking the best people on the jobs market. It is therefore investing in its future by working in collaboration with academic institutions in a bid to produce graduates more suited to the contemporary working environment.

Another consequence of growth is that senior managers inevitably grow more remote from most staff. Sage is responding to this challenge by building an effective middle management layer which can communicate effectively in both directions. This should ensure that strategic decisions at the highest level take account of realities on the 'shop floor'.

This is an exciting time for the IT sector. The growing significance of the Internet and electronic communication is promising to revolutionise many spheres of commercial activity and Sage is at the heart of this development. It says that, in general, take-up of the new information and communication services and facilities has been limited as yet but is set to accelerate in the next few years. It intends to be there to take full advantage when this occurs.

J Sainsbury

One of Britain's leading grocery chains, founded in London in 1869 and at the forefront of supermarketing in the 1950s and superstore retailing in the 1980s and 1990s. It is part of a group which includes the Homebase Do It Yourself chain and Savacentre hypermarkets in the UK, and the company expanded abroad in the 1970s with Shaw's supermarkets in the US. It now employs more than 175,000 people (most of them part-time) and makes sales of £14.5 billion, £12 billion of them in UK food retailing.

Scorecard:

Remuneration and benefits	★★★
Progressive attitude	★★★★
Opportunity for promotion	★★★
Training, development and education	★★★★
Working atmosphere and environment	★★★

Biggest plus:
A market leader with a tradition of taking staff needs seriously

Biggest minus:
The necessity for tight control to cope with the scale and nature of the business and intense competition

J Sainsbury Plc
Stamford House
Stamford Street
London SE1 9LL
Tel: 0171 695 6000
Fax: 0171 695 7610
website: j-sainsbury.co.uk

SAINSBURY'S

J Sainsbury

The Business

Sainsbury pioneered supermarkets in the UK and became the market leader by rolling out the modern superstore format in the 1980s. In the 1990s it was overtaken by Tesco but remains a powerful brand and a highly professional operator. It moved from being a family company to the Stock Exchange in 1973 and the family influence was further diluted in 1998 when the last family executive director, David (now Lord) Sainsbury, stepped down from the chair to join the government as an industry minister.

The company saw the need to diversify from its UK supermarket base very early, and established interests in the US and in non-supermarket retailing in the UK. In the 1990s the group established the Sainsbury Bank to capture customers' savings and meet their borrowing needs. By the end of the 1990s the group was ready to invest further in international expansion. But the UK supermarket chain remains the dominant business, contributing nearly 90% of profits in 1998.

Company Culture and Style

Over the past two decades Sainsbury has emerged from its family company past to become a business which combines the best of the family tradition with a modern management approach appropriate to a large, international group. David Sainsbury's six years in the chair coincided with tough times, including the group being overtaken by Tesco as Britain's leading supermarket operator. It also saw the development of a new management style, aimed specifically at releasing people's potential and creativity.

In a large, fast-moving business like this it is essential to have effective control and monitoring systems, but they now operate to support initiative and innovation. 'Structures are necessary, and they can be frustrating,' said Caroline Gray, a senior manager for human resources. 'But we're not over-bureaucratic – not compared to other companies of the same size.'

The most concrete evidence of the changes at Sainsbury is the creation of staff councils. These operate throughout the business, from stores to the centre. At store or depot level the councils, consisting of up to 15 representatives from all areas of the unit, meet quarterly. They discuss any issues of concern, short of pay and conditions which are negotiated in the usual way, and are expected to resolve issues locally wherever possible.

The central council is chaired by the group chief executive and has 30 representatives elected from around the business. It meets twice a year and gives staff the chance to put issues to senior management – and to get answers.

The scale of the business means it is essential to have formal policies and clear procedures. But Caroline Gray explained that staff are no longer expected to wait to be asked their opinions: 'If you think something is wrong you can challenge it, so long as you can say how to make it better. We encourage challenge.'

Discipline is still essential, however. Whether at store level or in the key head office areas such as the buying teams, it is essential for everything to work smoothly if the right products are to end up on the shelves on a Saturday morning. And the intensity of competition from other superstore operators means there is sustained pressure for improvement.

'We want people who have a passion for constant improvement,' Caroline Gray said, adding that Sainsbury people need to be collegiate, and flexible enough to work across different departments.

Human Resources

People are key to delivering the service Sainsbury wants to provide so HR is a key discipline, represented at board level by John Adshead, who is also responsible for systems.

The value attached to staff relations is illustrated by the 'Talkback' programme of continuous attitude surveys, a rolling programme which involves every employee, to provide hard data on what people are worrying about and what they are enjoying. The survey achieves remarkable response rates, with one period in 1998 achieving a response of 91%.

'HR has got to be important in a business like this which is so labour-intensive,' Caroline Gray explained. 'It is the people at the front end who are going to make the difference for us. It is so important that colleagues are customer-focused, and they will be only if they feel they are being treated well.'

The HR function is represented right down the organisation, with a personnel manager in more or less every store and depot, supporting line managers in the management of their staff on a day-to-day basis, and in staff development activities.

Career Opportunity and Development

Sainsbury continues to grow, both in absolute size and in the diversity of its operations, and that growth inevitably brings opportunities for personal development. While the group includes DIY and the Sava-Centre hypermarkets, the supermarket business itself has grown more diverse in recent years. At the start of the 1990s the edge-of-town superstore was virtually the sole model, but developments in systems and distribution have enabled the company to open smaller stores in country towns, and 1998 saw the beginning of a trial of a convenience store format.

There are also plenty of opportunities in head office departments, in the buying and marketing teams which play a crucial role in determining what appears in the stores, as well as the usual functions such as human resources, finance and IT.

The group recruits around 600 graduates a year, with roughly 85% going in to the stores and the rest into head office departments. Caroline Gray said the company prefers recruits who have already gained some experience of the world of work, ideally in a retail environment. And as part of the selection process, applicants are put through their paces on the shop floor.

'We have previously lost graduates who found it wasn't what they were expecting,' she explained. 'Some of them thought being a manager meant sitting in an office and telling people what to do.'

The initial training programme is very structured to give people a thorough introduction to the business, and concludes with a formal panel assessment. Trainees only pass the panel if they can show they have the necessary understanding of the products and systems and of how to handle people. This formal approach is intended to ensure that recruits can handle the considerable responsibility which they can take on at an early stage in their careers.

'They can have financial and people responsibility at a young age,' Caroline Gray said. 'Then the opportunities for advancement are very, very good. You can be a store manager when you are still in your 20s, and that is like running a medium-sized business.'

As with all retailers, it then gets more difficult to progress, given the flat management structure. But Sainsbury provides ample opportunity for personal development without moving jobs, ranging from secondments to other parts of the business to MBA programmes.

Remuneration

Caroline Gray explained that Sainsbury 'aims to pay upper quartile salaries for upper quartile performance'.

That emphasises the stress on performance which runs throughout the business, and which has become more significant in determining pay in recent years. The company has long since moved away from rigid pay scales with annual increases to compensate for inflation. There are still salary bands, but they are fairly wide. For example, a store manager could be on anything from £32,500 to £56,000.

But performance review is now taken very seriously, with everybody in the company going through a review every three months at which performance targets are agreed and personal development discussed.

A company-wide bonus scheme has recently been introduced for managers, while Sainsbury also operates a formal profit-sharing scheme, with payouts which can be taken in cash or shares in the company.

The Future

The main HR challenge in the immediate future is to drive performance management and employee development throughout the business. 'We want to have an effective system of performance measurement so we can tell people how they are doing and relate that to their rewards, but more importantly to the recognition they get,' Caroline Gray said.

Communication and releasing the talents of all members of staff are the other big issues. The Talkback attitude survey and the staff councils have pushed forward the dialogue across the business, but there is more to do to capture the ideas and experience of people from the checkout to the buying office.

All this must be achieved while competing against tough rivals and satisfying the public (in the shape of the government) that the competition is genuine and to the public benefit.

Scottish Equitable

Edinburgh-based Scottish Equitable is a leading provider of pension and investment products and services through independent financial advisers. It is a member of the AEGON Group, one of the world's top ten listed insurers, and is one of only seven insurance companies in the UK to have been awarded the elite triple-A financial strength rating by Standard & Poors.

Scorecard:
Remuneration and benefits	★★★★
Progressive attitude	★★★
Opportunity for promotion	★★★
Training, development and education	★★★★★
Working atmosphere and environment	★★★★★

Biggest plus:
Financial clout to go for growth

Biggest minus:
Operating in a pensions sector subject to constant government scrutiny and review. That could also become its biggest plus

Scottish Equitable plc
Edinburgh Park
Edinburgh EH12 9SE
Tel: 0131 339 9191
Fax: 0131 339 9567

Scottish Equitable

The Business

Founded in 1831, Scottish Equitable rightly regards itself as a financial services company in the great Scottish tradition. That means the careful, long-term husbandry of other people's money – as well as its own – as evidenced by its profitability. It concentrates on its core pensions business, with a range of innovative products in a constantly changing market, and it capitalises on the skills it has as a leading pensions provider.

These skills include investment performance, which has helped the company to a period of prolonged and consistent growth and is now spearheading advances in the personal investment and fund management business.

Company Culture and Style

In 1993 Scottish Equitable was regarded by many as one of a small band of smaller Scottish life offices there for the taking into possible oblivion by a predator in a rapidly changing financial services sector. But the company was ahead of the game and forged a partnership with the Netherlands-based insurance giant AEGON which gave it financial muscle, a powerful backer and a measure of independence which has seen the Scottish Equitable name flying higher than ever.

AEGON and Scottish Equitable have played off each other's strengths, and their success has had a considerable impact on the jobs market in the Edinburgh financial sector. The growth that has been experienced – record-breaking figures all round in 1998 are a typical example – has created challenges and changes in the company's culture and style which it has moved swiftly to meet.

In the spring of 1996 it decided to abandon its head office in St Andrew's Square, Edinburgh – the traditional, but outmoded in technologically advancing times, heart of the Edinburgh life office sector – and move to magnificent purpose-built offices in a business park on the outskirts of the city.

It was a radical move, one which had to be handled delicately in terms of staff morale, especially in the face of a growing workforce which had to be settled in and motivated. Around 1,400 staff moved out to the new offices but by the end of this year that number will have gone up to 2,300.

As well as a large, subsidised staff restaurant, the building has two Astroturf pitches for football and hockey, an activity centre with an aerobics studio and gym, and an abundance of staff-run clubs and societies.

A company for the young and fit only? Scottish Equitable has recognised that it might be heading in this direction and has set out to recruit over-35s. Group personnel director Gareth Humphreys explained: 'We conducted an analysis of our activities in the recruitment market and one of the things that came up was that there is a big group of people out there who are older than we normally recruit and would be ideal for us.

'So far the response has been tremendous. We hope to fill about 150 jobs through this campaign. We have a very young staff and it will give us a better balance – it is hard to replicate experience.'

Other internal research on the impressions people have of Scottish Equitable showed that it is seen as a young organisation, fast-moving and very sociable. Gareth Humphreys asks and answers the question: 'Is that attractive? Not necessarily – there are lots of people who enjoy the social life attached to the office but there are a large number of others who enjoy a totally separate social life.'

Scottish Equitable has an enlightened corporate culture where intra-personal skills are highly valued and teamwork is genuinely central.

But Scottish Equitable is not just about Edinburgh. Around 2,300 work in the head office but there are a further 600 employees in the UK in a total of 32 branch offices. Add Scottish Equitable International, with offices in Luxembourg and Milan, and you have a team producing teamwork on a wide canvas.

Human Resources

Gareth Humphreys puts it simply: 'We specialise in pensions and that expertise is hard to replicate. That is why staff are a key element for us and staff retention is so important. We look at all the things we do and provide as a company to ensure staff retention. We want to make sure people understand that there is a purpose behind what is happening to make sure we develop their skills base.'

New members of staff take charge of their own development by working through a self-paced introductory course called Discovery, in which they learn about the company, its products and the marketplace.

Further professional development is planned in consultation with employees, managers and dedicated training staff.

The company is committed to heavy investment in its human resources and to ensure that employees stay and are able to progress.

Career Opportunity and Development

The selection criteria are pretty tough, but the opportunities and rewards make it worthwhile. The opportunities for graduates are in the actuarial profession, investment management, information systems, sales and marketing – and 'high calibre' are the two favourite words.

The company's links with independent financial advisers are crucial and there are many openings for what they call 'sales professionals', with flat corporate structures giving easy access to management.

A career in Scottish Equitable will be backed by thorough, structured training. There are opportunities for early responsibilities and good promotion prospects.

Remuneration

The company offers highly competitive salaries and generous bonus schemes, and provides an extremely competitive benefits package. It has implemented a flexible benefits programme, called EquiFlex, which features a wider range of benefits and levels of cover to give the employee a greater degree of control over the benefits received.

Gareth Humphreys explained: 'We are constantly looking to revise the benefits to enable people to get the right mix to take account of their personal priorities and the changes in their family and financial circumstances.'

The full EquiFlex package includes life assurance, dental insurance, private medical insurance, childcare vouchers and retail vouchers for High Street stores such as Marks & Spencer, Safeway, Boots and Thomas Cook. There are also interest-free loans for those who wish to buy annual season tickets for travelling to and from work, personal accident insurance, permanent health insurance and critical illness insurance. Staff are also eligible for bonuses, dependent on personal and company performance. While company bonuses cannot be guaranteed, the company's performance has consistently been excellent, so the bonuses keep coming in.

The Future

Scottish Equitable has a very favourable future. With a solid core business and financial base, a strengthened IT resource, asset management and customer service capability and a broadening product and service range well adapted to the all-important independent financial advisers, things are looking good. There is likely to be even more emphasis necessary on staff training and retention.

Opportunities abound. Scottish Equitable International, the Luxembourg-based subsidiary, has reported a 118% rise in new business, with particular success in Italy and a strengthening position in Europe.

The company has launched its own investment company, Scottish Equitable Asset Management, with the aim of doubling funds under management from £17 billion to £34 billion within five years.

A revamped corporate structure has seen the creation of a holding company, Aegon UK, with the Scottish Equitable chief executive, David Henderson, becoming its chief executive. He describes the move thus: 'A message to the market that our ambitions go beyond the boundaries of being a life and pension provider. It gives us the flexibility to seek out opportunities for the development of new business.'

This could mean acquisition. The determination and ambition are there, and the company undoubtedly has an impressive track record. Standard & Poors summed it up nicely when it stated: 'Scottish Equitable has a strong level of capitalisation and strong business position, excellent expense management and very good financial flexibility.'

Scottish Hydro-Electric

Scottish Hydro-Electric, a trading name of Scottish and Southern Energy plc, based in Perth, Scotland, is the most diverse of all the major electricity generators in the UK in terms of its fuel sources and is the largest generator of electricity from renewable sources. It generates power as well as distributing it, and one third of its electricity is sold in England. But that is set to grow dramatically with the company's merger with the Maidenhead-based Southern Electric, to form Scottish and Southern Energy, taking it into a new league.

Scorecard:

Remuneration and benefits	★★★★
Progressive attitude	★★★
Opportunity for promotion	★★★★
Training, development and education	★★★★★
Working atmosphere and environment	★★★★

Biggest plus:
Its ability to take advantage of enormous mass market opportunities

Biggest minus:
Eye-off-the-ball, executive time may be needed to bed-down the Southern Electric merger

Scottish Hydro-Electric
10 Dunkeld Road
Perth PH1 5WA
Tel: 01738 455040
Fax: 01738 455045
website: www.hydro.co.uk

Scottish Hydro-Electric

The Business

Scottish Hydro-Electric has come a long way since it was created in 1943 to bring electricity to the north of Scotland and replace the heat supplied by burning peat and the light from dirty, dangerous paraffin lamps. It still sticks proudly to its north of Scotland roots, but it is now an expanding energy company which serves customers throughout Britain, and expansion has not been at the expense of standards because it remains the utility highest-rated by its customers.

Its share of the British electricity market has doubled to 6% since privatisation and this will rise to almost 9% next year – without taking into consideration the benefits of the merger with Southern Electric, which will provide a customer base of 3.3 million and create a strong, new competitive force in the UK energy market.

From its traditional area in the north of Scotland, which covers 25% of the UK land mass but has only 2% of the population, it has successfully expanded into England and Wales with an £800 million investment programme in modern, efficient gas-fired power stations and combined heat and power plants while investing over £1 billion in Scotland in the period 1994–2001. It has a turnover of over £1 billion.

Company Culture and Style

The corporate mission statement says that the company's highest priority is delivering exceptional customer satisfaction, and it also aims to be recognised as an outstanding company by its customers, employees, shareholders, community and suppliers.

It has set consistent standards to help provide a unifying culture across the organisation which is made up of different businesses employing individual people.

Firmly to the fore are the company's values – nine of them, in fact – and they range from being customer-focused to caring for the environment. Other examples: High Integrity: 'we treat others inside and outside Scottish Hydro-Electric, in the way we would wish to be treated ourselves.' Teamwork: 'in meeting the needs of our stake-holders the contribution of the team working together is greater than that of the number working individually.' Far-sighted: 'we know where we are heading and what it takes to get us there.'

Teamwork is obviously one of the essentials in an organisation which has customers in the most remote and most populated areas and has an employee mass of 1,500 in Perth and a further 2,000, throughout the UK.

Alan Scott, director of human resources, says the aim is to liberate the potential of each employee, and when asked about the company culture he produces a sheet of paper which outlines what is called 'The People Vision'.

Liberating potential is one of the phrases listed there, but other words that leap out are superior business performance, satisfied employees, employees feel and know their value, reduction of barriers, and a learning organisation.

It is perhaps a bit hackneyed these days, but Scottish Hydro-Electric firmly believes it is all about people. The aim is to create a culture where all employees can use their talent and skills – 'liberating potential' – producing satisfied employees; this then is related directly to customer satisfaction and to sustained business success. Employee, customer and shareholder satisfaction are all inextricably linked.

There is a whole raft of initiatives, plans and programmes aimed at developing employees, keeping them happy and motivating them. Everybody gets a chance to assess the boss – comments are non-attributable – and the boss is expected to listen. The process goes right to the top, with the chief executive receiving any constructive criticisms from his directors.

Scottish Hydro-Electric believes in developing an 'Open Book Man-agement' culture, getting people to understand where they are going, where they fit into the bigger picture, and to participate in discussions about company strategy and changes in the industry in which it operates.

Learning maps are regarded as a primary tool; a series of three learning maps conveys a visual picture of the energy industry, business operations and the company's strategy. Employees follow the maps and discuss the issues in small facilitated groups, increasing their understanding through dialogue and self-learning.

The company operates an effective performance management system to provide a consistent framework and approach to managing personal performance across the company. This process involves setting objectives and reviewing performance within a coaching style of man-agement to improve individual performance, and thus overall company performance.

Human Resources

The four Scottish Hydro-Electric divisions of generation, power systems, commercial and corporate have their own arrangements for negotiating some business terms and conditions in the belief that they know best what terms and conditions apply in their areas of operation. About one third of employees are on personal contracts, the rest are part of collective bargaining. There is a partnership arrangement with the unions and the balance between collective and individually bargained terms and conditions requires careful consideration.

In recruiting the company looks beyond the job in hand. Pamela Zielinski, recruitment and selection adviser, explained: 'I am not just looking at whether or not they can do the job they are applying for, but at the scope they have for progressing and taking other roles within the company. If it makes good commercial sense it means you are also a good employer. To get the best out of people in the company you have to be a good employer.'

Existing employees are given an opportunity to apply for vacancies and if they don't succeed, every effort is made to explain why they have failed and to suggest how they might do better next time. External applicants who are unsuccessful are given the same courtesy.

According to Pamela Zielinski: 'There has to be transparency – sometimes people can devote up to a day coming here for an interview and we owe it to them to tell them why they have been unsuccessful. I spend a considerable amount of time with people who have been unsuccessful and sometimes when under pressure it is hard to rationalise, but we want these people still to think well of the company.'

Career Opportunity and Development

Scottish Hydro-Electric says it gives recruits the scope and support for a career path which is hard to beat anywhere. For those with flair and ability that path can take them to senior positions within the company.

Every encouragement is given to learn continually and improve individual knowledge and skills through the provision of appropriate training and development opportunities. The organisation development team at company headquarters has a consultancy role to facilitate continuous performance improvement throughout the organisation.

If an employee feels overlooked and is not being given the correct career path there are plenty of opportunities to speak up.

Remuneration

The pay is good, the benefits flexible. Management consultants are used to help benchmark the company's rates and the pay is described as being extremely competitive in some areas and around the median for others. Getting it right is not always guaranteed in different markets and with such large proportions of union and non-union employees.

Mary Robertson, compensation and benefits adviser, puts it this way: 'Some of our business principles are reflected in the way that we manage pay. For example, we need constantly to balance our reward approach to ensure that our shareholders and employees are both satisfied; in the same way we have to balance our energy portfolio to ensure that both purchase and sales commitments are met. A creative style is a definite requirement.'

Last year a second tranche of share options was granted to all employees and, in 1996, flexible benefits were introduced for the company's 1,000 personal contract employees. The company would like to extend that across the whole organisation as part of the drive towards the removal of status and barriers. The menu includes critical illness cover, dental insurance, financial counselling, private medical cover, holiday and personal accident cover. It is also the first company in the UK to use air miles as a flexible employee benefit and it is proving very popular.

The Future

Brighter than orange. The company will stick to businesses it understands and to which it can add value. It will develop and defend its Scottish business and continue to expand into England and Wales. And it says it will stick to Britain for the meantime, no doubt a little nudge at its big Scottish rival, Scottish Power, which has looked across the Atlantic for expansion.

The merger with Southern Electric creates a major new force in the market and removes the big risk that Scottish Hydro-Electric might be a take-over target. The strengths of the two companies are complementary: Scottish Hydro-Electric's generation experience and its energy trading expertise, coupled with Southern Electric's large customer base.

But a merger of this size creates employee uncertainty as well as promise. There will be a new chief executive and a close examination of the culture and values as seen by the new team. Challenges lie ahead, but the merged group has the management experience, financial resources and assets to turn those challenges into opportunities.

Sema Group

Sema Group is one of the world's most powerful information technology companies, delivering innovative IT solutions to many of the world's leading organisations. The company operates in 130 locations worldwide and has 15 UK offices. Sema Group employs 16,500 people, 6,000 in the UK. Annual turnover now exceeds £1.3 billion.

Scorecard:

Remuneration and benefits	★★★★
Progressive attitude	★★★★★
Opportunity for promotion	★★★★
Training, development and education	★★★★
Working atmosphere and environment	★★★★

Biggest plus:
An empowered company where you can really make a difference

Biggest minus:
Not yet a truly global player

Sema Group
Fulcrum House
2 Killick Street
London N1 9AZ
Tel: 0171 830 4444
Fax: 0171 830 4439
website: www.semagroup.com

Sema Group

The Business

Sema Group has over 35 years' experience in delivering IT solutions to its customers. Growth has been rapid, especially over the last five years during which Sema Group has grown at an impressive 24% compound per annum. This has been driven both by organic growth and acquisitions.

Today, the company operates in 130 locations, mostly in Europe but also in South-east Asia and North America. UK offices are in London, Birmingham, Wilmslow, Reading, Nottingham, Derby, Crewe, Darlington, York, Andover, Newcastle, Nantwich, Blackpool, Aberdeen and Glasgow. It employs 16,500 staff worldwide, 6,000 of whom work in the UK. Annual turnover now exceeds £1.3 billion.

Sema Group provides solutions to companies in the fields of telecoms, finance, energy, commerce, transport, public sector and industry. Its business systems operation combines expertise in outsourcing, consulting and systems integration, while Sema Group Telecoms is a leading provider of systems and services to the telecommunications industry. Overall, the company has a reputation for quality of delivery second to none. Not being tied to any particular supplier, it prides itself on being able to put together the best solution for every client.

Company Culture and Style

The company has a flat structure: not hierarchical, and certainly not bureaucratic. Individuality is promoted strongly at Sema Group. This is an empowered culture, essential because the company works across such a wide range of markets. The work is diverse, so it looks for diverse individuals.

The type of person who flourishes at Sema Group is very client-focused, able to communicate well in that environment. Tracey Yates, head of recruitment at Sema Group: 'We look for flexible people as much of our workforce is mobile. That work is likely to change many times over your career, so it's difficult to specialise in just one area.

Of course, if you enjoy different challenges, this is the ideal company to give them to you. Our people have the chance to work on major projects with some of the world's largest businesses.'

Teamwork is vital. The company structure is project-based with people working closely in teams. Everyone works hard at Sema Group, and the company expects a lot of its people. But the work is also exciting, challenging, stimulating and rewarding.

Without doubt, Sema Group people enjoy their work. It is a leading supplier of IT systems to major sporting events, including the Barcelona and forthcoming Sydney Olympiads. It was the systems integrator for Euro '96, and supported the Kuala Lumpur Commonwealth Games and the Bangkok Asian Games. It is also replacing IBM as the IT sponsor for future Olympic Games.

The company's work is so diverse that there is no such thing as a typical client. A common factor though is that Sema Group's philosophy is always to work in partnership with its clients. The effectiveness of this was demonstrated by its winning *Computing*'s Partnership of the Year award in conjunction with Conoco.

The company is keen to harmonise conditions and opportunities across its acquisitions. It is proud that it has never made a hostile acquisition, and intends to maintain this stance. Every company acquired wanted to join the group. Furthermore, many people who have joined in this way now work in totally new areas for them, right across Sema Group.

A large number of employees work at client sites. The approach here is distinctive: to work with the client in integrated project teams, not to impose methodologies or conventional IT wisdom. These ongoing projects are often long-term: five, seven, ten years or even longer. Employees may work on these for some time and then move to other areas to develop their careers. There are also many multinational projects. The only basis for selecting the people who work on these is their talent.

Human Resources

Sema Group has a substantial HR department, originally set up as a traditional administration service but now being rolled out across the business lines. Its task now is very much to put information in place to support the business, and dedicated HR professionals work to support staff.

All job vacancies are communicated to everyone in the company, using noticeboards and the Intranet. Communications are handled through the internal magazine *Optima*, which is produced in both a group-wide and UK-based version. Regular teamtalk sessions help to cascade information down the company. There are also Management

Question Times, held at various locations across the UK, where anyone can question the company's senior management about matters of concern or interest.

A top priority for HR is recruitment, which has led to considerable advertising, branding and marketing activity. A new HR IT system is now in place, offering significantly improved management information. Dedicated resource managers work across the business, encouraging people to talk about their career development.

Career Opportunity and Development

Approximately 25% of new recruits are graduates, of which the company takes on around 200 each year. The new entrant programme, which according to the business unit will last from four to twelve weeks, provides an excellent introduction to Sema Group. This may include live work almost immediately, or make use of dummy projects. At the same time, communication, business and teamworking as well as technical skills will be developed.

Imogen Trowse, analyst/programmer: 'Initially, I expected to be a small part of a very big team but I've gained experience so quickly that my career's advanced immensely.' James Parkhouse joined as a resource allocator: 'I came in with an MSc in Economics and Politics, and I've been astonished by how much potential there is for someone like me. So much of IT is about face-to-face contact and sharp business thinking.'

In 1999, the company will put in place a new career management programme. This will include mentoring schemes, a fast-track for those with strong management potential, and many other factors. It will look at business goals and build these into everyone's objectives, allowing them to see how to move both the business and their careers forward.

At Sema Group, the individual is in charge of career development: he or she makes it happen. This individual initiative is supported by excellent training, both in-house and external. The internal training department is large and provides classroom tuition, computer-based help, open learning, seminars and work groups. The company also sponsors people to acquire relevant professional qualifications by fee-paying, time off for study, and so on.

Remuneration

Sema Group generally pays market rates of salary in most areas. Pay rises are based on an individual's performance as measured by job appraisal, and also on the profitability of the company as a whole. Bonus incentives are offered to sales staff.

All employees have a highly flexible benefits scheme, allowing staff to vary their benefits according to their preferences. For instance, the basic scheme includes holidays, a company car (at appropriate levels), health benefits (including family member coverage), dental healthcare, accident insurance, travel insurance, life assurance, and a contributory pension scheme. An individual could choose to take a smaller car than standard and increase salary, pay more and have a bigger car, or have no company car at all and boost salary even further. And adjust the other variables in similar fashion.

The Future

The key requirement for the company is to attract, retain and develop the right people. Sema Group's only resource is its people. It is vital, therefore, that it has the right skills in place to take advantage of the growth potential of its markets – particularly the rapidly developing telecoms and finance sectors.

However, the company is confident about the future. The new career development management path will help ensure that the company develops its people skills to meet the needs of its fast-growing business. As a result of this and its other attractions for employees, Sema Group will undoubtedly continue to be an exciting and rewarding place to work into the next millennium.

Shell

The Royal Dutch/Shell Group of Companies (Shell) is a major player in the international energy business. With an Anglo-Dutch holding company structure, its operating companies are decentralised and focused on the key business areas of exploration and production, oil products, chemicals, gas and power, and renewables. Shell operates in more than 140 countries worldwide and employs over 100,000 people.

Scorecard:

Remuneration and benefits	★★★★★
Progressive attitude	★★★★
Opportunity for promotion	★★★★★
Training, development and education	★★★★
Working atmosphere and environment	★★★★★

Biggest plus:
Almost any career aim can be fulfilled, almost anywhere in the world

Biggest minus:
Don't expect your hand to be held all the way

Shell International Limited
Shell Centre
London SE1 7NA
Tel: 0171 934 3630
Fax: 0171 934 7606
website: www.shell.com

Shell

The Business

By many measures the largest company in the world, Shell is almost synonymous with unlimited career opportunity. This Anglo-Dutch giant is probably the most international of all companies, with an inherited culture and successful record of working with many different nationalities and cultures. Shell has many upstream and downstream operations in Europe, particularly in the areas of exploration and production on the UK Continental Shelf. It has six distinct businesses: the most recent additions are Shell International Renewals (a renewable energy business which brought together its solar energy, wind and biomass concerns and also researches new sources of energy) launched in 1997 and Shell Services International, a global IT consultancy and business services company, launched in 1998.

People joining the company will usually come into contact with other nationalities and high performers will probably work abroad early on in their career. They also have the advantage of fast development opportunities. What they make of these is up to them, but a career progression which includes working for operating companies overseas and stints at Shell's main offices in London and the Hague compares favourably with others in the industry.

Shell takes a long-term view of business, and with considerable amounts of its own cash always at its disposal, it has the financial muscle to invest in countries or risk scenarios that would be untenable or impossible for most companies. Clear thinking, analysis and scenario planning are vital in measuring this risk. However, Shell is not afraid of difficult business situations. It remained in South Africa when many companies left due to pressure from members of the international community. Today, it still receives tributes from Nelson Mandela acknowledging that staying was the best thing that Shell did for his country.

Anyone looking for a career that avoids risk, complex business situations and significant contact with governments would be best advised not to apply to Shell. If, on the other hand, that sounds exciting and challenging, Shell probably has no peer.

Company Culture and Style

A changing corporate structure is carrying traditional Shell values of integrity and professionalism into a new era where Shell is adding an emphasis on external focus. This includes valuing diversity and welcoming different lifestyles, working in teams and fostering ever more effective communication.

In addition, the culture is increasingly aware of the planet's resources and Shell seeks to play its part as a responsible world society member. Its recent ground-breaking report, *Profit and Principles – does there have to be a choice?*, was widely welcomed by the media, financial analysts and stakeholder groups as a sign of Shell's commitment and accountability on social and environmental issues. Shell also has a scholarship fund which promotes postgraduate study at a British university for students from the developing world.

As an equal opportunities employer, Shell is a member of Opportunity 2000 and is eager to recruit more women in technical roles. A woman now heads the gas business; a female board member sits on the Shell Transport and Trading Company board; and there are other examples. The company, however, recognises that more remains to be done in this area. Shell also seeks to recruit people from a variety of different nationalities, cultures and lifestyles. And while one third of Shell's high-level graduate intake is from the UK, increasingly this pool is drawn from many more countries.

Creativity is valued highly, in all areas of the company: flair and lightness of touch in engineering, innovation in partnerships and joint ventures, and flexibility during inter-government negotiations.

High-performing Shell people have the opportunity to spend a significant part of their careers overseas. Expatriate packages are attractive: tax-free salaries, paid accommodation, business class travel home, paid school fees, sports facilities, and often a more amenable climate than the UK offers!

Human Resources

Human resources management at Shell is now very much about encouraging individuals to take control of their own development, while providing all the tools, the environment and the support they need in order to do so. Another key role of HR is to give the organisation the right resources at the right time. Change happens quickly in the energy industry and sometimes this means moving people quickly too.

The company runs a global attitude survey with opportunities for local tailoring. Issues covered range from partner employment to provision of information. This survey works on multiple levels throughout the organisation, and its overall aim is to achieve greater co-ordination globally without losing Shell's flexibility and speed of response. The company now places far greater emphasis on employee communication and leadership visibility.

Open Resourcing is a system whereby jobs are advertised on the company's Intranet system. Each employee agrees with his or her manager to do a certain job for a specified period; at the end of that time, there is a window during which new jobs can be applied for. As well as the Intranet, the company uses Shell Business Television four to six times a year, allowing all its employees to be addressed at the same time. Furthermore, the Group Leadership Meeting brings together around 500 of the company's business leaders for an annual conference.

Career Opportunity and Development

With its huge global operation, Shell generates an abundance of career opportunity for talented people. Individuals can become general managers for Shell businesses in smaller countries at a relatively early age, providing a self-managed business opportunity with bottom-line responsibility, but backed by Shell resources.

Outside exploration and production, new recruits are likely to have their first one or two assignments in the UK, and thereafter have opportunities for overseas work once they have built up their skills. In the UK, some businesses have personnel development centres which help people decide what they want to do next: each career stream has a competency framework, combining technical and leadership skills.

Shell does not have a dedicated graduate training course. Instead, you do the job from day one, driven by the need to gain real experience. From there, people work out with their managers what their own training and development needs are.

In addition to graduate recruits, Shell is increasingly taking on skilled professionals from outside. A recent example is a senior-level appointment to strengthen its expertise in retailing. However, this desire to introduce new expertise has no adverse effect on the career development opportunities of existing employees, who continue to enjoy enormously wide career possibilities.

Remuneration

Shell pays well and compares to other blue-chip multinationals in terms of basic salary at executive and management levels. There is a significant variable pay element at all levels, more so for management where this includes share options. Variable pay, including bonuses, is dependent upon company performance and individual contribution.

Benefits are good and include the usual packages expected of a world-class employer. Shell provides particularly attractive benefits in the area of equal opportunity. It also offers career breaks, and its maternity arrangements are seen as among the best.

The Future

Shell believes it must demonstrate that being a professional in the oil and gas industry is not just about engineering but also about big business, people, fun and excitement. This shift of perceptions might seem unusual for such a successful company which clearly has fascinating jobs to offer, but Shell believes that it must mean what it says and deliver on its promises.

Employees recognised that recent corporate changes and restructuring were essential for the long-term success of the company, and that the challenges faced by both Shell and its employees – to be up-to-date and competent – were ongoing ones. The new structure should provide greater opportunities and challenges than ever before.

The focus is on recruiting people for the short and medium term. However, Shell recognises that a percentage of staff will enjoy opportunities with the company over a much longer timeframe. Certainly, with six businesses operating in over 140 countries, working for Shell can be like having many different careers – all with genuinely top employers. For those who relish challenge, excitement and working at the leading edge, there is every incentive to stay with Shell.

The Sheridan Group

There are probably few companies which so successfully merge entrepreneurial excitement, high finance and show-biz as the Sheridan Group, which in less than a decade has become the biggest leisure-oriented development company in Ireland and an increasingly significant player in Great Britain and further afield. It is currently involved in integrated entertainment projects costing up to £100 million, with many more on the drawing board, and is also moving into hotel and residential park developments. It now employs 260 people in Northern Ireland, Great Britain and the Republic of Ireland.

Scorecard:

Remuneration and benefits	★★★★
Progressive attitude	★★★★★
Opportunity for promotion	★★★
Training, development and education	★★★
Working atmosphere and environment	★★★★

Biggest plus:
Career opportunities in a wide range of exciting areas

Biggest minus:
The problems arising from a need for company restructuring

The Sheridan Group
35 Bedford Street
Belfast BT2 7EJ
Tel: 01232 244211
Fax: 01232 233946

Sheridan Group

The Sheridan Group

The Business

The Sheridan Group was formed in 1989 'to pursue the development and operation of unique, integrated entertainment centres in Ireland and the United Kingdom'. That legalistic statement of aim belies the excitement that permeates a company of relentless growth, built on one man's dream and his dogged determination to give it life, in the face of establishment scepticism and bureaucratic inertia.

The dream had occurred a few years earlier and it was that, contrary to the perceived wisdom at the time, the cinema industry in Britain was not dead and could be revived by making it part of a wider eating, drinking and fun package, offering people comfortable, multi-choice theatres, family entertainment, restaurants, bars, shops and convenient, secure parking all under one roof.

The dream became reality in 1993 with the opening of Peter Curistan's £16 million Virgin-anchored entertainment complex in Belfast. That success, and his realisation that property development need not be confined to 'safe' office and residential projects, led to the growth of what is now a £30 million turnover business. It is the biggest leisure sector developer in Ireland, of rapidly increasing significance in Great Britain yet it is, in Curistan's words 'barely out of the starting blocks'.

The company's sheer speed of growth has left many of his team breathless, and each new development seems to lead to others. After Belfast came the huge Parnell Centre in Dublin which, in addition to housing a multiplex Virgin cinema (Curistan always signs up blue-chip anchor tenants before moving on-site), has a simulation theatre, family entertainment centre, 40,000 sq. ft of shopping, 100 apartments and a multi-storey car park – and the first IMAX giant screen cinema in Europe. Built on a site on the 'wrong side of town' in Dublin, its runaway success says much about the sort of man Curistan is.

This led to the development contract for a 70,000 sq. ft integrated leisure centre on Bournemouth seafront and then the operating contract for the visitor attraction in Scotland's £60 million tourist development at Loch Lomond. These, and at least six other similar centres around Great Britain being negotiated at the time of writing, will also have IMAX theatres as their central attraction.

Other areas in which the Sheridan Group is now involved range from film-making (for the IMAX theatres), hotel and residential developments.

Company Culture and Style

A recent magazine profile of Sheridan Group was headed 'Curistan's Odyssey' and while this did refer to what is the company's crowning glory to date, the £100 million Odyssey Centre – Belfast's millennium entertainment, sports and educational complex and the biggest building project ever undertaken in Ireland – no phrase could more accurately sum up the course, the style and the culture of the group.

'A journey of adventure, with new excitements round every bend, and you never know what's coming next,' is how senior property director Simon Healy describes his years with Sheridan Group. And no-one who would like it any other way need apply.

Curistan likes to recount how one man in line for a senior post had a 'terms of employment' contract drawn up by his solicitor – 72 pages of it! 'All I want is one page. By the time I had finished reading through his, I had lost interest. I thought, if this man wants to do business with my customers the same way, he'll turn them off too.'

But though Curistan is an adventurous entrepreneur, he is no buccaneer and certainly no gambler with his resources or the 260 people in his employ. Although Sheridan projects at the leading edge of imagination and technology, it moves forward through a process of evolution rather than revolution.

In management style Curistan does not encourage a 'boss' attitude, preferring consensus and team-building. He is always the final decision-maker, but only after seeking the opinions of everyone involved; there is always plenty of opportunity for imaginative and constructive input. His 12-year grounding in accountancy with Price Waterhouse gave him first hand experience of how blue-chip companies manage their affairs and a healthy respect for the need to keep a careful eye on his financial back.

Human Resources

While responsibility for recruitment and human resource development within each enterprise is the responsibility of the unit manager, this is within the guidelines of the company culture of 'relaxed efficiency' which Curistan encourages, and for those who demonstrate ability, whether in accountancy, surveying, property management, law or hospitality enterprise, no career path is limited.

At management level Curistan admits that he keeps a 'guiding eye' on newcomers until they have shown what they can do and that they can take up projects and run with them.

Career Opportunity and Development

The structure and scope of the Sheridan Group presents two facets in terms of career opportunity.

On one hand, the core 'executive elite' is a comparatively small group, drawn mostly from accountancy and surveying backgrounds, who work closely with Curistan in seeking development opportunities, putting together proposals and seeing them through. This is a tightly focused group with each member being 'hand-picked', and his closest lieutenants have been with him a long time. Curistan boasts that they can put together a feasible development plan faster than anyone else in the field.

'Getting the right people is the answer,' says Curistan. And it is an increasing challenge as the number and scale of the projects the company is involved with, and their financial and legal complexity, grows. He knows he needs really top-flight people. 'The legalities, the planning, the finance demand such a lot of expertise.'

Curistan jealously guards his 100% ownership of the company, not as a control freak would, but because of the flexibility and agility it gives him in pursuing business opportunities without needing to look over his shoulder and be answerable to shareholders.

For that reason, he is reluctant to get involved in offering the sort of equity stake that is now often demanded by top-flight operators. For the same reason, he has never had a partner share any of his businesses, although all future development projects will almost certainly involve risk-spreading joint ventures with local money and expertise. He has been approached with proposals from as far away as South Africa and Poland.

In his entrepreneurial role he himself travels constantly, seeing what the competition is doing and keeping up-to-date with the latest technology. He is in the United States and Europe at least once a month and other areas such as Africa or the Far East about every three months.

That's why his staff never know what's coming next!

Curistan favours an 'over-dinner' approach to recruiting senior staff. 'You can usually tell pretty quickly if it is a person you can relate to, and that is vital in a compact, fast-moving team,' he says.

By contrast, the breadth of interest of the Sheridan Group, although generally in the area of 'hospitality and entertainment', offers scope for gaining experience and career development across a whole range of activities. It encompasses cinema technology, bar and restaurant management and operations, design and planning, promotions, car park management, sporting promotion and event management . . . the list is long.

Remuneration

As to be expected in a group as multi-faceted as Sheridan, remuneration policy is flexible. Below middle manager level pay rates are based on the going rate for each sector; above that, salary levels tend to be above average, and for key people, generous target-related bonus schemes operate.

Curistan emphasises the benefits of long-term career opportunities. Successful people will find themselves at or near the top of their relevant pay scales.

The Future

The primary corporate objective of the Sheridan Group is to become a significant international entertainment and property development group. With many projects already on the ground, and more in the pipeline, it's heading in the right direction.

The group is entering a new growth phase and this is creating problems which Peter Curistan is going to have to face up to. Even at its present level, he admits that he needs to strengthen his upper levels of management and as the group grows, decisions will also have to be taken on the actual structure of the company. This is going to open up career opportunities in a very exciting and creative area, where the whole entertainment market is improving and becoming more sophisticated.

Although he is loath to consider giving up his sole control, Curistan knows at the back of his mind that eventually, if he wants to recruit and keep the top executives he is going to need, he will have to bite the bullet and share equity.

Simply Travel Group

Simply Travel is a specialist tour operator, whose summer and ski package holidays and short breaks are aimed at the discerning independent traveller. Among its ten programme brands are Simply Crete, Simply Ionian, Simply Turkey, Simply Ski and Brief Encounters. Now part of the Independent Holiday Group, Simply Travel has been growing at around 30% annually over the last five years and the combined group expects to organise 65,000 holidays in 1999. Simply Travel has around 110 full-time employees in the UK, and a similar number of representatives and contractors overseas, often working on a seasonal basis.

Scorecard:

Remuneration and benefits	★★★
Progressive attitude	★★★
Opportunity for promotion	★★★★★
Training, development and education	★★★
Working atmosphere and environment	★★★★★

Biggest plus:
Freedom to achieve whatever you want with one of the leading, most distinctive specialist tour operators

Biggest minus:
For people who love the travel business rather than 'get rich quick' types

Simply Travel Limited
Chiswick Gate
598–608 Chiswick High Road
London W4 5RT
Tel: 0181 995 3883
Fax: 0181 742 3902
e-mail: stg@simply-travel.com

Simply Travel Group

The Business

Simply Travel has built its excellent reputation for providing a product of the highest quality. Its holiday offer is pitched at the middle market – typically discerning, professional people 'with a little more affluence' – who want a quality alternative to mass-market package holidays. Simply Travel aims to be a quality-driven, direct-selling organisation maintaining the 'Simply' image based on superior accommodation in tranquil and 'off the beaten track' settings. Its award-winning brochures are legendary.

Simply Travel realises that its loyal customers are intelligent people, prepared to pay a little extra on the basic cost to make the holiday run smoothly. Simply Travel is quite transparent over its prices, unlike many mass-market operators who strive to show a low headline price, but bury supplements and charges in the small print.

It's a formula that evidently works and competitors view Simply Travel with a certain amount of envy. The company features regularly and prominently in customer surveys and awards. In 1998 the *Observer* travel awards had readers voting in unprecedented numbers for the Simply Travel Group as best tour operator; and no fewer than four of the company's products scored in the top eleven places, with Simply Ionian coming in a close second. Simply Tuscany and Umbria won 'Tour Operator of the Year in Tuscany' sponsored by Alitalia in both 1997 and 1998. And in the 1998 *Holiday Which*? survey reported in February 1999, Simply Travel was voted Best Beach Operator and Best Greek Operator, and came second overall in the Best Tour Operator.

Managing Director Steve Rushton says, 'People vote for Simply Travel – and more importantly go on our holidays year after year – because we give our customers what they want. We always look closely at client feedback, so we would soon know if things were not going well.'

Company Culture and Style

Simply Travel has succeeded in delivering a quality holiday product in much larger volumes than are normally associated with a specialist operator, while still retaining the perceived exclusivity of its product.

That reveals a fairly rare and happy atmosphere. Steve Rushden notes that as the company has grown (the head office in West London now has nearly 100 people), the special culture and ethos has not changed.

'It's all about responsibility and each person knowing why they are there and what is expected of them,' he says. 'Our product is absolutely rooted in personal service and treating our customers as individuals. That means being flexible, and we push responsibility down the ranks so that whoever picks up the telephone can deal effectively with the customer and never let them feel that they have got lost in any bureaucracy.'

Simply Travel sets parameters so that its people feel that they 'own' their own product. The ten 'Simply' brands are each run by a programme manager, whose job remit is more than just selling the holidays. They are commercially responsible for their programme in the widest sense, which means close collaboration with (often senior) colleagues in marketing, pricing, quality control. But seniority is unimportant – only how people work together to support the special values of the 'Simply' products.

This devolved responsibility means that there is tremendous energy running through the organisation. It leads to enthusiasm, integrated teamworking and a supportive environment where everyone helps each other, especially in times of meeting tight deadlines!

This is a very happy company with an excellent working environment. It celebrates awards together and socialises actively, including company trips and twice-yearly parties.

Human Resources

Simply Travel has two full-time personnel professionals who Steve Rushton reckons are 'stretched'. It demonstrates how crucial people are to a customer-facing travel business like Simply Travel.

The company has been totally restructured over the past three years, moving from the necessarily 'flat management' associated with an owner-business (Simply Travel was founded by Graham and Yianna Simpson) to one that provides the necessary support structures needed by a fast-growing organisation. Simply Travel has just had its initial assessment with Investors in People and is determined to get its structure right first from the top.

There are perhaps two types of people working in the travel/holiday business: The 'old school', who might typically have worked in the travel business for 25 years, ten or so as a rep overseas. Then there is the 'new breed' – people not necessarily from a travel background but who 'know what they like' in a holiday. Both styles are found in Steve Rushton's balanced management team.

Young professionals joining the company are often language students who 'fell into the business by mistake', perhaps starting as a holiday rep, accumulating five years' experience and then finding themselves back in the UK and looking to use their travel experience in business. The current operations manager and head of marketing began in this way.

Career Opportunity and Development

Simply Travel is happy to accommodate different types of people in the company: the ambitious ones who are looking 'to climb the ladder', and those who just want to work in the travel business and 'do a good job'.

The company promotes internally wherever it can, while recognising that it has to be 'careful' in handling promotions. Globe-trotting travel professionals – expert in contracting accommodation overseas or looking after clients – may or may not take to an office role in line management. But Simply Travel allows 'travel specialists' to pursue their career interests, drawing upon their invaluable experience, while still employing 'engine room managers' who face customers, deliver programmes and manage the business.

'We don't force anyone to do anything,' says Steve Rushton. 'We're incredibly open in our style and don't have any political animals. If people say that they've reached their limit, we don't push them over the edge, and if people feel they can handle more responsibility, we give it to them. It makes my job of planning a bit easier because we're all dealing with what we understand.'

Ambitious people can do virtually whatever they like. Steve Rushton himself joined as group financial controller in 1996. Helen Awad, personnel manager, had no formal personnel experience and indeed was a former chef when she joined Simply Travel; but she wanted a hands-on role in recruitment, took Institute of Personnel Development examinations, and grew into her new role.

Zoe Bowyer, the programme manager for Simply Crete, started work in Simply Travel's post room. She doesn't speak Greek, but energy, enthusiasm and hard work have helped her to now run the company's largest programme. Amanda Fleming-Jones joined in 1997 as Steve Rushton's PA and is now running the support services for Simply Travel.

'I am a big believer in making your own luck,' says Steve Rushden.

'You must want to work here, enjoy the product, and dedication and intelligence are far more important than direct experience. Then you can go as far as you want to.'

The only caution is that there are so many opportunities that people could inadvertently specialise too early. This is a very young company – the average age is perhaps mid to late 20s – and the company encourages gaining experience, switching roles, perhaps working overseas as a rep, before deciding on a chosen career path.

To ensure familiarity with the Simply programmes, every member of the sales team spends 2–3 weeks a year, largely in the 'off season', actually visiting the villas and countries in which their programme runs.

Remuneration

At junior levels, Simply Travel pays above the industry average, and good performers enjoy good bonuses. There are also the perks of the job, which include very reduced rates for holidays and flights.

At senior levels, it is all about capability. There are no whopping 'welcome to Simply Travel' salaries, but the company certainly pays people well if they are producing results. Incentives in the form of bonuses play a prominent part.

The Future

The travel industry as a whole is saturated, and people are already travelling as much as they can. But in Simply Travel's middle market, specialist sector, customers are likely to become more discerning. When others ask Simply Travel 'what's your secret, having a better brand and higher profits?', the answer is always 'by paying attention to detail, giving customers what they want and employing committed people who know and like what they are doing'.

Simply Travel has an ambitious growth plan, identifying a real niche for medium-sized specialists. With the support of the Thomson organisation behind it, expansion might now mean buying up brands and straying into other areas of Europe, but at all times retaining the unique 'Simply' style and personal touch.

This growth plan challenges Simply Travel to find enough ambitious people who want to take the responsibility – and accountability – that the company believes it is vital to empower. It's a calculated risk rather than taking a chance, and Simply people with nous and who always think about what they are doing and why, can enjoy tremendously exciting careers with an extremely popular tour operator.

SmithKline Beecham

SmithKline Beecham is an international leader in the research, development, manufacture and marketing of healthcare products with global annual sales in excess of £8 billion. It's core businesses are pharmaceuticals and consumer healthcare. It has over 300 healthcare products and services, sold in over 160 countries. In 1998, over £900 million was spent on research and development, where more than 5,000 scientists worldwide focus their efforts on four therapeutic areas: neurosciences; inflammation, tissue repair and oncology; anti-infectives and biologicals (vaccines); and cardiopulmonary. SmithKline Beecham employs approximately 58,000 people worldwide, 8,500 in the UK.

Scorecard:

Remuneration and benefits	★★★★
Progressive attitude	★★★★★
Opportunity for promotion	★★★★
Training, development and education	★★★★
Working atmosphere and environment	★★★★

Biggest plus:
Working for a truly global organisation

Biggest minus:
Must be able to adapt to an environment that is continually changing

SmithKline Beecham
1 New Horizons Court
Brentford
Middlesex TW8 9EP
Tel: 0181 975 2230
Fax: 0181 975 2774
website: www.sb.com

SmithKline Beecham

The Business

The sheer size and scope of SmithKline Beecham allows it to produce results on a staggering scale. Every minute, nearly 400 prescriptions are written worldwide for SmithKline Beecham products and every second 20 doses of its vaccines are distributed somewhere around the globe.

SmithKline Beecham (SB) is now the world's second largest company in over-the-counter medicines and is the UK's second largest pharmaceuticals company. But SmithKline Beecham is not purely a pharmaceuticals company, although this represents 60% of sales driven by successful products in the field of antidepressants, antibiotics and vaccines. Its wider focus includes a broad consumer product portfolio of well-known brands such as Lucozade, Ribena and Aquafresh. It is also a leading player in the smoking cessation market, with Nicorette and NiQuitin CQ

Chief executive Jan Leschly says, 'In today's fiercely competitive healthcare environment, success hinges on two critical factors – the ability to change and the ability to do it faster than the competition.'

With a first-class reputation for scientific excellence in research and development, the SmithKline Beecham product pipeline is promising; and it has set itself stretching financial targets for the coming years – double digit sales growth and earnings growth in the mid teens. In Leschly's words: 'The driver of our success will continue to be the three key challenges we are facing: to become a world-class, customer-driven company; to develop pioneer products and services; and to continue to align our cost structure to our competitive environments.'

Company Culture and Style

SmithKline Beecham has self-styled the 'Simply Better' Way, a cultural initiative dedicated to continuous improvement. It is the framework that defines the systems and process by which all work is organised, and the methods and tools that are used to consistently achieve excellence.

'Simply Better' means building a working environment that motivates and then provides the means for personal and professional growth, grounded in strongly supported company beliefs. The company's 'leadership practices' go the extra step to ensure that its core values of customers, innovation, integrity, people and performance are translated into everyday behaviour.

Multinational SB is always sensitive to global cultural – and legal – differences. 'Simply Better' places great emphasis on cross-cultural teamworking as a way of making better use of people from diverse locations and functions. IT and telecommunications facilitate enormously in this regard, but also serve to highlight the 'fascinating' way in which people look at and read into things differently.

Diversity remains a prominent issue at SB but the company is far from complacent. It realises that if diversity as a policy, or even a way of life, is working well it can become embedded to the extent that people no longer hear about it.

SB is a highly ethical employer including equal opportunity and the role of women in business. It is also highly practical, making sure that it 'walks the talk', but after setting corporate goals then pursues pragmatic solutions at the local level.

Leschly suggests that there are five personal characteristics that SB seeks in people: street smart, with good judgement, energy, sense of humour and care for people. Asked what he likes best about working at SB, he says, 'Most of all, it's the people. Their ideas. Their energy. It's infectious. When it stops being challenging, when you stop being able to have fun, its time to do something else. I can tell you, its still as challenging for me today as it was on day one. I work with some of the industry's brightest minds. I'm able to watch good people rise up through the ranks and fulfil their potential. I can see our products making a difference everywhere in the world. That's very rewarding.'

Human Resources

HR is an integral part of the business, highlighting the premium SB places on 'people values'. Group HR director Dan Phelan is a member of the corporate management team, effectively the company's senior operating committee. He believes that 'The end product of the HR process is to have people organised in the right numbers, with the right skills, in the right place, at the right time, to achieve our goals.'

Among the usual remits, HR identifies important current trends as striking a better balance between work and lifestyle, and pressure management. Large companies are conscious that they ask a lot of their employees and so must be careful not to put too much pressure on them and to provide the tools with which to cope.

SB is very much at the forefront of recognising that today, people want a smoother blending of work and personal life. 'Companies have to accept that's the way it is heading, and look for ways to help people work smarter, not just harder,' says Sheila Boughton, manager, UK relations and diversity. SB also realises the dichotomy. People who enjoy their work will always want to put more in.

SmithKline Beecham aims to change mindsets so that there is a greater focus on outputs, not inputs, and to ensure that performance is measured and rewarded against meeting results.

SB's regular, extensive, worldwide employee survey is very practical in its construction. Managers are required to sit down with their people, consider the findings of the survey, and why the scores were arrived at. They then must develop a plan of action.

Although loyalty is always important, for many people the shifting psychological contract has lessened expectations of spending a really long-term career with one company. HR views a key task as helping people to accept this tacitly and then improve their overall employability during their time with SB by continually acquiring new skills.

Career Opportunity and Development

The enormous diversity of SmithKline Beecham's business creates a wide range of exceptional international career opportunities from scientific research and development to commercial activities. The company seeks people from a broad spectrum of academic backgrounds, from recent graduates and MBAs/ PhDs to direct hires from industry.

Jan Leschly says, 'As SmithKline Beecham continues its journey towards excellence, I welcome the daring spirit, the inquisitive mind and the relentless thinker to join us.'

Vacancies are advertised company-wide in the UK, with plans afoot to widen this to the US and Europe, and SB operates a global, comparable job evaluation scheme. There are many transfers around the business, particularly between the UK and US, but the cost and benefits to both company and individual are always evaluated first.

Self-managed careers have long since been a hallmark of SB, and the company knows that busy employees must be given full support and access to the necessary skills in order to pursue and achieve their own goals. The SB appraisal system elicits individuals' views and aspirations, and also plots a route on how to get there.

The company offers its Leadership Partnership to all management employees. While continuous self-improvement is considered a right of every employee, SB nevertheless places great emphasis on grooming its leaders of tomorrow. The programmes also help SB assess levels of competency when looking at promotions.

Remuneration

Pay is competitive, and benchmarked regularly. All employees receive an annual bonus based on their business area achieving profit targets. Further up the responsibility line, SB correlates pay and incentives even more closely to performance and the achievement of objectives.

SB has lowered the catchment level for share options by one management grade, bringing an additional 500 people into this incentive scheme, which over 1200 people in the UK now benefit from.

SB offers a generous benefits package, including a very good (and well-explained) company pension plan. SB has a 1–1 Share Matching Plan which encourages employees to identify with the overall fortunes of the business. Non-cash benefits include an employee assistance programme, childcare schemes, and a link line for those caring for elderly or disabled relatives.

The Future

SmithKline Beecham genuinely cares about its employees and is a very progressive employer. But the company itself wants to see actions rather than aspirations. It believes this must be a local business driver effect, tailored for each part of a complex, global business. SmithKline Beecham has recently re-focused its 'Simply Better' initiative as a 'tool kit' to guide managers on how to operate. Leschly says, 'We can free up under-utilised or wasted resources through the discipline of working the Simply Better way every day, focusing on customer requirements, good process management and continuous improvement to ensure that our work pays off. In other words, we are saving where we have to save, enabling us to invest where we would like to invest.'

While no multinational company can hide from the vagaries of the work economy, SmithKline Beecham has weathered the storms well. It is particularly encouraged by the number and quality of new products in the pharmaceutical pipeline. The company sets demanding stretch targets for itself for, as Jan Leschly puts it: 'Unless your reach exceeds your grasp, you'll never know how far you can go.'

Storehouse

Storehouse is one of the leading UK-based retailers of clothing and homeware products, nursery equipment and food services. Storehouse plc was formed in 1986, the result of a merger between British Home Stores and Habitat Mothercare. The group's annual turnover is in excess of £1.3 billion with 485 stores in the UK and 238 overseas. It has more than 21,000 employees worldwide, over 10,000 of which are full-time employees.

Scorecard:

Remuneration and benefits	★★★
Progressive attitude	★★★★
Opportunity for promotion	★★★
Training, development and education	★★★
Working atmosphere and environment	★★★

Biggest plus:
The Storehouse culture provides an attractive and stimulating place to work

Biggest minus:
Standards are high, the pace is fast, and change and improvement is a way of life – it may not suit the faint-hearted

Storehouse plc
Marylebone House
129–137 Marylebone Road
London NW1 5QD
Tel: 0171 262 3456
Fax: 0171 262 4740

STOREHOUSE PLC

Storehouse

The Business

Storehouse has a clear strategy for growth with a focus on the customer, product improvement, and store refurbishment and systems enhancement as the cornerstones. A significant investment is being made in the infrastructure of the businesses and in the quality and skills of the people who manage them.

The head office of the group, and of Bhs, is in Marylebone in the West End of London. The head office of Mothercare is in Watford, close to the M1 and M25.

Bhs has undergone a metamorphosis in the last ten years, moving from a solid, conservative but hierarchical organisation to a modern, dynamic and progressive force in the high street. It has made significant progress in modernising its brand by continued customer focus, improving the range and quality of its products, and creating attractive store environments. This has involved building upon, rather than departing from, the traditional product strengths of fashion, quality and outstanding value for money.

Storehouse chairman Alan Smith says the group owes its continued success to its recent streamlining, 'Having rebuilt profitability by completing the divestment of the remaining, poorly performing businesses in the portfolio and strengthening the two core brands, Bhs and Mothercare, the focus is now firmly on the future.'

Mothercare, which was founded in 1961 as the UK's first mother-to-be and baby specialist, is seen as the niche retailer in the group. The Mothercare brand remains a unique concept in providing everything for the mother-to-be, her baby and her young family. Mothercare has achieved an authoritative position on the high street, which was enhanced further by the acquisition of Childrens World in May 1996.

Through the growth of the businesses and major improvements, the turnover of the group has increased by 6.8% over the last year.

Company Culture and Style

The development of people at Storehouse remains a priority. Bhs runs a 'Spotlight on Success' programme which recognises employees for their contribution both as teams and individuals. Progressive training and remuneration policies together with flexible working arrangements provide a modern and attractive working environment.

Storehouse sees the skills and dedication of its employees as critical to the success of the company and places great emphasis on retaining staff and training them.

Reinforcing the strength of the culture, the most recent annual staff survey showed that over 80% felt part of a winning team and over 90% felt that they had the skills and confidence to do their job well. Kevin Heald says, 'It's really about building both individuals and teams. It's important to have stars, but it's the team that gets the result.'

Human Resources

Both Bhs and Mothercare recognise the critical importance of people to the success and future of their businesses and of the group. As a result, there is a coherent group human resources strategy within the business strategy, which aims to establish high quality, highly skilled and highly motivated individuals and teams. The focus of the strategy is to ensure that there are the right people policies, the right training, development and career progression processes, the right rewards, benefits and incentives, and the right culture and style.

There is a well-established mechanism for communication with and listening to employees, who are known as 'associates'. Both Bhs and Mothercare conduct annual staff surveys, which are seen as invaluable measures of feelings and attitudes as well as a means of capturing issues and ideas for the respective boards to examine and develop actions to address.

Human resources manager Kevin Heald says, 'In my experience the best businesses are really turned into what's happening at the sharp end.'

Career Opportunity and Development

Storehouse places a great emphasis on promotion from within the organisation.

Kevin Heald says that a feature of the group, which makes it an attractive employer, is it offers the opportunity to gain responsibility very early. 'Young people come in, get a good basic training and can move up the ladder very quickly. In general, retailing is a youthful industry – the average age of our board members is early forties.'

Over 40% of Storehouse managers have achieved their position by working through the ranks. Storehouse places great emphasis on identifying those with potential and supporting their development and career progression.

The two principal areas for career progression are buying and merchandising, and stores. In the former, graduates with relevant degrees or those with professional experience are actively sought and follow a structured development programme at associate level and progress towards junior and assistant buying and merchandising roles. Career progression is fully supported by the appropriate development programmes up to senior level.

In stores, the emphasis is more on practical and people skills, although the same process of structured development and career planning is applied. In each case, the opportunities for bright young people to obtain positions of real responsibility at an early stage are almost unmatched in any other industry.

Remuneration

Storehouse believes in being competitive on basic pay, rewarding financial results with bonuses and providing an attractive and varied set of benefits with individual choice at management level. According to Kevin Heald, Storehouse is a 'great believer in incentives' and many employees participate in at least two bonus schemes.

Full-time staff get standard benefits including annual leave, sick pay and maternity pay. For management staff the 'Choices' benefit scheme is a form of 'mix and match' benefits with the option of taking money in lieu of different benefits. Staff can choose whether to buy private medical insurance or increase the value of their company car. There is also an option to 'buy' extra annual leave or qualify for free dental treatment.

Storehouse is always on the lookout for alternative ways to provide new benefits without a hefty price tag; it has recently secured a free tax advice service for all employees.

Bhs has also set up a charitable trust to offer counselling and financial support to staff with difficulties. All staff qualify for a discount of 20% on goods and 40% on work clothing in the case of Bhs staff, who don't wear a designated uniform.

The Future

Storehouse has a clear strategy for growth. There is still much scope for new Bhs stores in the UK and new openings are running at five to eight stores per year. The 46 out-of-town stores in Mothercare, formerly Childrens World now trading as Mothercare World, are performing well. The extensive network of overseas franchises in both Bhs and Mothercare is expanding, particularly in Eastern Europe.

'The group has continued to invest in its people by promoting from within and by recruiting talented retail managers from outside,' says Keith Edelman, Storehouse Group chief executive. Within the past year the Group has appointed a new managing director for Bhs, Stephen Tague, Greg Tufnell joined the company as Mothercare's managing director the year before and Andy Meehan became managing director of the International Business. 'The Storehouse way of doing things is reflected in the policies which have been established, for example the group ethical policy and the group environmental policy.'

There are also new developments within the company's existing brands. The new style Homestore opened at Bath in 1998. Two further stores have opened in Birmingham and Watford and no doubt others will follow.

Another new concept is 'Bhs for Less' which opened recently in the Hatfield Galleria. This store sells end of season stock at up to 40% discount, thus helping other Bhs stores keep clean, new season ranges of stock.

Cafe Gio, an Italian style café, will be opening at the Trafford Park Shopping Centre followed by additions throughout the UK. If it is successful it may be added to the existing restaurant facility in other stores or introduced to stores presently without a restaurant facility.

The group is also introducing state-of-the-art technology systems throughout both businesses. This major investment will achieve significant efficiencies and enhance customer service and supplier partnerships to an even great degree.

The company prides itself on the fact that it actively encourages employees to communicate their ideas and concerns. In recent staff surveys, nine out of 10 employees felt that the company was always looking for a better way of doing things. This evidence certainly seems to support their perceptions.

TNT UK Limited

TNT UK Limited is a market leader in time-certain express delivery and logistics services in the United Kingdom. In 1997–98 it generated a turnover of £650 million and pre-tax profits of £54 million. The company employs 12,000 people and is part of the TNT Post Group which employs 100,000 people worldwide.

Scorecard:

Remuneration and benefits	★★★★
Company culture and style	★★★★★
Opportunities for promotion	★★★★★
Training, development and education	★★★★★
Working atmosphere and environment	★★★★★

Biggest plus:
An environment where everyone can succeed and everyone is valued

Biggest minus:
Operates in a hugely competitive marketplace

TNT United Kingdom
TNT Express House
Holly Lane
Atherstone
Warwickshire
CV9 2RY
Tel: 01827 303030
Fax: 01827 713746
website: www.tnt.co.uk

TNT UK Limited

The Business

TNT UK Limited started trading in 1978 when TNT acquired Inter County Express Limited, a successful carrier providing a profitable three-day parcels delivery service.

Almost from the first day, TNT UK was noted as an innovator. When it began, no parcel carrier in the country provided nationwide on-demand next-day-delivery services, and real-time communication with drivers on the road was almost unknown. Its TNT Overnite service, launched in 1980, offered both through a fleet of radio-equipped vehicles. This service was supplemented two years later with the introduction of TNT Sameday (the first nationwide door-to-door immediate delivery service), and by a range of other new services throughout the 1980s and 1990s.

TNT UK is the only organisation to have won four European Quality Prizes (in 1995, 1996, 1997 and 1998) for business excellence. These awards, given by the European Foundation for Quality Management, are widely regarded as the pinnacle of achievement in Total Quality Management. The best company among the prizewinners is also honoured with the European Quality Award, which TNT UK won in 1998.

The company has also won 15 Motor Transport Industry Awards in the last 13 years; the 1997 Management Today/Unisys Business to Business Overall Service Excellence Award; and was voted by 2000 members of the Institute of Transport Management as the 1998 Express Parcels Carrier of the Year. TNT UK has IIP status: one of the few multi-site businesses to win company-wide recognition. It was also one of only two companies highly commended for best practice in people management in 1997 by that organisation and is the winner of the Investor in People 1998 Key Champions Award.

Company Culture and Style

The company's culture is built firmly on nine key principles. The customer care principle requires that employees always listen to clients and build first-class relationships with them, so as to provide excellent standards of service and customer satisfaction. Leadership is about inspiring all staff to be outstanding achievers; the company believes that everyone at TNT is a leader in some sense. The people principle means that the business recognises achievements, promotes from within wherever possible and encourages people to enjoy rewarding careers which provide security and job satisfaction.

Other principles set similarly high standards in communication, resources, working with suppliers, continual improvement, impact on society and business results (where the aim is to achieve sustained growth and profitability by always striving to beat its previous best).

The culture is definitely one where everyone can flourish. Alan Jones, MD of TNT UK: 'We take on youngsters and train and develop them to achieve outstanding performance. Moving people up creates opportunities for others. We believe that the safest route is to promote from within and there are many advantages of using this approach.'

So what does the company look for in its new recruits? The most important attribute is having a positive mental attitude. Alan Jones: 'We want people who can make things happen even when problems occur – and when you're transporting the range and quantity of material we are on a daily basis, problems are bound to occur. But if you believe you can achieve anything, then the sky is the limit. We need to find positive people and equip them with the skills, the tools and the training they need to satisfy our customers.'

A clue to the culture is provided by the company's Product Knowledge Quiz, a University Challenge-style event which involves every depot in the country providing a team of six contestants. The final regularly fills a hotel with eager onlookers, impressed by the sheer amount of knowledge each contestant has acquired.

Another clue is offered by TNT's distinctive telephone policy, a 10-point list which includes no screening of calls and answering incoming calls within three rings. Suffice it to say that *Which?* magazine commented: 'If you want to know how to answer the telephone, call TNT.'

Above all, TNT is a people business. This applies to both the way it looks after its employees and the way it treats its customers. The culture is definitely one embodying the 'must-get-through' attitude. The style is open, friendly, informal and contented. Anyone can talk to anyone else, no matter how senior. Achievements are recognised and reported in a state-of-the-art range of communications media.

Human Resources

Alan Jones: 'People are our business. We want the best people because we insist on being the most successful organisation in all of our market sectors. This means providing our people with the best conditions: not only in terms of pay and benefits but in training, working atmosphere and environment. We have won national awards for our training programme, and in 1998 all departments won a major industry award of some kind. We make a huge investment in training each year, not surprising when you consider that our payroll comes to around £200 million – we naturally want to get best value for that money.'

HR is very much a personal thing at the company and when people do particularly well they are likely to receive an individual letter from the managing director. Currently this amounts to 40 or 50 letters each week. There is also a Hall of Fame where outstanding achievements of all kinds are recognised.

Career Opportunity and Development

The company almost never recruits from outside when making senior appointments. This means that the sky really is the limit for talented, committed and able people at TNT. To back this up, a considerable number of the current top managers started their careers as drivers and worked their way right up the ladder. The company takes on hundreds of graduates each year, some for its graduate training scheme and others on an ad hoc basis. It recruits all over the country, drawing on local pools of talent.

Young people may move in order to gain promotion. However, the company has a strong policy on families and prefers not to uproot people needlessly. Employees with families can carve out just as successful a niche by helping the company to expand in the local area in which they work.

For those who are keen to move, there is no shortage of opportunity at TNT. With 19 specialist express delivery and logistics divisions currently within TNT UK Limited, there are plenty of chances for upward movement. All jobs are advertised internally every week.

There are also overseas opportunities through the company's parent, the TNT Post Group. TNT's proud boast is that the group operates in more countries than are represented in the United Nations! Having said that, most TNT UK employees prefer to stay within the UK and build their careers here.

Remuneration

In terms of pay, the company seeks to offer upper quartile wages and salaries. These increased by 4.5% in 1999 and also in 1998. Everyone is on a bonus of some kind: individual, individual and team, or team incentives. Drivers receive bonuses linked to their productivity, while depot managers' bonuses are related to depot performance. Managers at the head office have bonuses related to the performance of their division or the company as a whole.

TNT offers all the benefits one would expect of a top employer: very good pension schemes, death-in-service cover, a car scheme which includes fuel and maintenance, and good holiday allowances. People are encouraged to take their full holiday allowance so as to return refreshed.

The Future

The future for TNT UK will undoubtedly be about providing an outstanding service for its customers, growing organically, and continuing to innovate and stay at the leading edge of the market. The company is already the market leader in many of its sectors it will need to maintain and build on that position. Doing so requires constant dialogue with customers which is something TNT is very good at.

There are two main challenges for the company. The first is the intensely competitive nature of the market. Alan Jones: 'We never rest on our laurels. At the moment, we don't have any real competitors – only weak opposition. But weak opposition can turn into strong competition tomorrow if you let it. That's why complacency is taboo.'

Creating sufficient expansion to satisfy the aspirations of its people is TNT's other major challenge. The company can only promote high-performing people and give them long-term careers if it grows. However, the company's deep-rooted desire to be the best in everything it does and to continually improve upon already impressive practices make its future look assured.

Unisys

Unisys is a major international information technology and computer services company. Its global revenues amount to $6.6 billion and its global gross profit to $2.2 billion. It employs 32,600 people worldwide, 4,000 in the UK.

Scorecard:

Remuneration and benefits	★★★★★
Progressive attitude	★★★★★
Opportunity for promotion	★★★★
Training, development and education	★★★★★
Working atmosphere and environment	★★★★

Biggest plus:
A focused, well-managed company with a clear direction

Biggest minus:
Not for people who want to work in traditional ways!

Unisys
Bakers Court
Bakers Road
Uxbridge UB8 1RG
Tel: 01895 237237
Fax: 01895 862093
website: www.unisys.co.uk

UNISYS

Unisys

The Business

Unisys can trace its corporate roots back over 100 years to Burroughs Corporation which invented the world's first commercial adding machine. In 1986 Burroughs merged with Sperry Corporation (which invented Eniac, the USA's first computer) to create the second largest mainframe company in the world. The debt created by this merger, increased by some other acquisitions, was a major problem in the early 1990s as world interest rates rose sharply. As a result the company made significant losses in the early 1990s, an additional cause being the fact that 80% of its revenues were sourced from mainframe sales at a time when customers were moving towards lower margin products and seeking service solutions from technology companies.

The company was also relatively unfocused. For instance, until 1995, each of its 16 European country operations was run on a semi-autonomous basis, with its own CEO, sales director, finance director, and so on. Each country had a very broad spread of programmes to sell, from hardware to systems to maintenance.

To improve this situation, Unisys embarked on a major reorganisation at the end of 1995. It removed much of the individual country management in Europe, thus cutting back heavily on the bureaucracy and becoming more responsive to the market. It also began the move from being a seller of hardware to being a solutions provider.

This strategy was implemented but the initial execution was flawed, and after 18 months of slow progress Unisys appointed a new chairman and chief executive, Lawrence Weinbach, in September 1997. Formerly the managing partner/chief executive of Andersen Worldwide, he had turned it into the world's largest professional services firm and quintupled its revenues. He was therefore well placed not only to transform Unisys, but to take an unemotional look at all its operations. Weinbach: 'The products were very good and the service capability was very good. The way the company went about expanding its product base and getting into the service business was not so good, and because of that, the company got into trouble.'

When Weinbach joined, the company was saddled with $2.3 billion in debt. It was also losing money in its personal computers and small servers area, had a tarnished reputation and a demoralised workforce. Weinbach promised to shave $1 billion off the Unisys debt and by December 1998 had reduced it by $1.1 billion (saving over $60 million a year in interest). He also took the company out of personal computers, outsourcing production to Hewlett Packard. Above all, he refocused the company. The stock price soared and the 1998 third quarter results (net income $250 million compared to $112 million in 1997 Q3) were the best for a decade. Not surprisingly, the company's reputation is revitalised and demoralisation is no longer an issue.

Company Culture and Style

'The culture at Unisys is very open,' says Martin Sexton, VP of corporate communications at Unisys EMEA. 'It's always been that, but it's now also a great place to work. There's a buzz about us. The people are really friendly and helpful. In my 36 years with the company, I've never found anyone I couldn't get on with, and lots of people have said similar things to me. In the end, the people make a company, and this truly is an excellent company because of the people.'

So what makes that culture so enjoyable? One reason is its attitude. The company has a youthful feel (although not every individual is youthful!): it has a go-ahead approach, a culture dominated by technical excellence, creativity and effectiveness. Unisys is the ultimate open-door environment, enhanced by its recent move to create business centres instead of traditional offices. Many of its staff, due to the nature of their roles, had to spend long periods away from their office – and when away, found themselves without support services. The business centre culture means that people can work in another city just by calling that business centre and booking facilities: a meeting room, a desk, a computer, or whatever. Once there, they simply insert their floppy disks, sign on and have complete computer access. They also benefit from full secretarial support. Homeworking is also increasing, aided by the extension of the Unisys global telephone network system to homes.

Martin Sexton: 'This is a major move. It means that we've had to supply our mobile staff with laptops and mobile phones, and change the traditional way of working. But everyone who's tried it loves it. Furthermore, here in the UK we reduced office space by 30% over the last two years, while increasing staff numbers by 20%.'

The company is rapidly becoming flatter and less hierarchical. In the past, the company had 6,600 different job descriptions and a very complex structure. This is now down to 400 job descriptions with just six bands. The type of person who flourishes at Unisys is creative, problem-solving and tenacious; he or she is not afraid to stick with the problem until it's solved.

Human Resources

At Unisys, old-style personnel management has given way to HR Business Partners. Far from being a mere cosmetic change, this name reinforces the HR objective of serving the business, and of working with managers in a given business operation to help it perform better. Martin Sexton: 'Our HR activities are more pragmatic these days. They're also much more proactive in helping people get the right training and development.'

An annual survey measures employee satisfaction with the company, the results of which are taken seriously and often lead to improvements throughout the organisation.

Career Opportunity and Development

Martin Sexton: 'The opportunities for development at Unisys are as broad as your imagination. As an example, I've never done the same job for more than three years.' If you want to do different things at Unisys, there is plenty of opportunity to work elsewhere. With a global operation and 33,000 employees worldwide, the scope is huge. In Europe alone, Unisys is represented in 16 countries. There are also many opportunities in emerging market sectors. One example is call centres, an area where Unisys is strongly represented today – and yet this sector did not exist in 1995. Similarly, its work on newspapers and magazines (most leading European titles either use Unisys systems or are considering switching to them) is a relatively new development.

Unisys has a Career Fitness Centre, a web-based set of tools and online advice to support employee development. Unisys people are encouraged to register with this and define their objectives, identify their skills (both technical and soft skills such as communication), and plot their development. At Unisys, it is certainly true that everyone is in charge of his or her own career. Moving that career forward became even easier and more effective in January 1999 with the opening of the Unisys University, a virtual college devoted to training excellence which was the result of a huge amount of development and planning.

Remuneration

The company plans to pay the market rate for its people. Certainly, staff turnover has fallen from around 15% to 8% or so, and the company is now an employer of choice for its sector. Pay rises are a function of an individual's performance as measured by a rigorous performance planning and review summary. People are rated against objectives previously agreed with their managers. Top performers are very well rewarded, above the market rate. Sales people can earn bonuses, and all UK staff can make use of an attractive share purchase (15% discount on the market rate, with employees able to spend up to 10% of their salary each month this way), introduced in October 1998.

Other benefits include a pension plan which recently changed to a money-purchase scheme in response to people's demand for mobility (earlier joiners are ring-fenced into a final salary scheme); a car for appropriate levels, health cover, dental cover, life assurance, and indeed all the perks expected from a blue-chip employer. Unisys operates a highly flexible benefits scheme which allows employees to trade these variables up or down. For instance, a staff member could take more holiday, either by reducing other benefits or taking less salary – or take less holiday and add to the salary.

The Future

The company's future looks extremely positive following its reorganisation and new sense of direction. It is also clearly a great place to work. Its growth is being driven by continuing deregulation of telecommunications, more competitive financial markets, and Internet expansion. The biggest single challenge it has is finding enough of sufficiently skilled, motivated and ambitious people. However, it continues to recruit heavily at universities and other recruitment fairs, and it also has a strong intern scheme. The future at Unisys looks highly attractive.

United Biscuits

UB is an international food business whose main strength is biscuits. The group has a dominant position in the UK biscuit market through McVitie's brands such as Digestive, Penguin and Go Ahead! It also has an international business ranging from Finland to China which accounts for a quarter of its £1.6 billion annual sales. The group has interests in snacks and frozen foods in the UK including KP and Phileas Fogg, Young's seafood and Linda McCartney vegetarian dishes. 14,000 employees work in the UK, out of a total of 22,000.

Scorecard:

Remuneration and benefits	★★★
Progressive attitude	★★★★
Opportunity for promotion	★★★
Training, development and education	★★★★
Working atmosphere and environment	★★★

Biggest plus:

A British consumer goods business with a long-standing international presence

Biggest minus:

A relative minnow in the global world of fast-moving consumer goods

United Biscuits (holdings) plc
Group Headquarters
Church Road
West Drayton
Middlesex UB7 7PR
Tel: 01895 432100
Fax: 01895 448848
website: unitedbiscuits.co.uk

United Biscuits

The Business

UB was created 50 years ago through the merger of two Scottish family businesses, Macfarlane Lang and McVitie & Price, the latter lending its name to the famous digestive biscuit and leading brand. The group was farsighted enough in the 1970s to diversify from that fairly narrow base, both geographically, by making acquisitions in the US and on the continent, and by developing interests in snacks and other areas of the food industry.

The international acquisition strategy produced mixed results. Biscuit companies were profitable, but on the whole were very localised operations. Snack acquisitions, on the other hand, proved impossible to make sufficiently profitable because they tended to be competing with the powerful brands of PepsiCo. The 1990s refocusing has seen the group withdraw from such an unequal struggle to concentrate on its more promising areas. That process of focusing on its key strengths has continued, although UB still operates in 21 countries and its products are sold in many more.

The new vision statement, adopted early in 1998, talks of an international food group 'incorporating the best biscuit business in the world' – but it lays equal stress on 'sustainable profitable growth' and shareholder value.

That new vision signifies a more robust attitude to underperfoming businesses and a more active approach to managing the business portfolio. It has been accompanied by a number of deals which strengthened the biscuit business in Europe and extracted the group from difficult situations such as the snack operation in Australia. And the emphasis now is on melding the collection of local products into more significant global brands. 'We have very strong local brands. We want to drive those to become international power brands,' explained corporate affairs director Tim Way. The first of those can be seen in the low-fat product range, Go Ahead!

Company Culture and Style

The UB culture has been evolving as part of the new international awareness. The change programme is now in its third, and most positive, stage. After shuffling the portfolio of businesses to concentrate on the best, there came a concentration on improving businesses which were performing badly. Now it is time to put the accent on growth, innovation and internationalisation.

Increasing the emphasis on innovation and product development comes naturally to a group with a strong record of new product introduction. For example, Go-Ahead! has created a whole new low-fat product category.

Changing the mindset from being a British business with interests abroad, to one which regards itself intrinsically as a forward-looking international operation, is likely to be more challenging.

It will be helped by a new organisation structure which has replaced the previous regional approach. Now there is a worldwide McVitie's Group which is managed separately from UK Foods. UB believes this approach will help to focus managers on delivering growth in their area of responsibility, and that the new structure puts together businesses where the transfer of skills and best practice will be easier.

'We were very UK-focused but now we are increasingly international,' explained Claire Dickson, group management development director. 'People now have to be international in their perspective. It is a real mindset shift.'

UB is not shy of demanding a lot from staff, based on the overriding need to deliver improved shareholder value. But the group has not allowed the heightened financial focus to overwhelm its tradition of treating people well, stressing communication with staff and the importance of the human dimension in the business.

'Sometimes you get someone who is good with people but not focused on making returns. Others are focused but can't take people with them. We're working hard to develop a senior management cadre which combines the necessary people skills with the ability to deliver in difficult circumstances,' explained management development manager Steve Pierce.

The changes at UB will not affect the group's strong sense of social responsibility, typified by its commitment to the Business in the Community programme.

'We encourage managers to be involved in community work and particularly with education,' Tim Way said. That includes graduates, who are encouraged to work with schools and act as mentors for new businesses.

Human Resources

UB has always paid great attention to its people and to industrial relations – it was the first British company to set up a Europe-wide works council, for example. But in the new UB, the HR function has a new prominence. 'It has a key strategic role in the business. It has never been more influential than now,' said Mike Wilkinson, group HR director. The function is playing a key role in the management of the change process throughout the business.

The second key challenge for HR is to develop the organisation's skill set. That means ensuring, first, that key people are equipped with the right capabilities and second, that the right management processes are in place.

The top management team meets five times a year specifically to review senior management performance and development needs, as part of the succession planning process. UB also operates a system of 'godfathering', which means that each function has a senior 'sponsor' whose responsibilities include ensuring that functional abilities of staff are up to, and where possible ahead of, industry standards. These godfathers are supported by senior human resources and training personnel, creating a high-level team in each function capable of advancing professional development.

UB has also implemented 360-degree feedback, a process by which managers can learn more about aspects of their management style through feedback from colleagues. 'It has been quite challenging personally,' Tim Way said, 'but people have responded positively. It has helped foster a better understanding about behavioural requirements – that how you do something is every bit as important as what you do.'

Career Opportunity and Development

The group aims to recruit people with high abilities, preferring those with an ambition to develop and move on to more demanding jobs. As a result the recruitment process has become more rigorous in recent years, but so have the opportunities for those who are successful become more rewarding.

'We have raised the bar for graduate recruits,' Steve Pierce said. 'We are very much looking for future senior managers, not just people to fill current roles. We want to attract the very best.' He stressed that once these potential high-flyers have joined UB, the company is also keen to ensure that they do not fly off elsewhere. 'It's not just about getting the best people in, it is also about getting them to stay with us', he explained.

UB recruits about 60 graduates a year. At the moment, recruitment is predominantly on a country by country basis, although languages are sought and some movement across borders is beginning to take place.

On-the-job training includes an opportunity to experience the commercial realities of the business over the first six months, including a period with the sales force. Many graduates will then move annually for the first few years to ensure that they acquire a broad perspective on the business and the different challenges and cultures in factories and head office departments.

A comprehensive development programme for young managers, tailored to suit the individual, ensures that graduates progress at a sensible pace. This includes professional mentoring and functional development programmes leading to qualifications such as IPD and CIMA. UB has also created an understanding business course leading to a Diploma in Management with the Henley Management College, which counts towards Henley's MBA.

Remuneration

UB has a philosophy of paying well to attract and keep the best people and the remuneration package aims to be competitive with the market, especially the food manufacturing sector. Graduates joining in 1999 can expect a starting salary of £19,000 together with a favourable range of benefits. Managers' remuneration is increasingly based on performance. Share schemes are offered at all levels in the UK, with share options available to senior managers worldwide.

The Future

As UB becomes more international in outlook and strives to produce growth from existing and new businesses, the drive will continue to push the necessary cultural and behavioural changes further down into the business. 'To achieve our vision we must become truly international, not just in geography but also mindset,' Mike Wilkinson said.

In HR the consequence of that is a sustained programme of development to nurture in all staff the imperative of broadening their thinking to embrace the ultimate necessity of improving shareholder value. Given the group's patchy financial record during the mid 1990s, from which it has recovered strongly, it is also imperative to drive home the message that promises must be kept – whether at plant or at corporate level.

The biggest challenge, perhaps, is to ensure that employees continue to feel valued in the midst of the changing culture, and continue to be motivated to deliver the kind of performance that UB is now looking for.

United Utilities

United Utilities is a group of businesses that make up the UK's first multi-utility. The company was formed when privatised North West Water took over power firm Norweb in 1995 and spread its interests from water, wastewater, and electricity distribution to telecommunications and business outsourcing. In addition it is heavily involved in winning customers in the deregulated electricity and gas supply markets.

Scorecard:

Remuneration and benefits	★★★★
Progressive attitude	★★★★
Opportunity for promotion	★★★
Training, development and education	★★★★
Working atmosphere and environment	★★★★

Biggest plus:
High levels of customer satisfaction and staff job satisfaction

Biggest minus:
Still a feeling that managers remain a little out of touch with the workforce but this is improving

United Utilities
Birchwood Point Business Park
Birchwood Boulevard
Birchwood
Warrington
WA3 7WB
Tel: 01925 285000
Fax: 01925 285199
website: www.united-utilities.co.uk

United Utilities

United Utilities

The Business

United Utilities plc is a multi-utility business with a strong presence in the North-west of England. The company evolved from North West Water, the public service provider that was privatised nine years ago. When the water company took over regional electricity company Norweb for £1.8 billion following a bitter takeover battle the combined business transformed itself into United Utilities. The new business comprises the water company itself, Norweb Distribution and Contracting, ENERGi, Norweb Communications, Vertex and the group international operations arm.

United Utilities was much criticised in its infancy when media comment over executive remuneration was at its height. When Sir Desmond Pitcher vacated the chairmanship at the behest of institutional investors, he was replaced by Sir Christopher Harding, who introduced a new sense of stability.

Now, as well as providing water, wastewater and electricity distribution, it has expanded into telecommunications and business operations outsourcing. Additionally it is successfully driving for more customers in the deregulated electricity and gas supply markets.

In 1998 the company employed a workforce of 9,902 with a minority involved in overseas operations where executives hope to take advantage of the need for expertise in countries that are privatising utilities systems. The business turned over more than £2 billion with profits of £460 million before tax and exceptional items.

Company Culture and Style

Company culture has by necessity undergone a sea-change transformation since North West Water was privatised under a Conservative government. The outdated idea of a utility simply providing a public service and employment with negligible regard to customer relations has long since disappeared. Now the focus is on growing the company while emphasising the requirement to look after customers, especially in those areas where competition is keenly felt.

No employee is under the illusion that everyone is entitled to a job for life and they are now aware that performance targets have to be aimed for. Far from disillusioning staff, especially long servers, it has helped add an impetus and recognition that company and personal development can be a twin goal.

To help imbue the business with a progressive outlook the company has joined the British Quality Foundation with the idea of striking a balance between the firm itself, its employees and local communities. This ethos pervades throughout United Utilities, although each of its businesses may vary its approach in striving to achieve similar objectives. Each has nine specific aims geared towards business excellence, as human resources director David Scott explains: 'We have generally similar sets of values throughout the businesses. Our people are now held to performance standards and let's not underestimate the value of this because it is a dramatic change for a privatised company.'

The workforce is committed but can also have fun; hence the particularly varied community schemes that staff members volunteer to take part in. There are links with environmental education, a swim safe roadshow, work with age concern and charity events like a sponsored cycle that attracted 600 entrants. Staff have also volunteered their time to Young Enterprise and the Duke of Edinburgh award scheme. A partnership with Forest in the Community intends to plant one million trees to celebrate the millennium.

North West Water became the first of the big ten water companies to achieve Investors In People recognition while Norweb did likewise, adding to a national chartermark for customer service and a Crystal Mark award for the use of plain English.

In fact performance is now measured against Business in the Community models, requiring the investment of at least 1% of pre-tax profits. Sir Christopher says: 'It's good common sense for businesses to implement corporate citizenship. We believe we should care about issues such as the skills of young people, the environment and those with special needs.' There is general agreement that the company should have a big social responsibility and employees are willing to play their part.

Human Resources

And, indeed, an in-house survey discovered impressive levels of job satisfaction among employees, running at over 80%. With equally eye-catching figures for customer satisfaction it is clear that the workforce plays a full part in serving customers.

Chief executive Derek Green says: 'As one of the region's biggest businesses serving seven million people in the North-west, it is very important that we get the balance right between satisfying our customers, rewarding our employees and meeting the aspirations of shareholders.' While relationships within the business continue to evolve, the company reckons that further improvement must be achieved. For instance, only one in three employees believes that senior managers are in touch with what happens at grassroots. But the important measure is that figures are improving year on year.

A new director of human resources, David Scott, was appointed in 1998 to lead the way in this important area and to embrace the chairman's philosophy that it is the quality of staff and managers that counts. To this end a key policy is to develop and retain its quality staff.

Mr Scott says: 'It is a two-way situation. We encourage training and development but also staff must invest in their own careers.' All the technology, products and services in the world will not function unless those involved convert these advantages in a positive way.

United Utilities is eager that everyone plays his or her own part and is fully knowledgeable about the businesses, hence a high degree of internal communications and information passed via company publications. Fewer than 50 employees are on a flexible working hours scheme. Managers are contracted to work 'as required' to do their jobs, while field staff operate to scheduled hours to react to the needs of customer service.

Career Opportunity and Development

United Utilities has a wide spectrum of interests both in the UK and overseas although the chances of working outside the country are currently limited. For capable and motivated members of staff, however, there are clearly opportunities to be grasped.

In North West Water alone, £3 million is being spent in 1998/9 on staff training, amounting to 36,000 training days across the business (equivalent to nine or ten days for each individual). There is a performance appraisal scheme which involves managers and staff reaching agreements over individual objectives. Indeed, line managers are especially trained to coach their staff as another way of enhancing overall performance. Wherever possible, business development plans are partnered with best practice training opportunities.

The company took on 30 apprentices in 1998 – 23 process workers, five craft, and two laboratorial. Both process and craft trainees spend the first eight months off-site at a skill centre where they work towards an NVQ level 2. A further placement follows with a view to delivering level 3 qualifications. All trainees study for BTEC national or higher national certificates and a learning-to-drive package involves the company paying for up to 10 driving lessons. Managing director Harry Croft says: 'Achieving Investors In People status is a welcome recognition of our commitment to invest in people.'

The Group's employment policy involves improving the skills of employees and making them feel valued. It is also laid down that business issues and developments should be delivered via formal and informal processes.

Staff are recruited by a variety of means – through modern apprenticeships, graduate recruitment and the open market.

Remuneration

The company aims to be competitive across the board, including salaries and benefits. One key policy objective is to ensure that packages are directly related to the performance of the group. Salaries are reviewed annually, taking into account personal performance for those on individual contracts. A Sharesave scheme is in operation, based on SAYE savings contracts. In addition the Qualifying Employee Share Ownership Trust (QUEST) was established to satisfy options under the Sharesave scheme. Trade unions in United Utilities companies are openly involved in collective bargaining on pay and terms on behalf of around 3,500 employees. Management salaries range from £21,200 to £98,000 and for other employees range from £9,000 to £26,000. In 1998 a series of productivity schemes was negotiated with unions which could produce up to 5% of salaries if targets are met.

The Future

Chairman Sir Christopher Harding has placed a firm emphasis on developing the quality of staff across all areas of the business. When he joined he said immediately that his priority was getting to know as many people as possible – and he was pleased with what he saw. His maxim is 'put people first', whether in the workplace or the marketplace. This philosophy has generated a feeling among staff that they are worthy and regarded and that a motivated workforce is a productive one.

However, there is still a need to improve communications between senior managers and the grass roots of the company. Some still believe that there should be more feedback to staff but this is a problem that is acknowledged and is being tackled.

Certain areas of the operation face a challenging period, especially in water where a price review in 1999 could have an effect on future profits.

Vanco Euronet

Vanco Euronet manages wide area networks for companies throughout Europe. It has offices in the UK, France, Germany, Italy, the Netherlands and Spain, and an array of support locations from Athens to Zurich. As at January 1999, turnover was £20 million and pre-tax profits £1.6 million.

Scorecard:

Remuneration and benefits	★★★★★
Progressive attitude	★★★★★
Opportunity for promotion	★★★★
Training, development and education	★★★★★
Working atmosphere and environment	★★★★

Biggest plus:
Operates in a huge and growing marketplace

Biggest minus:
Finding enough high-calibre people to sustain growth could be a challenge

Vanco Euronet
John Busch House
277 London Road
Isleworth
Middlesex TW7 5AX
Tel: 0181 380 1000
Fax: 0181 380 1001
website: www.vancoeuronet.com

Vanco Euronet

The Business

Chairman and managing director Allen Timpany formed Vanco Euronet to take advantage of a massive new industry created by four market developments. These are: the liberalisation of telecommunications monopolies throughout Europe; the expansion of businesses to become pan-European players in the European Union; the need for greater business efficiency through the use of telecommunications; and the dramatic advances in the functionality and cost efficiency of equipment and circuits.

Indeed, it would be hard to overestimate the opportunity. In the 1970s, back-office automation spending was around $50 billion a year. The PC and front-office revolution increased this to $500 billion a year; and the networking of IT is increasing this at the beginning of the new millennium to $800 billion a year. Vanco Euronet is a key enabler in this massively growing market.

European deregulation of telecommunications companies is certainly one of the key drivers. In the UK, where there was previously one licensed operator – BT – there are now 168. Less dramatic but still significant growth is evident in continental Europe where numbers have burgeoned from 20 to 260. Vanco Euronet was formed to take advantage of this and other market opportunities. The essentials of the company are to offer businesses solutions and provide business benefits through a team of high-calibre, highly intelligent network people who understand fully the needs of their corporate customers.

Company Culture and Style

The company is entrepreneurial, fast-moving and dynamic. Currently, it employs around 150 people, although numbers are set to grow rapidly. Nevertheless, it plans to retain its distinctive structure. Employees work in small business groups, which are effectively companies in their own right. Each has its own account managers, salespeople, finance, technical and administrative staff. Not surprisingly, the ability to work within a team is vital; but so is the ability to come up with your own innovative and creative ideas.

Allen Timpany: 'Vanco Euronet is a company where people have a chance to make a difference to improve what they do, what the company does, and the way our clients work. Our staff are the owners of our competitive, advantage; this really is a people business, and we value and reward those people accordingly.'

Vanco Euronet people tend to be highly able, intelligent and unafraid of hard work. They also relish the opportunity to have a real input, often very early on in their career path. They are enthusiastic, embrace change, and enjoy working at the leading edge of technology. Vanco Euronet is an independent organisation, and as such can choose from the complete mix of hardware, software and circuits to put together effective business solutions for its many clients. This means that its people need wide business knowledge and technical skills, but the effort they put in to acquire those skills is put to effective use and is well rewarded.

Andrew Cushing is the company's marketing coordinator who joined Vanco after two years with Rolls-Royce Motor Cars' marketing department. 'I wanted to move somewhere I'd have more influence and the chance to implement my own ideas. Vanco Euronet is certainly that. If you have the ability to think, senior people here will always listen to what you have to say.'

The culture is also a multicultural one. Nine different nationalities work at the company's head office in Isleworth, Middlesex. And, given its pan-European operations, much of the work is for a broad span of different continental companies in centres such as Amsterdam, Paris, Frankfurt, Madrid, Milan and Prague, as well as London.

Vanco Euronet is not a hire and fire organisation, but it is a demanding one. It makes clear at the recruitment stage exactly what working for it involves, and believes it selects the right people at least eight times out of ten. Anyone wanting a highly structured organisation where all the processes are already developed should look elsewhere. Conversely, anyone looking for a company with enormous potential, opportunities for change and the chance to make a genuine contribution could hardly find a better place to work.

Human Resources

The company places a high priority on human resources: particularly in the areas of recruiting, retaining and motivating top quality people. It tends to look for those of at least upper-second degree level standard, of which it recruited 20 in 1998 and intends to hire 30 to 40 in 1999. A computer networking background is not essential in order to join Vanco; what is, though, is a bright mental approach.

One benefit of this is that Vanco Euronet is fun to work for. Tony Nester, European business director, comments: 'Vanco Euronet attracts the highest calibre staff from around Europe which creates a very stimulating working environment.'

HR is handled by managers at a detailed level, rather than having a top-heavy HR function. There is of course a central department to administer the usual necessities of employment, but HR at a motivational and day-to-day level is very much the province of business unit managers.

Career Opportunity and Development

Once on board, staff usually work in the UK for six months. This includes lots of job mobility and the chance to communicate with senior people. Thereafter, employees can be moved overseas if they want to work abroad. The option to do so is always there with the company's European operations continually expanding, and staff are positively encouraged to work on the continent.

Training and development is a significant function at Vanco Euronet: no surprise for a large corporation, but perhaps less common for an operation the size of Vanco. Training takes the form of defining a job role and splitting it up into its constituent parts. To move from one grade to the next, the candidate needs to demonstrate not only the specific skills for his or her job but for general development, for example the ability to manage people effectively, budget accurately and so on. Employees liaise with their managers to map out development, and a sophisticated review process gives them what they need to move up, including training and development requirements.

Training is handled both in-house and through outside organisations, and might include several hours of evening work. Employees are encouraged to extend their knowledge in given areas, and all the support they need to do so is likely to be provided. These areas include general business as well as more specific product and industry skills.

The company operates WINCOs ('winning through continuous improvement'), based on the Japanese idea of continual improvement. All technical staff belong to WINCO teams of seven or eight people, and meet as often as they wish. The approach is to consider their work and think of better ways of handling what they do. Improvements are therefore driven by people who actually do the day-to-day work.

Remuneration

Financially, Vanco is an above-average payer, with industry-standard pay scales and an above-average bonus scheme. More significantly, the company has a policy of making every employee a shareholder.

Everyone is eligible to join the share scheme after one year. Graduate recruits can expect to make several thousand pounds out of this in two years; senior technicians, £40,000 to £50,000 over five years; while business managers may reap as much as £250,000 in six or seven years.

Benefits include a pension plan and a generous car scheme which compares very well with the industry norm. The whole company is also taken each year on a three-day overseas conference, the latest one being held in the Algarve.

The Future

Not surprisingly, Allen Timpany is enthusiastic about the future of his company. It is operating in what is today the world's biggest market-place, and doing so with great success. Business opportunities in Europe can only continue to expand, and Vanco Euronet is very well placed to take advantage of those.

The company will remain focused on the European opportunity for the time being. It already has offices in Amsterdam, Paris, Frankfurt, London, Madrid, Milan, Copenhagen, Manchester and Prague. Over the next year it plans to add Athens and Warsaw, together with another 20 locations with mobile sites in places such as Stockholm. It also aims to expand its UK offices.

The challenge for the company will be finding sufficient numbers of the right people in order to maintain its impressive growth rate sustained to date. Allen Timpany: 'The problem for the company creates an opportunity for the individual. The right people have almost boundless opportunities here, and their future success is clearly linked to the success of the company. It will be difficult, but not impossible, to find enough top rate people to go forward at the rate we would wish.'

Viacom Europe

Viacom Europe is part of media giant Viacom Inc., a diversified entertainment and publishing company with operations grouped in four main activities: Networks and Broadcasting, Entertainment, Video and Music/Theme Parks, and Publishing. Familiar brands include Paramount Pictures and Paramount Television, MTV, VH1, Showtime, Nickelodeon, Blockbuster and Simon and Schuster. In 1997 Viacom Inc. had revenues of $13,206 million and operating profits of $752 million. Of 85,000 employees worldwide, 8,581 are in Europe and 5,041 in the UK. Viacom's European head office is in London.

Scorecard:

Remuneration and benefits	★★★
Progressive attitude	★★★★★
Opportunity for promotion	★★★★
Training, development and education	★★★
Working atmosphere and environment	★★★★★

Biggest plus:
Team culture, friendly, interesting people working with a 'fun' product

Biggest minus:
Long hours typical, even if some are a spillover into social life

Viacom Europe
180 Oxford Street
London W1 0DS
Tel. 0171 478 6000
Fax 0171 478 6945
website: www.viacom.com

Viacom Europe

The Business

Viacom is one of the world's largest entertainment and publishing companies and is a leading force in nearly every segment of the international media marketplace. Creative content in programming is the heartbeat of Viacom. As Sumner M. Redstone, chairman and chief executive of Viacom Inc., puts it: 'All of our resources are focused on what we do best – to create great entertainment, package it, brand it, distribute it and extend it.'

It's easy to be impressed by Viacom's powerful brands. Try Paramount winning three of the last four Academy Awards for Best Picture, including *Titanic*, for starters and throw in *Frasier*, *Star Trek* and joint production of *Saving Private Ryan* for good measure. MTV Networks owns and operates five of the most popular cable television programming services including MTV: Music Television, VH1 and Nickelodeon. Showtime Networks owns and operates premium subscription television programme services. Blockbuster is the global brand name leader in video, with over 6,000 stores in 24 countries.

A glamorous and fast-growing business, yes. But tough also. Shareholders demand strong financial performance and Viacom is intent on delivering. That means hard work.

Company Culture and Style

Led by aggressive, bright and energetic management, Viacom is about much more than the bottom line. Redstone believes that you have nothing to show if you don't have people, and what Viacom has is a lot of motivated, creative people.

The individual businesses in networks, television, motion pictures, video and publishing have their own distinct cultures. Viacom says it would be 'presumptuous' to try and homogenise these cultures, but recognises that there is a single thread running through the whole fabric of the organisation – the way that it treats people.

Externally it is tough-minded, but also fair and honourable. Inside, it is a demanding organisation, but is always willing to 'go the extra mile' for its staff. 'People are the greatest asset we have,' says Dwight Tierney, vice president, HR and administration at Viacom Europe, 'and we must take care of them and meet their needs.'

This is a highly collaborative environment. Highly relevant for creative collaborations across the businesses, but at employee level too. Information committees, best practice presentations, 'think tanks' are all ways that Viacom gets its people talking together and thinking and acting outside their business silos. And it's all about Viacom at the centre adding value. 'How can we help you' is the message to the businesses.

Into the workplace and it's everything you would expect. Viacom's offices just off Oxford Street in London's bustling West End are energetic, trendy, atmospheric – and full of young people. Music television is playing everywhere, rocking the senses of sight and sound simultaneously. And you get the impression that people at Viacom enjoy each other's company.

Viacom is doing good things with its name. 'Viacommunity Day' celebrates its employees' strong tradition of volunteerism and reaches out to the communities in which Viacom does business. In 1997, 'Viacommunity Day' involved an enormous effort, with thousands of employees worldwide redirected on a single day to a web of community projects. In London, around 170 people out of a total complement of 500 joined in. This is very much a grassroots thing – employees choose and drive the charity projects – but Viacom gains valuable spin-offs as people feel good about themselves, learn more about the organisation and network with new contacts.

Human Resources

HR at Viacom Europe is a strategic business partner, helping individual businesses to map where they are going and how to get there. A business-oriented HR most definitely has a voice at the table, around which sit the most senior managers of the organisation. HR is actively involved in decision-making – whether to buy a business, expand a brand, or close down an operation. Consequently it strives for excellence in 'the flawless delivery of HR products and services throughout the organisation'.

Viacom Europe's HR team led by Dwight Tierney puts tremendous effort into resourcing, heightening employees' awareness of different parts of the group, enabling postings and encouraging cross-fertilisation. 'If you get your people moving for you, it's a home run every time,' says baseball fanatic Tierney.

Promotions are not always about higher remuneration, and HR people invest time in getting to the heart of individual aspirations, making sure that the person is certain what they really want before moving.

Individual businesses handle their own recruitment, but Viacom is increasingly gaining a reputation for supporting the businesses centrally and finding good people. With HR professionals across the organisation increasingly working together, and sharing becoming a way of working life, one key objective is to make sure that the businesses first exhaust all internal opportunities. A richer variety of career opportunities throughout Viacom beckons.

Career Opportunity and Development

This is a fast-growing, profitable company, and there is nothing like success to present a world of opportunity. Conquering the world seems to be on the agenda, and Viacom views Europe as a huge opportunity for it to extend its brands.

And the jobs at Viacom are diverse. Producers, designers, IT specialists, media sales, engineers, scriptwriters, marketers, sales assistants as well as professional support functions in legal, human resources and finance all blend together happily in support of the cause.

One of Viacom's recruitment consultancies once asked 'where will we find the people you need?'. A Viacom HR executive interjected with the shrewd observation: 'we find them here'. HR specialists throughout Viacom are already collaborating to foster best practice sharing. Now Viacom Europe is co-ordinating much more in terms of overall personal development across the group, although each business still does proprietary training specific to its needs.

Grabbing development by the scruff of the neck, the needs of the individual and of the business are identified through the performance appraisal process involving the individual, line manager and HR. Customised training programmes are being expanded. Competencies, skills development, leadership and self-management courses are numerous, and a new management development scheme is gathering pace.

Talented individuals are also recruited from the 'classic' areas, meaning other television and entertainment companies, advertising agencies and marketing firms. Viacom also looks laterally, and Internet companies, software houses and satellite/digital technology businesses are seen as fertile areas for talented people. Indeed, anyone who understands brand value and marketing might be in the frame.

Not that Viacom is just a poacher. It gets poached too. The Viacom alumni reveals many former employees now heading up leading TV and entertainment enterprises – a clue to the prominent and successful careers people can carve at Viacom.

If it's hard to get into the media business, it can be just as hard to get out – particularly if you succeed in your job and produce results.

Remuneration

Viacom pays fairly and competitively, without needing to stretch to the highest end of pay scales. But Viacom ensures that people are recognised and rewarded consistently and equitably for their contribution to the achievement of business objectives.

Short-term bonus incentives are not 'give-aways' and are linked closely to strong performance. Senior managers are also eligible for the share option programme. Remuneration is deliberately made transparent and easy to understand. 'If people cannot leave my office and calculate what they can earn, then we've made it too complicated,' suggests Dwight Tierney.

There are the usual benefits such as company pension and medical insurance, but there is also the so-called 'psychic income'. Working in the entertainment business provides a 'feelgood' factor that costs nothing, and the glamorous environment is regarded as a perk in itself. Certainly Viacom people enjoy their fair share of parties, concerts, film premières and screenings, music awards and all the other attractive 'goodies' that the entertainment business generates.

The Future

Europe is a huge market for Viacom. The Paramount Channel is just launching in Spain, and Viacom's existing activities in the Benelux countries, Scandinavia and Eastern Europe are ripe for expansion. More jobs and new jobs are in the pipeline, as the HR team braces itself for the task of suitable recruitment.

And the Internet, with the myriad of entertainment possibilities this exciting media is spawning, must be of great significance to Viacom sooner rather than later.

With so many revolutions happening simultaneously (pick from technical, media, digital, virtual and more), the questions for Viacom are where will it find the right people to exploit these opportunities and how will it develop them? The convergence of media will create lots of opportunity and certainly lots of competition. And while it cannot lose competitive edge, Viacom doesn't want to lose the human dignity and respect factor that it values so highly. A balancing act. But the success of Viacom to date suggests that it knows how to continually press the right 'hot buttons' to keep talented people motivated.

Virgin

Virgin is one of the UK's largest private group of companies, bound together by one of the most powerful brand names around. Virgin Group has grown in size 30 times over the last 14 years through a series of alliances, joint ventures and outsourcing. In this time it has catapulted from a modest music and entertainment company with revenues of £50 million to a diversified global conglomerate with revenues in excess of £2.5 billion. The group of Virgin companies and their joint ventures currently employ over 24,000 staff, and operate in at least 24 countries with a mix of media, entertainment, retailing, publishing, financial services, merchandising and travel activities.

Scorecard:

Remuneration and benefits	★★★
Progressive attitude	★★★★★
Opportunity for promotion	★★★★★
Training, development and education	★★★
Working atmosphere and environment	★★★★★

Biggest plus:
Total belief in the company, the brand, the values and the leadership

Biggest minus:
Work hard as well as play hard

Virgin Management
120 Campden Hill Road
London W8 7AR
Tel. 0171 229 4738
Fax 0171 229 5834
website: www.virgin.com

Virgin

The Business

Virgin is not really a 'group' as such – financial results are not aggregated centrally – and each business runs its own affairs. But there is a collection of shared ownership, shared leadership, and shared values. In many respects, Virgin resembles a *keiretsu* – a society of business. The Japanese think so anyway.

And oh what a brand. According to a recent survey, 96% of British consumers have heard of Virgin and 95% can correctly name Richard Branson – 'Richard' to everyone – as its founder. People know about Virgin and expect extraordinary things from it, putting Virgin in a unique position of trust and strength, but also handing it the responsibility not to disappoint.

Virgin companies are now too numerous to list (visit the website). How does one begin to describe a group which includes air travel, cola, radio and entertainment, financial services, retailing, trains and bridal wear? The amazing portfolio includes wholly-owned businesses, alliances, joint ventures and outsourcing arrangements.

But all Virgin businesses grow around a name which must stand for something. Anything which employees do must fit the corporate brand values, which is how the Virgin 'group' works. But Virgin is not a brand extension – as a 'house' brand, it adapts to diverse types of businesses and services.

Richard Branson's business style has sometimes been viewed as slightly eccentric, but few can deny his success. Virgin has a sizeable global presence, and incredible name recognition. It is profitable and growing fast, entering and claiming significant share in new markets. But all this has come about without most of the trappings of the multinational. There is no head office, board meetings have been held in a pub, there is little sense of management hierarchy and the minimum of corporate bureaucracy. This is the ultimate lean enterprise.

Company Culture and Style

Richard Branson identifies the key Virgin values which must be instilled in any new business venture: 'Virgin is about doing things which really work, not just looking the part. We are passionate about running our businesses as well as we can, which means treating our customers with respect, giving them good value and high quality, and making the whole process as much fun as it can be.'

According to Will Whitehorn, Virgin's director of corporate communications and one of Branson's closest lieutenants, Virgin's core competency is the ability to identify relevant business opportunities, move quickly and manage the growth of new businesses. And of the hundreds of business proposals that Virgin receives, only a few pass 'Go'. These are always ones which will be faithful to the Virgin values.

As Branson has explained: 'If we launch a new product, people assume that we will come up with something a bit different. But it's also synonymous with fun and with entertainment in the broadest sense. The value of the name is enormous. We get asked to put the Virgin name to many things, but we say no to most of them.'

Virgin focuses on businesses that can generate their own growth potential. So it is easy to see why some of Virgin's target markets are those occupied by near-monopolies or where cartel-like behaviour is evident. Not only are there fat margins to cut into, but you can be the people's champion while you are doing it.

Each business inevitably has its own manifestation of the Virgin culture. In terms of employees, Virgin Travel and Virgin Retail are the largest, closely followed by Virgin Rail. By turnover, Virgin Direct is near the top. Virgin Radio, the Megastores, the London Broncos, Storm Model Agency, and Virgin Net just highlight the diversity.

Virgin Atlantic Airways has really flown the flag of the underdog in its struggles with the major airlines. Virgin Direct confounded the conventional industry wisdom that you cannot sell non-obligatory financial services over the telephone, by introducing its own PEP. Virgin Cola, in a joint venture with Canadian partner Cott Corporation, took on Coke and Pepsi (one of the world's most entrenched duopolies) and shifted £50 million of product after three months with only four employees.

Co-operation is integral to Virgin's culture, and imbues the style in which people work. Employees of joint ventures – for example Virgin Direct is a 50:50 venture with AMP – think that they work for Virgin. Identifying with the Virgin group, or the Virgin name, instils confidence, a belief that they cannot fail to succeed, as well as helping to open doors.

Virgin managers believe passionately in the Virgin values and in what they are doing, and are convinced that together they can build a British, truly global brand name. Realising this ambition is a great challenge, and a highly motivating one at that.

Human Resources

Virgin really has little need for central personnel policies, although each individual business will have its own personnel professionals to manage the core tasks of recruitment, training, remuneration. The personnel process at Virgin is more behavioural and instinctive than written policy. If people are inculcated with the ways and values of the business, knowing that everything (including their livelihood) depends upon outside perceptions of the Virgin brand name, motivation and behaviour is instinctive.

Individuals are encouraged to speak their mind, however, and in the absence of hierarchies managers are the first port of call. There is no atmosphere of retribution, and the system works well. The 'myth' of all employees having Richard Branson's home telephone number is actually true. Maybe 150 employees call each week and despite globe-trotting business schedules and hot air ballooning exploits, Branson succeeds in answering around half of these personally. He talks to 'his people' a lot.

Everything relating to employees and the company comes back to the brand. If employees have no confidence in a company, this soon works its way through to the customer. That's why Virgin knows that employee perceptions are extremely important.

A belief in fun and enterprise does not make life one big party. Nor is there mayhem. People work very hard at Virgin. The airline and financial services industries have demanding regulatory standards; at Virgin Atlantic Airways, these necessary regimentations (including the three allowable colours of nail varnish for stewardesses) are conveyed during a six-week induction programme which everyone must attend. High street retailing is a tough, competitive business. And the entertainment industry is famous for gruelling schedules.

Career Opportunity and Development

You are less likely to join Virgin Management, but more probably one of the individual businesses. But Virgin people can and do move around a lot.

Virgin is not a good company to work for if you are disinclined to take the initiative. The cliché 'self-starter' really applies here, and people typically stay either for six months or for life, especially at management level.

One of Branson's philosophies in building the record business was instead of trying to make a good business even larger, he preferred to start a new one and take the management with it. A regular diet of fresh challenges is one reason why he has kept his management team together for so long. In a way, the *keiretsu* developed naturally, without anyone ever realising it was becoming one.

Remuneration

Pay and benefits will vary across the businesses, but Virgin generally pays market levels. It is not a 'get rich quick' proposition, yet levels of employee satisfaction are high. There is a central principle that people should share in the profitability of the business. For example, Virgin Direct salespeople are paid a salary, not a commission, and a flat bonus based on the company's – not their own – performance.

All employees get other Virgin benefits – discounts at the Megastores or cheap flights, for example, and the all-important invite to the famous Virgin annual party.

The Future

Things just keep happening at Virgin, and the pace shows no signs of abating. Virgin Atlantic is taking on another 1,500 staff before Spring 2000. 'We're backing young British people to help us take on rival airlines from the UK and around the world,' says Richard Branson.

Virgin probably has its work cut out most in the much-scrutinised UK rail industry, particularly on its high-profile West Coast line. But ever on the side of the customer, many will be backing Virgin to get it right. And guess who has launched Millennium Drivers, an initiative to provide some 2,200 new train drivers by 2006 for all train companies from three new training centres in the UK? That's right. Virgin.

The biggest challenge for Virgin will be maintaining a flow of good people into the business, particularly relevant in its quest to become a global brand. The company needs and wants to hire local people in new countries, but it also wants Virgin people, living and breathing the Virgin culture with the skill and sensitivity to adapt and apply the Virgin brand to local cultures.

But one thing is virtually certain – the Virgin *keiretsu* will make an impact whatever it does and wherever it goes.

Vodafone Group

Vodafone is the world's largest mobile telecommunications company and the leading service provider in the UK with some 40% of the market. Vodafone has expanded into twelve other countries, from France to Fiji. Vodafone's annual turnover in 1997/98 was in excess of £2.4 billion, representing annual growth of 41%, with profits growing at similar levels. Vodafone had over nine million customers worldwide at the beginning of 1999, some 59% higher than the previous year and a figure which is rising all the time. There are around 12,000 employees in the Vodafone Group worldwide, 7,000 based in the UK.

Scorecard:

Remuneration and benefits	★★★★
Progressive attitude	★★★★★
Opportunity for promotion	★★★★★
Training, development and education	★★★★
Working atmosphere and environment	★★★★

Biggest plus:
The future is brilliant

Biggest minus:
Don't expect a 35-hour week

Vodafone Group plc
The Courtyard
2–4 London Road
Newbury
Berkshire RG14 1JX
Tel: 01635 33251
Fax: 01635 45713
website: www.vodafone.co.uk

Vodafone Group

The Business

Vodafone is a very young company, not something obviously apparent from its current position among the top 10 companies by market capitalisation in the FTSE-100 index. But this is a tremendous success story, a story that is a long way from over.

Vodafone was formed in 1983 as a subsidiary of Racal Electronics. Sir Ernest Harrison, then chairman and chief executive of the parent company, ensured that the development of the Vodafone network was given the highest priority in terms of financial and human resources and he moved with Vodafone Group when it floated on the London Stock Exchange in October 1988 with a value of £1.7 billion. Vodafone was demerged from the Racal Group in September 1991 'in order to create increased shareholder value'. By early 1999, Vodafone's market capitalisation had reached £30 billion.

The company has grown phenomenally on the back of the explosion of mobile telecommunications. It is the undisputed market leader in the UK, and growing its networks overseas all the time.

In the UK Vodafone perhaps accounts for at least 28% of all new connections. It now has some 5 million UK customers, representing a market share of 40%. Vodafone UK continues to be the mainstay of the group's turnover and profitability, despite increasing competition and Vodafone's spiralling investment in other markets.

By 1999, Vodafone had over 4 million customers outside the UK, representing 41% of the group's total, although UK activities account for around 70% of group turnover. Vodafone presently operates in France, Germany, the Netherlands, Sweden, Greece, Malta, Australia, New Zealand, Fiji, South Africa, Gibraltar and Egypt. These investments in networks became profitable very quickly.

Vodafone's strategy is, quite simply, to concentrate on providing mobile telecommunications services worldwide.

There's a huge demand to satisfy. In the words of Chris Gent, chief executive, 'We now expect total market penetration in all the major markets in which we operate to reach 50% by the end of 2003, a year earlier than we projected in 1997. Mobile telephony is becoming the preferred means of personal communications and Vodafone is at the leading edge of the industry's development.'

Vodafone even had time to come up with a new corporate identity, following extensive research into the way it was perceived in the marketplace and how its core identity could be more powerfully expressed. Few can remember the old one.

Company Culture and Style

As the company puts it, 'the word is "Change"'. The mobile telecommunications industry moves so fast that things become out of date very quickly. Constant change is the only constant.

But Vodafone is the kind of place where ambitious people really want to work. Technical excellence. Value-added service. Diversity. Expansion.

'A typical day? There's no such thing as a typical day,' says James Taylor, telecoms engineer.

Vodafone fosters a friendly, open culture where people feel genuinely appreciated. Recognising that most people spend a great deal of time at work, the company thinks it is 'vital' that people enjoy what they do.

Teamwork is a fundamental way of working and, given the rate of recruitment, a previous year's intake looks after the latest crop of recruits. There's a lot of interaction, socialising and even house sharing!

Vodafone is fully aware of the way its products and services can contribute to community life and takes great pride in its reputation as a good corporate citizen. Last year, Vodafone donated over 250 computers to schools close to its Newbury headquarters. Potential victims of crime are able to use the Vodafone 'hotline to help' Safelink scheme, under which police issue people believed to be at greatest risk with a pre-programmed Vodafone which can be used to summon police help in seconds if an individual is threatened. The Safelink scheme is used by 14 police forces in the country.

Human Resources

With Vodafone growing its revenues at 40% annually, and extending its mobile telecommunications networks into new countries, it needs the very best people – people who, in the company's own words, 'see opportunity, and go for it.'

Expect to find all the professions, functions and specialisations which go with a major company, but Vodafone seeks in particular people in the areas of information technology, engineering, marketing, operations, human resources and finance.

Vodafone recruits graduates each year, but given the rapid growth of the business, many people with business experience join directly.

Career Opportunity and Development

Vodafone offers terrific career opportunities for people in all manner of directions and specialisations, and has created more than one full-time job every day for the last seven years.

For graduates, real responsibility comes on day one. On-the-job exposure ensures that people quickly learn the needs of the business. This is supplemented by technical training specific to the business area and job. Vodafone also supports individuals pursuing related formal qualifications.

Training is ongoing, and applies to all people in the business. Vodafone ensures that there are enough incentives and further development opportunities to keep people 'fresh'. It's a two-way deal: the company gives people the opportunities. People take Vodafone's business further.

Michelle Fox joined in 1997 as a marketing officer: 'I feel really passionate about Vodafone, which I think is pretty essential when you work in Marketing. I think we are the best at what we do, and have the best products.'

'I don't think people realise the international opportunities available at Vodafone. I certainly didn't,' says Peter Kearney, signalling engineer. 'But within two months in testing, my boss came in one day and said, 'How do you fancy going to Holland?' And I said, 'Yeah. Great.' And he said 'Tomorrow?' It was a great time. We set up 40 radio base stations in three months, and living in Amsterdam was just fantastic.'

Remuneration

Vodafone's broad policy on remuneration is to provide packages which are highly competitive and which ensure the right rewards are given to motivate, incentivise and retain people who are making important contributions to the success of the company. This certainly applies not only to the senior management population, but to most levels of the organisation as reward is increasingly correlated to performance.

Salaries are reviewed regularly and achievement is recognised and rewarded. Benefits include a company pension, share schemes and, it goes without saying, staff discounts on Vodafone products and services.

The Future

Vodafone's outstanding financial performance continues to surpass expectations of even the most optimistic analysts and forecasters. There is a growing belief that all estimates for the international mobile tele-communications market might be too conservative.

Vodafone's launch of 'Pay As You Talk' at the end of 1997, the upgraded version of its original 'prepay' service launched a year before, is set to revolutionise the mobile telecommunications sector making mobile telephony accessible to a whole new sector of the market. It's already enjoying significant success.

Deregulation and increasing competition are creating uncertainty in many major European markets, for both fixed and mobile telecom-munications. Vodafone has got a wealth of experience already under its belt in competing in a diverse range of markets. This differentiates it from most of its peer group and leaves it better positioned to cope with a market which is likely to become more competitive and less predictable.

But at the start of the 1990s, it was not immediately obvious that mobile phones would become an everyday item. They did, and how. Voice communication is going mobile and 100% penetration – not 50% or even more conservative forecasts made previously – may be feasible for some markets. Vodafone has achieved its market position entirely on its own merits and seems poised to profit substantially from the explosive growth of mobile telecommunications worldwide.

Whitbread plc

Whitbread is a leading British retailer in drinks, eating out, hospitality and leisure. It also has interests in two German restaurant chains. In the year to 28 February 1998, its turnover was nearly £3.2 billion and its pre-tax profits were £354.8 million. Whitbread employs 90,000 people in the UK, approximately half of which are part-time workers.

Scorecard:

Remuneration and benefits	★★★★
Progressive attitude	★★★★★
Opportunity for promotion	★★★★
Training, development and education	★★★★★
Working atmosphere and environment	★★★★

Biggest plus:
A highly customer-focused business which nurtures its people

Biggest minus:
No time to sit around and drink up the profits!

Whitbread plc
Chiswell Street
London EC1Y 4SD
Tel: 0171 606 4455
Fax: 0171 615 1000
website: www.whitbread.com

WHITBREAD

Whitbread plc

The Business

Founded in 1742, Whitbread is one of Britain's oldest-surviving beer producers. The Whitbread Beer Company markets such leading brands as Stella Artois, Heineken, Boddingtons, Murphy's and Flowers.

Nevertheless, beer accounts for less than 10% of the group's profits. Nowadays, Whitbread plc is probably the leading marketer in the UK leisure sector. The Restaurants Division includes the Beefeater, Pizza Hut and TGI Friday chains along with Bella Pasta and the Costa coffee stores. The Hotel Company consists of Travel Inn, the UK's fastest growing hotel chain, and the UK hotels franchise of Marriott International. Whitbread has a 50% interest in First Quench, the leading off-licence chain. The group is the premier operator in private health and fitness through its ownership of David Lloyd Leisure. Overseas, Whitbread is the leading steakhouse operator in Germany with its Maredo and Churrasco chains.

In addition, Whitbread Inns is one of the UK's leading pub retailer with brands such as Brewers Fayre, Hogshead ale houses and Wayside Inns, while Whitbread Pub Partnerships leases over 1,700 pubs to licensees.

David Reed, director of corporate affairs: 'Whitbread will continue to apply its skills to new areas where lifestyles are changing. Those skills include hospitality management – ensuring customers have a great time in our pubs, hotels and other leisure outlets; marketing skills to differentiate our brands; and property skills (we have over 6,000 locations but never open a new one without knowing the locale's demographics and ensuring that they fit our model). These skills help us to take a good idea, test it, and then grow it into a nationwide chain of 200 to 300 units.'

These successful moves are often the result of research. David Reed: 'We spend more on market research into the UK leisure sector, than any of our competitors. As a result, we know more of our marketplace than most companies.'

Company Culture and Style

Of Whitbread's 90,000 UK employees, at least 70,000 of them deal with customers face-to-face everyday. And as leisure becomes a more important part of everyone's lifestyle, Whitbread is convinced that its future lies in being better than anyone else at giving its customers a really good time.

'Meeting, and wherever possible exceeding our customers' expectations is at the core of our strategy,' says Chris Bulmer, human resources director. 'Our word for it is "wow" – and if we're going to wow our customers, we have to start by wowing our people through training, incentives, but most of all by recognising them as individuals who make a personal contribution to customer satisfaction.'

People work hard at Whitbread, but they also enjoy their work. There's a real sense of teamwork. Integrity is also a key element in everything the company does. Despite its many different outlets, there is a genuinely shared desire to make Whitbread the leading leisure company.

Improving internal communication within the group has been a major focus in recent months. Much effort has gone into improving the quality of team briefings. In effect, a central news service now exists, giving line managers all the information they need to brief staff. Currently comprising paper and e-mail dissemination methods, this will switch to an Intranet system in spring 1999 allowing people to download as much information as they require, even outside office hours.

Whitbread takes its role in society seriously: its Business in the Community Unit invests around £2 million a year and thousands of voluntary man-hours on charitable work. This includes such efforts as management projects to build community centres, refurbish local schools, etc. Perhaps not surprisingly, Business In The Community gave Whitbread its 'Best Company in Britain Award' recently for such work.

Human Resources

The human resources function is important at Whitbread, although much of the work which was once handled centrally has been devolved to the operating companies. The head office continues to address policy issues such as health & safety and equal opportunities, while the operating companies focus on specifics. Common standards exist, but are interpreted according to each business and each market.

The essential Whitbread HR policy comes down to a firm belief that the way to get the best from its people is to manage them properly. There is a constant two-way dialogue. People are also surveyed annually: how they are treated, what they feel about company strategy, how satisfied they are with their benefits and so on. The latest survey placed Whitbread in the top 10% of the top 10% of companies! Employee knowledge of group strategy, pride in the company and belief in leadership could not have been higher, and Whitbread also rated very highly compared to other high-performing UK businesses. David Reed: 'Obviously we are very pleased about these results, but we still seek to tackle any problems or gaps revealed by the survey as soon as possible.'

Career Opportunity and Development

Structures across the group are becoming flatter and hierarchies less pyramidal. As a result, people are more empowered than ever before. This process has meant that promotions are fewer than in the past, although more meaningful when they do occur. Performance management, reviews and psychometrics help select people who really want to delight customers. People have the opportunity to move from one type of outlet to another within the group, or alternatively develop within the same outlet.

There are opportunities to move between the operating companies to gain greater knowledge, which is actively encouraged. For instance, the marketing director of the beer company recently became the managing director of Beefeater, while his predecessor is now managing director of David Lloyd Leisure.

Each business recruits independently for its own needs. Some functions have formal graduate training and induction, but most graduates join on an ad hoc basis, many of them having already gained experience of one of the companies by working there in the kitchen or behind the bar during term evenings or vacation. Indeed, the group is keen that graduates should have some practical knowledge before joining full-time.

Training is vital. Each business has its own training functions, with badges denoting the level of training achieved (which also impacts on pay rises). There is a great deal of in-house training, covering technical knowledge such as wines and spirits, hotel catering and so on. There is also a range of specific training modules from outside. The company has links with the London Business School and Ashridge, as well as the Open University Business School. These run a range of courses for Whitbread covering marketing, planning and financial skills – everything needed to grow into management, in fact.

Remuneration

Whitbread acknowledges that it needs to offer top levels of pay to get the quality of staff it wants. Often, the pay can be increased as experience rises and the employee learns more about the job. At all levels pay is reviewed annually, and discussions and consultations are held to explain the pay awards. Across the board, Whitbread is seen as competitive for pay in its industry sectors.

Benefits include free shares to all staff after three years, a contributory pension scheme, an SAYE scheme after one year, subsidised meals, good sports and social clubs and a Whitbread card giving discounts across the group's products and services. There is also a free issue of products or leisure vouchers every month, and a purchasing scheme allowing staff to buy anything from conveyancing services to electrical goods at discount levels.

Managers enjoy a flexible car scheme which can be upgraded by 20% above salary level or downgraded and the difference taken in cash; a private healthcare plan for partners and family; and for senior managers an executive share-option scheme.

The Future

David Reed sees two main challenges for Whitbread. 'The first is customer service. Primarily, people want high quality of service when using leisure outlets. That makes them come back – and choose our venues over our competitors'. We focus strongly on building our service standards. As an example, our Executive Committee meets monthly and the first item discussed is always our service quality report. As well as the usual methods, this makes use of group representatives using our services incognito in order to check on standards. Our aim is always to compare ourselves with our competitors in each sector and try to stay ahead.

'The other challenge is how to differentiate our brands even more effectively. This is all about offering consumers more choice and is relatively new to the leisure industry. I believe we're probably leading the marketplace – but undoubtedly there are lots of fascinating challenges ahead.'

WHSmith

WHSmith is the UK's leading seller of books, newspapers, magazines and stationery, and supplies more magazines and newspapers to retailers than any other organisation. WHSmith is one of the most recognisable and reliable retailers on the high street and has successfully exported its retailing skills into travel niches in the USA, Europe and beyond and developed these as separate operations. It also owns an online book-selling company.

Scorecard:
Remuneration and benefits ★★★★
Progressive attitude ★★★
Opportunity for promotion ★★★★
Training, development and education ★★★★★
Working atmosphere and environment ★★★★

Biggest plus:
Team-based culture offering great opportunities in retailing

Biggest minus:
Process of cultural change will take time to filter down

WH Smith Group plc
Nations House
13 Wigmore Street
London W1H 0WH
Tel: 0171 409 3222
Fax: 0171 629 3600
website: www.whsmithgroup.com

WHSmith

The Business

WH Smith Group has decided to focus on its core brand and a tighter group of businesses comprising WHSmith High Street, WHSmith News, WHSmith USA Travel Retail and WHSmith Europe Travel Retail. Specialist retail operations Waterstones (book chain), Virgin Megastores and Our Price (music retailing) and The Wall (music retailing in the USA) have all been sold, while in the other direction, WHSmith bought the John Menzies Retail chain and The Internet Bookshop.

WHSmith is without doubt one of the most familiar names on the British high street, where it has been represented for 203 years. It has over 730 stores with the inclusion of John Menzies's chain of 232 stores, and better geographical coverage (Menzies has a strong presence in Scotland). WHSmith is essentially a 'popular specialist', selling books, newspapers, magazines and stationery.

WHSmith Europe Travel Retail consists of 184 stores and concessions located in UK and European stations, airports and hospitals. WHSmith News is the biggest wholesaler of newspapers and magazines in the UK, delivering to thousands of independent newsagents and multiple retailers.

WHSmith USA Travel Retail currently has 409 stores in airports and hotels across the United States, Canada, the Caribbean and Southeast Asia, in hotels, holiday and gaming resorts, and convention centres. The Internet Bookshop – www.bookshop.co.uk – is the leading European Internet bookseller currently offering 1.4 million titles from the UK and USA.

Company Culture and Style

Management style under new chief executive Richard Handover has become much more informal, and the company has evolved an open, honest culture. It is now much more team-based, and in the process, WHSmith has also become more customer-focused and results-oriented.

'Customer service excellence across the range of our operations is vital to our future. We want to be one of the best companies in the world,' says Richard Handover. 'We aim to please our customers by providing a standard of service that is consistently better than our competitors.'

'Our people are very much a part of the mission of the company and our human resources policy is bound into our overall business philosophy. The reason is simple. There's a clear link between satisfied staff and satisfied customers.'

The company is developing a flatter management structure. 'We say that everyone can make a contribution, so the organisational structure must put this into action,' says Richard Handover. The businesses have been drawn much closer together, and managers spend more time together mixing, sharing experiences and ideas, and cultivating Richard Handover's message of 'one brand, one company'.

Recognising that step, rather than incremental change was needed to achieve real results, WHSmith initiated a comprehensive business transformation programme. This commenced with top management, through the next level of 500 managers and will, as part of a three-year plan, eventually embrace everyone in the organisation. Staff throughout the group are aware that, even if not yet themselves an integral part of the change process, that change is happening. Management is spending much more time in the stores and communication is rife. Richard Handover leads from the front and is regularly found talking to staff in warehouses and stores.

People enjoy working for WHSmith, and think it is 'fun'. Staff surveys in the high street chain reveal higher levels of satisfaction than in competitors' businesses, with 93% saying that they enjoy working in WHSmith stores. Some 90% said that their colleagues supported and helped each other, evidence that the team-based culture is working.

Human Resources

HR is now represented at executive level for each WHSmith business, providing a fuller service and being a lot more supportive of the business in all aspects.

Group-wide, HR is looking at the whole equation of reward, recognising the need to clarify and communicate a 'sensible' reward strategy. Some years ago, WHSmith had a share-profit scheme based on the company reaching specified earnings-per-share targets. This has since stopped, with each individual business linking reward to its own fortunes.

This must be a flexible package to meet the flexible ways of working in a modern world. Changing family structures, a shift away from 9–5 jobs, and the need to capture the best talent in the market have all helped WHSmith to realise that its terms and conditions and benefits must reflect these trends.

Career Opportunity and Development

One of the attractions of retailing is that it is very much about dealing with people – particularly at the customer interface. If you don't relate to this, then it is the wrong career for you.

Retailing develops many other areas of expertise, including business and financial acumen, teamworking, marketing and merchandising, making it one of the few industries which bring this broad set of skills together. Increasingly, retailing is being recognised as offering an extremely rewarding career attracting higher-calibre graduates.

Graduates may work in the stores initially (occasionally directly into head office) and then progress through the business. There's a fantastic choice of jobs and graduates can request in which part of the business to start and will have three different assignments in their initial two-year period, before starting a permanent position. WHSmith is very flexible about where this might be.

'We want our people to feel that their jobs are interesting and rewarding, and thereby build up mature, long-term relationships with them,' says Richard Handover. 'Working for WH Smith should give people real satisfaction, wherever they work and whatever they do within the group.'

The HR heads in each business meet regularly to hold career planning discussions across the businesses. All positions in the group are advertised internally. There are travel opportunities, and the company has sent people to the US and Europe on projects, secondments and to fill full-time positions.

More recently, WHSmith has introduced some people from outside 'to check what's going on out there, especially in store retailing,' suggests Richard Handover. With a lot of young people in the company the need was felt for bright senior people who could 'kick-start' the youth policy and pass on their expertise.

Each individual business has its own training and development department and the company expects, rather than hopes, that people progress through each stage of the extensive training 'package'. Even if people remain in a store rather than pursue a glorious management career, every effort is made to ensure that they stay motivated and learn all the time. Training is generally regarded even by outsiders as first-class: everything from basic till training to courses at INSEAD, and at higher management levels, leadership training.

WHSmith boasts a high average length of service among its staff (5–6 years despite the naturally high turnover of the industry, many temporary staff and a big recent influx). That's supporting evidence that people can pursue excellent careers at one of the UK's leading retailers.

Remuneration

WHSmith aims to pay upper quartile for the retailing sector. In return, it expects upper-quartile performance. People are expected to work hard at WHSmith and the company therefore believes that it should pay well. It is not necessarily the top payer at store staff level, but pay is hardly ever the reason why people work for WHSmith.

The company also rewards exceptional performance, which includes team-based awards. Flexible benefits also feature in the package.

In parts of the business, WHSmith would like to slow down staff turnover (although much of this is planned) and is giving better recognition to weekend and part-time workers as well as full-time staff.

The Future

The future beckons for the retailing business, and words like 'uncertain' and 'exciting' can be found in the same sentence. In theory, everything that WHSmith sells could be sold over the Internet, but no-one knows how quickly this will develop (although there are some very positive forecasts). WHSmith remains committed to the high street, but buying the Internet book retailing business looks like a good punt.

The modern WHSmith is characterised by a flatter structure, shorter lines of communications and flexible, adaptable people not set in their ways. Mobility and flexibility are a way of life and if WHSmith wishes to recruit and retain its people, it will need to build 'emotional capital' among its workforce.

Communication is very high on the agenda – 'inside-out communications' according to Tim Blythe, corporate affairs director – and the company's internal communications strategy recognises the special challenges posed by a retailing operation. WHSmith is proud of the fact that when its financial results are announced externally, staff hear about them simultaneously.

Retailing is as competitive as it has ever been, and electronic shopping and other trends are changing all the rules. But WHSmith intends to be at the forefront of changes. 'Our challenge is to refine our understanding of the skills and competencies we need to respond to this fast-changing environment. That means repositioning ourselves to focus on what we do best, and of course acquiring and keeping the best people,' says Richard Handover.

Willis Corroon

Willis Corroon is a worldwide knowledge-based company providing risk management solutions, risk transfer expertise and specialised consultancy services. Represented worldwide through over 250 offices in 69 countries, the group employs 9,400 people in subsidiaries and branches, together with over 2,000 staff in associate companies. Its main offices are in London, Ipswich, and Nashville, Tennessee.

Scorecard:

Remuneration and benefits	★★★★
Progressive attitude	★★★★★
Opportunity for promotion	★★★★★
Training, development and education	★★★★
Working atmosphere and environment	★★★★

Biggest plus:
Positively encouraged to take control of your career

Biggest minus:
Not for the nine-to-fivers!

Willis Corroon
10 Trinity Square
London EC3P 3AX
Tel: 0171 488 8111
Fax: 0171 488 8223
website:www.williscorroon.com

Willis Corroon

The Business

The roots of the group go back to 1828 when insurance brokerage Henry Willis & Co. was founded in London. Seventy-seven years later, RA Corroon & Co. was formed in New York. After a series of consolidations, the UK firm of Willis Faber and the US company of Corroon & Black merged in 1990 to create Willis Corroon Group, now one of only three insurance brokers with a truly global basis of operations.

Over the 1990s, Willis Corroon has continued to develop rapidly. The company is now in the process of becoming a professional services firm, shifting emphasis away from traditional insurance broking and focusing more on providing risk management advice. Accompanying this change is a transition to fee-based rather than commission-based remuneration. The most significant development, however, is in the group's structure: a leveraged buyout in 1998 took it out of the public arena and into a new era. This was good news for staff, shareholders and customers alike; allowing the firm to react with greater flexibility, speeding the transition to a professional services firm, and ending unsettling media speculation about the company's future.

Today, the group operates in six main business segments: global reinsurance, global specialities (specialist broking and consulting services to clients with exposure to large or unusual risks), UK retail, North American retail, US wholesale and international.

Company Culture and Style

Stephen Maycock, group HR director: 'We are a people business and we recognise that our people are our greatest asset. Despite all the technology now in use in our industry, clients still prefer to be dealt with by humans. As a result, we value our people highly. Teamworking is vital, but we treat people as individuals within their teams. This is quite unusual for such a large, complex company.' The corollary of this trust and respect is that Willis Corroon attracts and fosters people who take on responsibility at an early stage and can initiate ideas. 'Our organisation is all about relationships: with clients, and within the company. These relationships are often independent of the traditional hierarchies seen in large firms.'

Willis Corroon people are highly committed. This is essential, given the importance of client relationships and the fact that the business is global. Staff can find themselves working until midnight, coming in at 7 am, taking two hour lunches; flexibility is vital. This means that working for Willis Corroon can be demanding. But it is also satisfying. This can be seen in the long service levels of many members of staff. The company culture is friendly, informal and geared towards problem-solving. All these are facilitated by the company's structure, which is matrix-based rather than hierarchical. The rigid structure of some firms gives way at Willis Corroon to a more fluid, yet highly effective, mesh. In particular, decision-making is rapid.

The core of the organisation's culture is knowledge-sharing. Willis Corroon has long been known as a knowledge-based company, drawing on and disseminating knowledge right across the industry and indeed beyond it. In the days when telex was a key means of corporate communication, the company accounted for an amazing 1.5% of the entire UK telex traffic. Today, that knowledge-sharing is even more important, but vehicles such as faxes, e-mails and video conferencing now bear the brunt of it. The importance of knowledge-sharing is underlined by the presence of a group knowledge director, and the company's ability to communicate worldwide is now very advanced. The culture is also one of continuous improvement, and here too the company is keen to take the best ideas from this and other sectors and introduce them wherever they can prove effective.

As Stephen Maycock says, one of the most intriguing and appealing aspects of working for the company is its flexibility. 'We're not bogged down with huge amounts of procedural infrastructure; quite the reverse. In many cases, the rules haven't been written. Some people find this disconcerting, but creative, ideas-initiating people thrive in this sort of culture. After all, our business continues to move forward, and we need to move with it if we're to stay on top of it.'

Human Resources

The Group Executive Committee meets fortnightly, and a significant proportion of its agenda is taken up with HR-related items. Recruits have mentors: this is a voluntary programme, organised through the company's Intranet service. The mentor programme is now being expanded beyond the recruit stage.

The philosophy behind the company's HR approach is for managers to treat employees as they themselves would like to be treated. This attitude clearly works well, so much so that there are no unions at

Willis Corroon, and no formal union recognition claim has ever been put forward.

An annual Employee Attitude Survey helps monitor the effectiveness of the HR policies. The results of this survey are published globally across the group, and the key issues tracked for at least three years – ensuring that any areas of weakness are rapidly tightened up.

Vacancies at a senior level are advertised internally and on the Intranet, worldwide throughout the group. As a result, mobility within the group, both across operating areas and across countries, is good, and better than in most companies of comparable size.

Career Opportunity and Development

At Willis Corroon, people are encouraged to take responsibility for their own careers. Stephen Maycock: 'We will give all the support, counselling and training required. Really, the sky's the limit, but the individual members of staff say what they want. This proves to be an effective way of selecting the best talent; with this system, the best people tend to percolate to the top.'

Development aids include an assessment culture, formalised 360-degree appraisal programmes, an extensive HR site on the Intranet, and much more. A 'virtual university', in the shape of the Willis Corroon Institute, is in embryonic form. The company is now embarking on a more formalised MBA recruitment programme. It also has INSEAD affiliation, and is developing stronger relationships with a number of business schools in Europe and North America. High-performing staff are invited by the Group Executive Committee to join the company's 'conceptualised' partnership plan, encouraging them to take even more control of their careers.

For many, a major attraction of the company is its diversity and hence opportunity for development. The group offers three primary career paths: management, client relationships and technical professional. A recruit could enter in a finance area (within Technical Professional) and then decide that a role within Client Relationships would be more suitable. By acquiring the relevant knowledge and behaviour skills, the recruit could work towards making that crossover. Stephen Maycock: 'Willis Corroon is a fascinating place to work for because our business is so extensive: everything from satellites and racehorses to fine arts and crude oil shipping. Whatever your interest, we're likely to have something to appeal to you.'

The same is true of the location. Some people at the company spend as much as four months in the year on an aeroplane! Others prefer to locate in a particular country, and here again this is usually possible thanks to the company's wide global coverage. The company has a substantial number of expatriates, dotted throughout its worldwide network.

Remuneration

The company sees itself as a median payer within its marketplace, but the emphasis is shifting to bonus programmes and performance-related pay (as measured by quantitative and qualitative assessment). The leveraged buy-out has brought with it a buy-in equity plan for, initially, 400 people. This is a major management incentivisation and one which promotes, in Stephen Maycock's words, 'An ownership mentality in a complex organisation.'

Additional benefits with some national variations include an occupational pension plan, usually on a final salary basis; an AVC or a 401K scheme (in the USA); assistance with medical plan; company cars at middle-management level with a cash alternative; and a number of insurance benefits.

The Future

The challenges for the future at Willis Corroon are change, development, growth and profitability, in that order. The company and its sector are undergoing remarkably rapid change in a very short period. This is both a challenge and an opportunity. Stephen Maycock: 'If you thrive on change and wish to be with a company where you can contribute and influence its direction, you couldn't join a better company than Willis Corroon.'

WPP Group

WPP is one of the world's largest advertising and marketing services groups. The 60 companies in the group offer clients – local, multinational and global – a comprehensive and, when appropriate, an integrated range of marketing services, including advertising, market research, media consultancy, public relations, sales promotion, direct marketing, identity and design, and other specialist communications. WPP employs more than 30,000 people in 835 offices across 91 countries, with some 3,600 people in the UK. In 1997 the company had revenues of £1.8 billion.

Scorecard:

Remuneration and benefits	★★★★
Progressive attitude	★★★★
Opportunity for promotion	★★★★★
Training, development and education	★★★★
Working atmosphere and environment	★★★

Biggest plus:
Wonderful group of companies, professional approach to people development

Biggest minus:
No marketing business is for people who want security

WPP Group plc
27 Farm Street
London W1X 6RD
Tel. 0171 408 2204
Fax 0171 493 6819
website: http://ww.wpp.com

WPP Group plc

WPP Group

The Business

WPP companies live by their wits. Clients come to them for intelligence, experience, inventiveness and imagination, in order to gain competitive advantage. The management of its people and the maximising of their talents are, therefore, central to the success of the group.

WPP aims to be the preferred provider of advertising and marketing services. Increasingly sophisticated clients are looking for a more coordinated, global approach, and meeting this need is at the core of WPP's strategy. The client lists are impressive. The group's 60 companies together served more than 300 of the *Fortune* 500 companies in 1997 and more than 60 of the FTSE-100.

As the sum of many individual operating companies, WPP is also a thoughtful parent company which plays an active role in adding value to clients' businesses and the careers of its people across the group. In certain defined activities, WPP can free up its companies to be of even greater value to clients and also provide richer careers, opportunities and rewards for its people as part of a group. But if centralising an activity threatens the autonomy or identity of an operating company, it is left de-centralised.

Company Culture and Style

WPP has no wish or intention to change the individual and special cultures of its operating companies. With such impressive names as J. Walter Thompson, Ogilvy & Mather, Hill & Knowlton, Enterprise IG, Millward Brown, Research International and the Henley Centre in the fold, no wonder . . . these are very prominent and powerful brands.

Instead, through communication of its vision and standards, WPP provides an overlay to the individual cultures of its companies. Like placing an emphasis on what individuals actually deliver and achieve, rather than the way they work; implanting the notion of *ownership* of the business; and working together in teams.

Chief executive Martin Sorrell has worked hard to improve the degree of cooperation among the many disparate parts of the WPP empire. Much effort has gone into helping individual operating companies improve the quality of their service offer, and facilitating cross-company partnerships and initiatives including training, recruitment, career development, incentive and stock ownership schemes, information technology, property, procurement and practice development.

WPP is full of talented people and aims to keep it this way, helping make its companies even more attractive to talented people throughout the world. Creativity remains absolutely central, but this is not the sole preserve of art directors and copywriters who produce tangible creative work – everyone is encouraged to take a creative approach to problem-solving.

Risk-taking is also valued – something which requires constant attention and analysis given the propensity for most organisations to revert to conservatism if the culture does not remain open. Openness is encouraged at WPP, as is the exchange of ideas and a diversity of viewpoint, and there is considerable flexibility in the workplace relating to hours and style of working. Diversity is almost an end in itself, in a business which is all about reflecting what consumers think.

Human Resources

The parent company takes an active approach to personal and professional development, identifying people with the potential to take on leadership roles in the group. This professional approach to human resources is more akin to its client companies than to communications agencies.

WPP recognises that it is a global business, not a craft or a cottage industry. It needs – and has – highly creative people, yes, but it refuses to rely only on instincts and raw talent when it comes to recruitment and personal development. 'Without the strategic perspective,' suggests human resources director, Brian Brooks, 'talented people can easily fall through the cracks. It comes down to facilitating learning and development. There really is no other way to help our people exploit their full potential.'

Competing directly with investment banks and management consultancies for the cream of talent from universities and business schools, WPP goes to lengths to recruit people interested in a career in multi-disciplinary marketing communications. Such people are likely to have stronger creative instincts and interests, and also be comfortable with ambiguity and a relative lack of structure that belongs to all marketing services consultancies.

The group is introducing 360-degree performance appraisal systems in each of its companies; the process may take years, but is highly relevant to a business like WPP, with its heavy emphasis on teams, performance and interaction, including the all-important *client* perspective.

Remuneration is of course important, but WPP defines remuneration strategy in terms of what it wants to accomplish as a business, and how individuals can help it get there.

Internal communication is rife within WPP. Martin Sorrell's monthly CEO Report goes out to 1,500 senior people, which generates vital feedback, while the group's newspaper *The Wire* goes to 20,000 people worldwide. Each individual possesses the group bible *The Navigator*, to guide them to companies, contacts, resources and capabilities. WPP also has a busy Intranet and website. And an electronic job posting system is developing which will make it easier to initiate moves, creating an internal but international job market.

Career Opportunity and Development

Many WPP companies are growing fast, and offer a range of challenging, rewarding and exciting careers in all marketing disciplines. People who can deliver integrated business solutions to clients, drawing upon strategic consultancy and creative services, can enjoy a fast-track management career within WPP.

Flexibility is also a watchword when it comes to pace of career progression – WPP judges people only on what they contribute to the business. Evidence? Shelly Lazarus is the only woman heading up a global advertising agency and Chris Jones, the CEO of JWT Worldwide, is just 43. But if individuals are happy in specialist areas, and delivering, there is no pressure to move inevitably into management.

The '100 Club' comprises the key people who are running the businesses and are therefore most responsible for delivering value to shareholders. The '300 Club' trawls for the highest potential people not yet in leadership roles. Management development programmes, customised for WPP by the London and Harvard Business Schools (WPP even has its own MBA programme), are aimed at both clubs.

Individual companies run their own training programmes, but the parent company increasingly initiates and sponsors additional training. These include brand leadership courses and 'community interest' workshops, which bring together WPP professionals from different disciplines and different companies. Other initiatives are aimed at developing competencies which people might not have, but will need – leadership and people management skills for instance. A training task force is being piloted in the UK to encourage individual companies to integrate their training efforts.

Remuneration

WPP applies the notion of having fewer but better-paid people. Staff cost-to-revenue ratios have fallen by over 7% during the 1990s, while profit margins have improved by even more than this. Yet the top 400 people earn considerably more, largely due to incentive remuneration. WPP spent £52 million on incentives in 1997, preferring to reward senior people for performance. This indicates a strong belief in the potential of the individual to make a difference, and its wish for everyone to think and act like an owner.

WPP is publicly committed to wider internal share ownership, and various programmes have been developed to enable a large number of WPP professionals to participate actively in the growing value of the company. In 1997 WPP introduced its Worldwide Ownership Program and granted stock options to 12,000 people, including special executive option programmes for the top 400 people.

The Future

Arguably, marketing services always has a future with companies needing constantly to innovate, create or grow markets, and grab market share. WPP is extremely well positioned in marketing services worldwide – in diverse geographical spread as well as breadth of services – and has grown faster than the sector as a whole. The downside is that marketing services budgets have always proved to be particularly sensitive to economic trends because they are controllable, and less growth would mean fewer opportunities for people to grow. Another vulnerable target – the training budget – is something WPP is committed to.

The effective use of technology in terms of business efficiency, ways of working, communications and knowledge-sharing represents a major challenge to creative businesses like WPP which tend to be more comfortable with creative or 'soft' information rather than hard data. WPP is also committed, through its Space Program, to restructuring the workplace and transforming organisational structures, aimed at delivering the best client service in the industry and 'better work, faster'.

Non-financial factors are increasingly important to people in their employment choice – such as development opportunities, quality of lifestyle, level of involvement in the business, and flexible working. The younger the age group, the more prominent these factors are. All of these trends are in WPP's favour. 'Pay can be a source of dissatisfaction, but it rarely produces satisfaction in itself,' adds Brooks.

WPP believes strongly, and therefore has challenged itself to prove, that the value of the group to client companies can be a great deal more than the sum of its parts.

Shopping around

Of all the choices we are faced with every day, choosing an employer is one of the most difficult and stressful. Making the right choice has long-lasting positive effects, whereas a career mistake can cause considerable damage; not only in personal terms but the evidence remains on your CV for the world to see and question.

Many individuals take more care and concern in making a big consumer purchase than they do in analysing a potential employer. They typically research a selection of competing products, analysing and comparing features and benefits across a range of factors, and choose the one which meets a balance of needs. How many people can say they analyse a prospective employer as closely?

Some employment needs are relatively easy to articulate, for example reward, training and career development, but there are wider issues to consider. How important is it for your employer to be well known? What kind of values could you work with, or more importantly not work with? What kind of working environment would you find acceptable? How well do you cope with change? Are you looking for a highly dynamic or stable organisation? These are just a few examples of employment factors which are of varying importance to employees. In essence, each individual has to balance their own needs and priorities, and be critical about the 'product' on offer.

Employers need to heed this too. They should start valuing employees as they value their customers. They can achieve this by defining the overall employment offer – identifying the kind of employees they want to attract, motivate and retain. In support they should research, measure and monitor needs, satisfaction and retention. Thus, employers are more likely to get a greater return on their investment in training and development and meet their organisational objectives.

In addition, as responsibility for career planning and development is devolved, a higher level of confidence and greater communication is required between employer and employee. That confidence emerges when the employment offer is delivered as promised, in a way which is relevant and meaningful to meet the needs and expectations of both parties.

Thinking about the kind of employer you are in traditional marketing terms, and treating your employees as you would a valued customer creates a win/win situation in terms of loyalty, commitment, motivation and becoming an employer of choice.

Sue Clemenson
Consultant at People in Business

Pay and Benefits

Recent evidence shows that pay increases have been falling recently and are likely to stay low – the current average is 4.2%. With inflation and pay increases so closely linked, and the need to maintain the UK's global competitiveness, maintaining low pay rises is important and this would appear to have been achieved. There has been astonishing stability in company pay settlements, at around 3.5% for over 3 years and earnings movements are now stabilising after some volatility over the last 12 months.

There is also a general feeling that the 'feel good factor' is now improving.

Differing economies within the country and industry groupings naturally have different pay levels that translate into regional pay differences. Percentage pay differentials for management jobs between the UK national median and the regions show the following pattern. Eastern Counties: –8.3%, London: +13.5%, North-east: –3.5%, Northern Ireland: –9.9%, North-west: +2.6%, Scotland: +7.2%, South-east: +4.5%, South-west: –4.7%, West Midlands: –5.7%.

When we speak of pay and benefits, we are considering the total package that comes with a job. A list of pay and benefit related items that could be included in the total package follows – other items may also feature.

Pay: Basic pay, bonus, commission, performance-related pay, profit-related pay, overtime, shift allowance, call-out allowance, market supplement.

Benefits: Holidays, sick pay, pension, company car, private health insurance, long-term disability insurance, life assurance.

Clearly not every package would include all of these items, but a remarkably large number would be included and are often forgotten by the employees when speaking of their package.

If a value is placed on each of these, it can be seen that the typical package can be quite substantial and can cost the employer a large additional amount on top of the basic salary. When this is added to employer's National Insurance contributions, the costs of employing an individual are often between 50% and 60% above the basic salary.

As might be expected, as seniority increases so does the level of benefits: a graduate trainee's typical package might be basic salary, company pension and life assurance, possibly with profit-related or performance-related pay. A middle manager would normally have private health insurance and performance-related pay, plus life assurance increasing to about three times annual salary and perhaps long-term disability insurance. For a senior manager, a company car would typically be around 1800cc and above, but more organisations are offering contract hire and leasing arrangements giving the individual more choice. Health and long-term insurances would increase.

The way forward over the next few years appears to be low economic growth, an improvement in the 'feel good factor', small fluctuations in inflation and pay levels and a drifting upwards of benefit packages.

Steve Flather
The Reward Group

Career Management – A Challenge for Organisations and Individuals

The issues surrounding career management have been hotly debated during the nineties but all the talking has resulted in very little action. Human resources directors, consultants, facilitators and general managers are all agreed that individuals and organisations should be working together to reconcile corporate and personal employment goals whilst employees talk about taking responsibility for managing their own careers.

Career management can broadly be summarised as 'finding a way to enable individuals and organisations to construct realistic career plans which meet business and personal needs'. It should be a lifelong process of evaluation and re-direction which reflects changing patterns in employment, domestic and personal circumstances, priorities and whole life management. If we accept that the traditional career is dead, even for those still pursuing a single employer route, then our duty to facilitate individual and organisational harmony is even greater.

There are many reasons why the challenge of introducing successful and cost-effective career management programmes is proving difficult. However, probably the most challenging obstacle to overcome is building a business case to persuade senior management that investment in career management is worthwhile and has a payoff for both parties. We are all prepared to refer to our people as 'our single most important asset', 'key differentiator' or 'greatest competitive advantage', but putting a plan in place which helps deploy that resource better, to motivate and energise them to be more productive through job satisfaction, seems to continually slip from our priority list.

Building a business case is vital in order to secure funding from budgets which are under increasing pressure, but it is a complex calculation that puts numbers against what are often termed as 'soft' benefits. There are considerable benefits for those organisations able to convince themselves of the commercial equation.

First, it is possible to quantify savings in recruitment and retention which result from realistic expectations and a more satisfied workforce.

Very often, the direct result of major change in an organisation follow-ing downsizing, mergers/acquisitions, change of CEO, introduction and commitment to new working practices, etc., is that the very indi-viduals you most want to retain are the ones who feel uncertain and leave. This does not only mean 'high fliers', our key players are more often than not the solid core of our workforce and not simply our stars. The cost of recruiting and retaining can be looked at over varying periods, quantified and expressed as a cost benefit.

Second, a good career management programme will help us under-stand individual and collective strengths and thereby clearly target training and development expenditure. This has cost benefits in ensur-ing that a blanket approach is not applied when it is neither necessary nor worthwhile

Finally, productivity can also be improved with fewer corridor chats, coffee machine conferences and other instances of worried employees taking time out to debate what is happening, to bemoan their fate, to resist moves to force change, and generally to worry over their personal and collective futures. Providing a creative outlet, whether through individual or group opportunities to plan and consider their own direc-tions, can do much to increase commitment and productivity. Encour-aging our human resources professionals to build a real business case to work with the people we claim to value so much must surely be the first step in ensuring that career management becomes a reality rather than a fantasy. The UK's top companies are beginning to make this move and there is every evidence that employees value this benefit as highly as more tangible rewards. It is an investment in their futures that pays dividends all round.

Frances Cool
Managing Director of Sanders & Sidney plc